Commercial Interiors

Version 2.0

REFERENCE GUIDE

Third Edition October 2006

LEED for Commercial Interiors Reference Guide

Version 2.0

ISBN #1-932444-08-4

Copyright

Trademark

Disclaimer

U.S. Green Building Council
1800 Massachusetts Ave., NW
Suite 300
Washington, DC 20036

Acknowledgements

The LEED for Commercial Interiors Reference Guide has been made only possible through the efforts of many dedicated volunteers, staff members and others in the USGBC community. The Reference Guide drafting was managed and implemented by USGBC staff and included review and suggestions by many Technical Advisory Group (TAG) members and the Commercial Interiors Core Committee. We especially extend our deepest gratitude to all of our LEED committee members who participated in the development of this guide, for their tireless volunteer efforts and constant support of USGBC's mission. They are–

LEED for Commercial Interiors Core Committee

Penny Bonda (Chair), Environmental Communications
Keith Winn (Vice-Chair), Catalyst Partners
Gina Baker, Burt Hill Kosar Rittelmann Associates
Kirsten Childs, Croxton Collaborative Architects, P.C.
Holley Henderson, H2 Ecodesign, LLC
Don Horn, U.S. General Services Administration
Scot Horst, 7 Group
Liana Kallivoka, Austin Energy Green Building Program
Jill Kowalski, EwingCole
Fran Mazarella, U.S. General Services Administration
Roger McFarland, HOK
Denise Van Valkenburg, Steelcase Inc.
Ken Wilson, Envision Design
Theresa Hogerheide-Reusch (Advisor), Catalyst Partners
John Stivers (Advisor), Catalyst Partners

Special thanks to: John Stivers, Catalyst Partners for his significant contributions to the creation of the LEED for Commercial Interiors Reference Guide

Energy & Atmosphere TAG

Greg Kats (Chair), Capital-E
Marcus Sheffer (Vice-Chair), 7group
Saad Dimachkieh, HOK
Chad Dorgan, Farnsworth Group, Inc.
Jay Enck, Commissioning & Green Building Services
Donald Fournier, Building Research Council
Jonathan Heller, Ecotope Inc.
Tia Heneghan, Sebesta Blomberg
John Hogan, City of Seattle Department of Design, Construction, and Land Use
Bion Howard, Building Environmental Science
Michael Lorenz, Kling
Cheryl Massie, Flack + Kurtz
Brenda Morawa, BVM Engineering, Inc.
Erik Ring, CTG Energetics, Inc.
Mick Schwedler, Trane Company

Indoor Environmental Quality TAG

Bob Thompson (Chair), EPA Indoor Environments Management Branch
Steve Taylor (Vice-Chair), Taylor Engineering
Jude Anders, Johnson Controls, Inc.
Terry Brennan, Camroden Associates
Brian Cloward, Mithun
Larry Dykhuis, Herman Miller, Inc.
Greg Franta, Ensar Group, Inc.
Francis Offerman, Indoor Environmental Engineering
Christopher Schaffner, The Green Engineer
Dennis Stanke, Trane Company

Materials & Resources TAG

Nadav Malin (Chair), BuildingGreen, Inc.
Kirsten Ritchie (Vice-Chair), Scientific Certification Systems
Paul Bertram, PRB Design
Chris Dixon, Mithun
Ann Edminster, Design AVEnues
Lee Gros, Austin Energy Green Building Program
Debra Lombard, RETEC
Nancy Malone, Siegel & Strain Architects
Dana Papke, California Integrated Waste Mgmt. Board
Wayne Trusty, Athena Institute
Denise Van Valkenburg, Steelcase
Melissa Vernon, Interface Flooring Systems
Mark Webster, Simpson Gumpertz & Heger
Gabe Wing, Herman Miller, Inc.

Sustainable Sites TAG

Bryna Dunn (Chair), Moseley Architects
Susan Kaplan (Vice-Chair), Battery Park City Authority
Ann Abel Christensen
Gina Baker, Burt Hill Kosar Rittelmann
Ted Bardacke, Global Green USA
Stephen Benz, Judith Nitsch Engineering, Inc.
Mark Brumbaugh, Brumbaugh & Associates
Meg Calkins, University of Illinois at Urbana-Champaign (and ASLA representative)
Stewart Comstock, Maryland Department of the Environment
Jay Enck, Commissioning & Green Building Services
Jim Frierson, Advanced Transportation Technology Institute
Ron Hand, G&E Environmental
Richard Heinisch, Acuity Lighting Group
Michael Lane, Lighting Design Lab
Mark Loeffler, The RETEC Group, Inc.
Marita Roos, Andropogon Associates
Zolna Russell, Hord Coplan Macht, Inc.
Eva Wong, U.S. EPA Heat Island Reduction Initiative (HIRI)

Water Efficiency TAG

David Sheridan (Chair), Aqua Cura
John Koeller (Vice-Chair), Koeller and Company
Gunnar Baldwin, TOTO USA, INC
Neal Billetdeaux, JJR
David Carlson, Columbia University
Bill Hoffman, City of Austin - Water Conservation
Heather Kinkade-Levario, ARCADIS
Geoff Nara, Civil & Environmental Consultants
Shabbir Rawalpindiwala, Kohler Company
Stephanie Tanner, National Renewable Energy Laboratory
Bill Wall, Clivus New England, Inc.
Bill Wilson, Environmental Planning & Design, LLC

USGBC Staff for their invaluable efforts in developing the LEED for Commercial Interiors Reference Guide.

This reference guide was printed on 100% post-consumer waste paper, process chlorine free, and printed with non-toxic, soy-based inks using 100% wind power. By using these materials and production processes, the U.S. Green Building Council saved the following resources:

Trees*	Solid Waste	Liquid Waste	Electricity	Greenhouse Gases	Sulfur & Nitrogen Oxides
51,250 lbs. of virgin wood, equal to 89 trees	7,988 lbs.	74,932 gallons	11,468 kWh	14,712 lbs.	31 lbs.

*One tree = approx. 575 lbs.

Table of Contents

Indoor Environmental Quality 261

Innovation & Design Process 373

Foreword from USGBC

The built environment has a profound impact on our natural environment, economy, health and productivity. Breakthroughs in building science, technology and operations are now available to designers, builders, operators and owners who want to build green and maximize both economic and environmental performance.

The U.S. Green Building Council (USGBC) is leading a national consensus to produce buildings that deliver high performance inside and out. Council members work together to develop industry standards, design and construction practices and guidelines, operating practices and guidelines, policy positions and educational tools that support the adoption of sustainable design and building practices. Members also forge strategic alliances with key industry and research organizations, federal government agencies and state and local governments to transform the built environment. As the leading organization that represents the entire building industry on environmental building matters, our unique perspective and collective power provide our members with enormous opportunity to effect change in the way buildings are designed, built, operated and maintained.

USGBC Membership

The Council's greatest strength is the diversity of our membership. USGBC is a balanced, consensus nonprofit representing the entire building industry, consisting of over 5000 companies and organizations. Since its inception in 1993, USGBC has played a vital role in providing a leadership forum and a unique, integrating force for the building industry. Council programs are:

- **Committee-Based.** The heart of this effective coalition is our committees in which members design strategies that are implemented by staff and expert consultants. Our committees provide a forum for members to resolve differences, build alliances and forge cooperative solutions for influencing change in all sectors of the building industry.

- **Member-Driven.** The Council's membership is open and balanced and provides a comprehensive platform for carrying out important programs and activities. We target the issues identified by our members as the highest priority. We conduct an annual review of achievements that allows us to set policy, revise strategies and devise work plans based on members' needs.

- **Consensus-Focused.** We work together to promote green buildings and in doing so, we help foster greater economic vitality and environmental health at lower cost. The various industry segments bridge ideological gaps to develop balanced policies that benefit the entire industry.

Contact the U.S. Green Building Council

1800 Massachusetts Ave., NW
Suite 300
Washington, DC 20036
(202) 828-7422 Office
(202) 828-5110 Fax
www.usgbc.org

Introduction

What Does "Green" Mean?

"Green" has become the shorthand term for the concept of sustainable development as applied to the building industry. Also known as high-performance buildings, green buildings are intended to be environmentally responsible, economically profitable, and healthy places to live and work.

I. Why Make Your Building Interiors Green?

The building sector has a tremendous impact on the environment. Buildings in the United States consume more than 30% of our total energy and 60% of electricity annually. They consume 5 billion gallons of potable water per day to flush toilets. A typical North American commercial construction project generates up to 2.5 pounds of solid waste per square foot of floor space. The industry appropriates land from other uses such as natural habitats and agriculture. These are just a few examples of the environmental impacts associated with the construction and operation of buildings.

Green building practices can substantially reduce these negative environmental impacts and reverse the trend of unsustainable construction activities. As an added benefit, green design measures reduce operating costs, enhance building marketability, increase worker productivity, and reduce potential liability resulting from indoor air quality problems. For example, energy efficiency measures have reduced operating expenses of the Denver Dry Goods building by approximately $75,000 per year. Students in day-lit schools in North Carolina consistently score higher on tests than students in schools using conventional lighting fixtures. Studies of workers in green buildings reported productivity gains of up to 16%, including reductions in absenteeism and improved work quality,

based on "people-friendly" green design. At a grocery store in Spokane, Washington, waste management costs were reduced by 56% and 48 tons of waste was recycled during construction. In other words, green design has environmental, economic and social elements that benefit all building stakeholders, including owners, occupants and the general public.

II. LEED® (Leadership in Energy and Environmental Design) Green Building Rating System™

History of LEED®

Following the formation of the U.S. Green Building Council (USGBC) in 1993, the membership quickly realized that a priority for the sustainable building industry was to have a system to define and measure "green buildings." USGBC began to research existing green building metrics and rating systems. Less than a year after formation, the membership followed up on the initial findings with the establishment of a committee to focus solely on this topic. The diverse initial composition of the committee included architects, realtors, a building owner, a lawyer, an environmentalist and industry representatives. This cross section of people and professions added a richness and depth both to the process and to the ultimate product.

The first LEED Pilot Project Program, also referred to as LEED v1.0, was launched at the USGBC Membership Summit in August 1998. After extensive modifications, the LEED Green Building Rating System v2.0 was released in March 2000. This rating system is now called LEED for New Construction and Major Renovations, or LEED for New Construction.

As LEED has evolved and matured, the LEED program has undertaken new initiatives to address the many different stages and sectors of the U.S. building market aside from LEED for New Construction.

LEED for Commercial Interiors is part of the growing portfolio of Rating System products serving specific market sectors (see chart, below).

Rating System Product Portfolio

under development as of September 2006

New Construction

Existing Buildings

Commercial Interiors

Core & Shell

LEED for Homes*

Neighborhood Development*

LEED for Multiple Buildings/Campuses

*LEED for Retail***

*LEED for Schools***

*LEED for Healthcare***

*LEED for Retail***

*LEED for Laboratories***

U.S. Green Building Council

Features of LEED

The LEED Green Building Rating System™ is a voluntary, consensus-based, market-driven building rating system based on existing proven technology. It evaluates environmental performance from a whole building perspective over a building's life cycle, providing a definitive standard for what constitutes a "green building." The development of the LEED Rating System was initiated by the USGBC membership, representing all segments of the building industry and has been open to public scrutiny.

The Rating System is organized into five environmental categories: Sustainable Sites, Water Efficiency, Energy & Atmosphere, Materials & Resources, and Indoor Environmental Quality. An additional category, Innovation & Design Process, addresses sustainable building expertise as well as design measures not covered under the five environmental categories.

LEED is a measurement system designed for rating new and existing commercial, institutional and high-rise residential buildings. It is based on accepted energy and environmental principles and strikes a balance between known established practices and emerging concepts.

It is a performance-oriented system where credits are earned for satisfying each criterion. Different levels of green building certification are awarded based on the total credits earned. The system is designed to be comprehensive in scope, yet simple in operation.

The Future of LEED

The green design field is growing and changing daily. New technologies and products are coming into the marketplace and innovative designs are proving their effectiveness. Therefore, the Rating System and the Reference Guide must evolve as well.

USGBC will highlight new developments on its Web site on a continuous basis at www.usgbc.org.

III. LEED for Commercial Interiors Overview and Process

The LEED for Commercial Interiors Rating System provides a set of performance standards for certifying tenant projects with USGBC. The specific credits in the rating system provide guidelines for the design and construction of tenant spaces in government and private sectors for office, retail, restaurant, healthcare, hotel/resort and education building applications. Tenants are defined as those who pay rent to use or occupy a building, occupants who dwell in a place, and/or holders of buildings such as ownership or lease. The intent of LEED for Commercial Interiors is to assist in the creation of high performance, healthful, durable, affordable and environmentally sound commercial interiors. LEED for Commercial Interiors addresses:

❑ Sustainable Sites

❑ Water Efficiency

❑ Energy & Atmosphere

❑ Materials & Resources

❑ Indoor Environmental Quality

❑ Innovation in Design

When to Use LEED for Commercial Interiors

Many projects will cleanly and clearly fit the defined scope of only one LEED rating system product. For other projects, two or more LEED rating system products may be applicable. USGBC encourages the project team to tally a potential point total using the rating system checklists for all possibilities. The project is a viable candidate for LEED certification if it can meet all prerequisites and achieve the minimum points required in a given rating system. If more than one rating system applies, then it is up to the project team to decide which one to use. For assistance in choosing the most appropriate LEED rating system, please e-mail *leedinfo@usgbc.org*.

LEED for Commercial Interiors Registration

Project teams interested in obtaining LEED certification for their projects must first register their intent with USGBC. Projects can be registered on the USGBC Web site (www.usgbc.org) in the LEED section, under Register Your Project. The Web site includes information on registration costs for USGBC member companies as well as non-members. Registration is an important step that establishes contact with USGBC and provides access to the LEED-Online software tool, errata, critical communications, and other essential information.

About LEED-Online

As of January 2006, project teams pursuing LEED for Commercial Interiors certification are required to use LEED-Online, which enables teams to submit 100% of their documentation online in an easy-to-use format. LEED-Online stores all LEED information, resources, and support in one centralized location. LEED-Online enables team members to upload credit templates, track Credit Interpretation Requests, manage key project details, contact customer service, and communicate with reviewers throughout the design and construction reviews.

Credit Interpretation Rulings

In some cases, the design team may encounter challenges in applying a LEED for Commercial Interiors prerequisite or credit to their particular project. These difficulties arise from instances where the Reference Guide does not sufficiently address a specific issue or there is a special conflict that requires resolution. To ad-

dress such issues, USGBC has established the LEED for Commercial Interiors Version 2.0 Credit Interpretation Ruling (CIR) process (separate from the CIR page for version 1.0 CIRs). See the LEED for Commercial Interiors section of the USGBC Web site for more information at www.usgbc.org. The Credit Interpretation process is summarized as follows:

1. Project teams should review the CIR Web page to read previously posted credit interpretation requests and USGBC responses. Many questions can be resolved by reviewing existing CIRs and the Reference Guide. Note that CIRs for other rating systems (LEED for Existing Buildings, LEED for Core & Shell, LEED for New Construction, and past versions of LEED for Commercial Interiors) are not necessarily applicable.

2. If no existing Credit Interpretation Rulings are relevant to the project, the LEED project team should submit an on-line credit interpretation request. The description of the challenge encountered by the project team should be brief but explicit; it should be based on prerequisite or credit information found in the LEED for Commercial Interiors Rating System and Reference Guide; and it should place a special emphasis on the intent of the prerequisite or credit. If possible, the project team should offer potential solutions to the problem and solicit approval or rejection of their proposed interpretation. Follow the detailed instructions in the "CIR Guidelines" document available on the CIR Web page in the LEED section of the USGBC Web site.

3. USGBC will rule on requests electronically according to the posted schedule, either through a posting on the CIR Web page or via e-mail correspondence.

LEED for Commercial Interiors Application

Once a project is registered, the project design team begins to collect information and perform calculations to satisfy the prerequisite and credit submittal requirements. Since submittal documentation should be gathered throughout design and construction, it is helpful to designate a LEED team leader who is responsible for managing the compilation of this information by the project team. Use the LEED-Online Submittal Templates that are provided through the LEED project resources Web page located in the LEED section of the USGBC Web site. These templates contain embedded calculators, and are instrumental in documenting fulfillment of credit requirements and prompting for correct and complete supporting information.

Two-Phase Application

A new feature of LEED for Commercial Interiors v2.0 is the option of splitting a certification application into two phases. Rather than submitting all documentation for a project at the end of the construction phase, project teams will be able to submit designated "design phase credits" at the end of the design phase for review by USGBC. Design phase credits are those credits that USGBC can reasonably adjudicate based on design phase documentation. For example, if a project site meets the LEED for Commercial Interiors Sustainable Sites Credit 3.1: Alternative Transportation, Public Transportation Access, USGBC can assess the likelihood of the project achieving this credit prior to the completion of construction.

It is important to remember that LEED credit is not awarded at the design review stage. Project teams are notified of the likelihood that their project will achieve a LEED credit if construction is executed in accordance with design phase plans. Projects must submit verification that design

elements were implemented as planned after completion of construction.

A list of the potential design phase credits can be found in the LEED section of the USGBC Web site. Project teams are allotted one design phase review. At the completion of construction, the balance of attempted credits, verification of design phase credits, and additional documentation for those design phase credits that have changed since the design phase review, are documented and submitted for USGBC review. See below for more details regarding the two-phase review.

Review and Certification

To earn LEED for Commercial Interiors certification, the applicant project must satisfy all of the prerequisites and a minimum number of points to attain the established LEED for Commercial Interiors project ratings as listed below. Having satisfied the basic prerequisites of the program, applicant projects are then rated according to their degree of compliance within the rating system. All projects will need to comply with the version of LEED for Commercial Interiors that is current at the time of project registration.

Design Phase Review

Once USGBC has received the complete design phase application and the design phase fee (which is a portion of the total certification fee), USGBC will formally rule on the application by designating each attempted credit as either Anticipated or Denied. No certification award will be given at this time, nor will any credits be awarded. This process gives project teams the opportunity to assess the likelihood of credit achievement, and requires follow through to ensure the design is executed in the construction phase according to design specifications.

Construction Phase Review

At the completion of construction, the project team will submit all attempted credits for review. If the project team had elected to have a design phase review, and any of the design phase Anticipated credits have changed, additional documentation must be submitted to substantiate continued compliance with credit requirements. For design phase Anticipated credits that have not substantively changed, the project team must submit verification that the design has been executed in the construction phase per requirements. Once USGBC has received the complete application and fee (the remainder of the total certification fee, if a design review has been conducted), USGBC will formally rule on the full application. All applicant-verified design phase credits that were designated as Anticipated and have not changed since the design phase review will be declared as Achieved. All other credits will be designated as either Achieved or Denied.

Appeals

Appeals may be filed after either the design phase review or the final review. Please see the LEED for Commercial Interiors section of the USGBC Web site for more information on appeals.

Fees

Certification fee information can be found in the LEED for Commercial Interiors section of the USGBC Web site. USGBC will acknowledge receipt of application and proceed with application review when all project documentation has been submitted. The LEED for Commercial Interiors ratings are awarded according to the following scale:

❑ Certified 21-26 points

❑ Silver 27-31 points

❑ Gold 32-41 points

❑ Platinum 42-57 points

USGBC will recognize buildings that achieve one of these rating levels with a formal letter of certification and a mountable plaque.

Updates & Addenda

This current version is the third edition of the LEED for Commercial Interiors Reference Guide dated October 2006. As LEED for Commercial Interiors continues to improve and evolve, updates and addenda will be made available to substitute and augment the current material. USGBC cannot be held liable for any criteria set forth herein, which may not be applicable to later versions of LEED for Commercial Interiors. Updates and addenda will be accumulated between revisions and will be formally incorporated at the major revision points approximately every three years. In the interim between major revisions, USGBC may use its consensus process to clarify criteria.

When a project registers for certification, the prerequisites and credits current at the time of project registration will continue to guide the project throughout its certification process.

IV. LEED for Commercial Interiors Reference Guide Version 2.0

The LEED for Commercial Interiors Version 2.0 Reference Guide is a supporting document to the LEED for Commercial Interiors Green Building Rating System™. The Reference Guide is intended to assist project teams in understanding LEED for Commercial Interiors criteria and the benefits of complying with each criterion. The Reference Guide includes examples of strategies that can be used in each category, case studies of buildings that have implemented these strategies successfully, and additional resources that will provide more information. The guide does not provide an exhaustive list of strategies for meeting the criteria as subsequent strategies will be developed and employed by designers that satisfy the intent of each credit. Nor does it provide all of the information that design teams need to determine the applicability of a credit to their project.

Prerequisite and Credit Format

Each prerequisite and credit is organized in a standardized format for simplicity and quick reference. The first section summarizes the key points regarding the measure and includes the intent, requirements, required submittals for certification and a summary of the referenced standard. The subsequent sections provide supportive information to help interpret the measure and offer links to various resources and examples. Also, please note that each credit section lists the additional documentation you may be asked to present in the event of an audit.

If your project team encounters an out-of-date Web link in the Reference Guide, please go to the root Web site, which should take the form of www.organization.com with no additional text following. Then you may be able to navigate through the Web site to find the referenced document. Please contact USGBC at (202) 828-7422 if you have trouble finding a resource.

Sustainable Sites

Overview

Buildings affect ecosystems in a variety of ways. Development of greenfield or previously undeveloped sites consumes land, may encroach on agricultural lands, compromises existing wildlife habitat and exacerbates local and regional erosion. Stormwater runoff from impervious surfaces may impact water quality in receiving waters. Sedimentation caused by erosion may hinder regional navigation, disrupt aquatic life and reduce the quality of local/regional recreation areas. Heat from the sun is absorbed by buildings and paved surfaces and is radiated back, increasing temperatures in surrounding urban areas. External night lighting systems may cause light pollution to the night sky and interfere with nocturnal ecology.

A building's location also affects ecosystems based on the occupants' options for travel to and from the site. According to the Federal Bureau of Transportation Statistics, vehicle use in America has nearly tripled, from 1 to 2.85 trillion miles per year, between 1970 and 2002. Vehicles are responsible for approximately 20% of U.S. greenhouse gas emissions annually (NRDC). Vehicle fuel consumption and emissions contribute to climate change, smog, acid rain, and particulate material released in vehicle exhaust have been linked to numerous health problems. The infrastructure required to support vehicle travel (parking and roadway surfaces, service stations, fuel distribution networks, etc) increase the consumption of land and nonrenewable resources, alter stormwater flow and absorb heat energy, exacerbating heat island effect.

Project teams undertaking commercial interior projects should be cognizant of the inherent impacts of development on land consumption, ecosystems, natural resources and energy use. Preference should be given to buildings with high performance attributes in locations that enhance existing neighborhoods, transportation networks, and urban infrastructures. During initial project scoping, preference should be given to buildings that are either LEED certified or that have incorporated key sustainability concepts and practices into design, construction operations and maintenance activities.

Establishing sustainable design objectives and integrating building location and sustainable features as a metric for decision making encourages development and preservation or restoration practices that limit the environmental impact of buildings on local ecosystems.

Credit Timing

As **Table 1** shows, achievement of many LEED for Commercial Interiors Sustainable Sites credits is contingent upon the selection of a building and project location where key sustainability features already exist or can easily be incorporated during project development. Corporate executives and tenant real estate representatives responsible for selection of the project location have a significant opportunity to positively affect the project's success in the Sustainable Sites category and are therefore critical players in the overall LEED for Commercial Interiors project's success.

When considering building and site alternatives, it is important to establish environmental criteria (such as selection of a building that has achieved LEED certification) that can be referenced throughout the evaluation and selection process. The selection of a building and location with existing sustainable attributes will impact the ability to earn several credits and may also reduce the degree of difficulty for credit achievement and documentation.

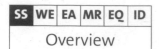

Tenant projects are served well when key players representing the tenant and the design team are included in the establishment of building selection criteria prior to the pursuit of a tenant space and lease negotiations.

Table 1: Timing on Credit Decisions and Actions

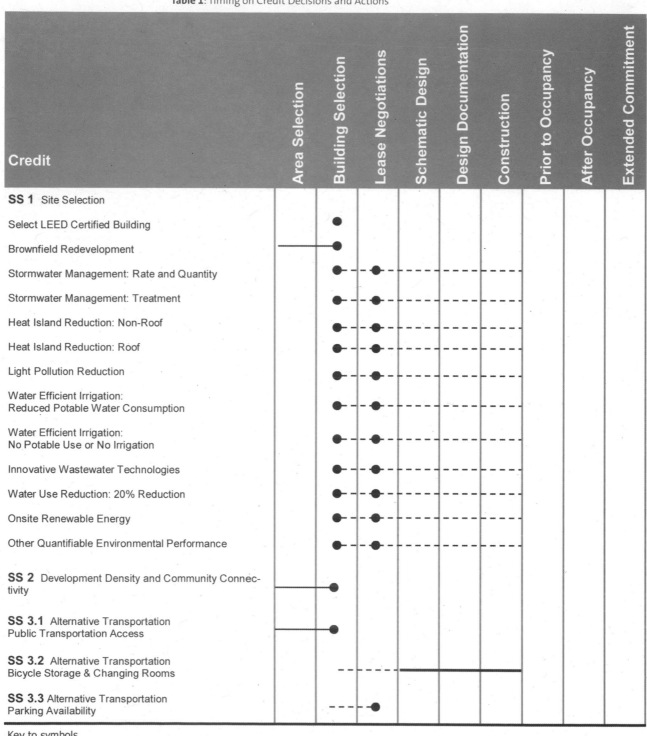

Credit	Area Selection	Building Selection	Lease Negotiations	Schematic Design	Design Documentation	Construction	Prior to Occupancy	After Occupancy	Extended Commitment
SS 1 Site Selection									
Select LEED Certified Building		●							
Brownfield Redevelopment	——	●							
Stormwater Management: Rate and Quantity		●	●						
Stormwater Management: Treatment		●	●						
Heat Island Reduction: Non-Roof		●	●						
Heat Island Reduction: Roof		●	●						
Light Pollution Reduction		●	●						
Water Efficient Irrigation: Reduced Potable Water Consumption		●	●						
Water Efficient Irrigation: No Potable Use or No Irrigation		●	●						
Innovative Wastewater Technologies		●	●						
Water Use Reduction: 20% Reduction		●	●						
Onsite Renewable Energy		●	●						
Other Quantifiable Environmental Performance		●	●						
SS 2 Development Density and Community Connectivity	——	●							
SS 3.1 Alternative Transportation Public Transportation Access	——	●							
SS 3.2 Alternative Transportation Bicycle Storage & Changing Rooms			- - -	——					
SS 3.3 Alternative Transportation Parking Availability		- - -	●						

Key to symbols

●	Critical decision point
———	Period of critical activity
———	Period of activity
- - - -	Period of possible activity

Site Selection

Three points may be earned for locating the tenant space in a LEED Certified Building,

OR

Up to a total of 3 points may be earned in 1/2-point increments if the building in which the tenant space is located meets any of the stated requirements. Two 1/2 points are needed to earn 1 point; no rounding up is permitted. In the case of exceptional performance (for example, exceeding stated thresholds) an additional 1/2 point may be achieved; however, no single requirement may earn more than 1 point. The requirements below have been gathered from other LEED Rating Systems, and are elaborated on in the LEED for Commercial Interiors Reference Guide.

Intent

Encourage tenants to select buildings with best practices systems and employed green strategies.

Requirements

- Select a LEED Certified Building

OR

- Locate the tenant space in a building that has in place two or more of the following characteristics at time of submittal:

Option A. Brownfield Redevelopment: (1/2 point)

A building developed on a site documented (by means of an ASTM E1903-97 Phase II Environmental Site Assessment)

OR

A building on a site that has been classified as a Brownfield by a local, state or federal government agency. Effective remediation of site contamination must have been completed.

Option B. Stormwater Management, Rate and Quantity: (1/2 point)

A building that prior to development had:

Less than or equal to 50% imperviousness and has implemented a stormwater management plan that equals or is less than the pre-developed 1.5-year/24-hour rate and quantity discharge.

OR

If greater than 50% imperviousness has implemented a stormwater management plan that reduced pre-developed 1.5-year/24-hour rate and quantity discharge by 25% of the annual stormwater load falling on the site. (This is based on actual local rainfall unless the actual exceeds the 10-year annual average local rainfall—then use the 10-year annual average.) This mitigation can be through a variety of measures including perviousness of site, stormwater retention ponds, capture of rainwater for reuse or other measures.

**3 points
for
LEED Certified
Building
or
1 point
for any two
requirements
up to a
maximum of
3 points**

Option C. Stormwater Management, Treatment: (1/2 point)

A building that has in place site stormwater treatment systems designed to remove 80% of the average annual site area Total Suspended Solids (TSS) and 40% of the average annual site area Total Phosphorous (TP).

These values are based on the average annual loadings from all storms less than or equal to the 2-year/24-hour storm. The building must implement and maintain Best Management Practices (BMPs) outlined in Chapter 4, Part 2 (Urban Run-off), of the United States Environmental Protection Agency's Guidance Specifying Management Measures for Sources of Nonpoint Pollution in Coastal Waters, January 1993 (Document No. EPA 840B92002) or the local government's BMP document, whichever is more stringent.

Option D. Heat Island Effect, Non-Roof : (up to 1 point)

A building that provides shade (or will have within 5 years of landscape installation) and/or uses light-colored/high-albedo materials with a Solar Reflectance Index (SRI) of at least 30, and/or open grid pavement, that individually or in total equals at least 30% of the site's non-roof impervious surfaces, which include parking areas, walkways, plazas, fire lanes, etc.,

OR

Has placed a minimum of 50% of parking spaces underground or covered by structured parking,

OR

Used an open-grid pavement system (less than 50% impervious) for 50% of the parking lot area.

Option E. Heat Island Effect, Roof: (1/2 point)

A building with roofing having a Solar Reflectance Index (SRI) greater than or equal to the value in **Table 1** for a minimum of 75% of the roof surface;

Table 1

Roof Type	Slope	SRI
Low-Sloped Roof	≤ 2:12	78
Steep-Sloped Roof	> 2:12	29

OR

A building that has installed a "green" (vegetated) roof for at least 50% of the roof area.

OR

A building having in combination high SRI roofs and vegetated roofs that satisfy the following area requirement:

Total Roof Area ≤ [(Area of SRI roof x 1.33) + (Area of vegetated roof x 2)]

Option F. Light Pollution Reduction: (1/2 point)

A building that meets or provides lower light levels and uniformity ratios than those recommended by the Illuminating Engineering Society of North America (IESNA) *Recommended Practice Manual: Lighting for Exterior Environments (RP-33-99)*. The building must have designed the exterior lighting such that all exterior luminaires with more than 1000 initial lamp lumens are shielded and all luminaires with more than 3500 initial lamp lumens meet the Full Cutoff IESNA Classification. The maximum candela value of all interior lighting shall fall within the property. Any luminaire within a distance of 2.5 times its mounting height from the property boundary shall have shielding such that no light from that luminaire crosses the property boundary.

Option G. Water Efficient Irrigation, Reduced Potable Water Consumption: (1/2 point)

A building that employs high-efficiency irrigation technology OR uses captured rain or recycled site water to reduce potable water consumption for irrigation by 50% over conventional means.

Option H. Water Efficient Irrigation, No Potable Use or No Irrigation: (1/2 point in addition to Option G requirement)

A building that uses only captured rain or recycled site water to eliminate all potable water use for site irrigation (except for initial watering to establish plants), OR does not have permanent landscaping irrigation systems.

Option I. Innovative Wastewater Technologies: (1/2 point)

A building that reduces the use of municipally provided potable water for building sewage conveyance by a minimum of 50%, OR treats 100% of wastewater on-site to tertiary standards.

Option J. Water Use Reduction, 20% Reduction: (1/2 point)

A building that meets the 20% reduction in water use requirement for the entire building and has an on-going plan to require future occupants to comply.

Option K. On-site Renewable Energy: (up to 1 point)

A building which supplies at least 5% of the building's total energy use (expressed as a fraction of annual energy cost) through the use of on-site renewable energy systems.

Table 2

On-site Renewable Energy as Percent of Total	Points
5%	½
10%	1

Option L. Other Quantifiable Environmental Performance: (up to 3 points)

A building that has in place at time of submittal other quantifiable environmental performance characteristics, for which the requirements may be found in other LEED Rating Systems.

Submittals

- Provide the LEED for Commercial Interiors Submittal Template, signed by the architect, interior designer, building owner, engineer or other responsible party, declaring compliance with each claimed requirement based on the standards as defined in applicable LEED Green Building Rating System.

Potential Technologies & Strategies

During the building selection process, give preference to those properties employing the highest and best green building strategies.

Approach and Implementation

The intent of LEED for Commercial Interiors SS Credit 1 is to encourage project teams to select buildings based on their green qualities. Locating the project in an existing LEED certified building is the most straightforward path to both achieving and documenting this credit.

Project teams may also earn SS Credit 1 by selecting a base building that has not achieved LEED certification but possesses performance characteristics associated with some LEED certified buildings. Options A through K lay out requirements that have been used in the rating systems for Existing Buildings, Commercial Interiors, New Construction and Major Renovations, and Core and Shell Development. These requirements are established performance criteria that contribute to SS Credit 1 points if they are in place at the time of completion of a LEED for Commercial Interiors project.

Review the list of LEED certified projects, available at www.usgbc.org, to find local LEED certified buildings or regional USGBC Chapter representatives who will be able to identify buildings with preferred performance characteristics.

In the following narrative for SS Credit 1, the submittal criteria for each option are presented in further detail. The requirements and submittal criteria represent the approach being used, or under consideration, in the corresponding LEED rating system, from which the LEED for Commercial Interiors SS credit has been drawn at the time LEED for Commercial Interiors v2.0 was approved by USGBC membership.

As LEED Rating Systems evolve, criteria for Options A through K may also evolve. Project teams may choose to follow the existing compliance path as outlined in LEED for Commercial Interiors v2.0 but should be aware that alternative compliance paths may be considered from other Rating Systems that are deemed equivalent for point achievement in LEED for Commercial Interiors.

Option L

Other Quantifiable Environmental Performance.

Option L is provided to accommodate credits from other LEED Rating Systems not specifically itemized in Options A through K. Option L may also be used when the building selected meets the exemplary performance criteria specified for some of the requirements of Options A through K. One additional half point may be attained for each.

Credit Interpretation Rulings

Credit Interpretation Rulings concerning the Options included in this credit may be made for LEED for Commercial Interiors v2.0 project requests and apply to LEED for Commercial Interiors projects. LEED for Commercial Interiors Credit Interpretation Rulings, available at www.usgbc.org, will provide updated information on a regular basis.

As it relates to a specific registered project, a Credit Interpretation Ruling (CIR) may be made for clarification on a given Option in the same manner as a CIR for any other credit in the Rating System. It should be noted that CIRs pertaining to other LEED Rating Systems may have an impact on a LEED for Commercial Interiors credit Option–these CIRs will be cross-referenced for easy access by LEED for Commercial Interiors project teams when applicable.

Submittal Documentation

The submittal requirements for SS Credit 1 sub-credits draw heavily from the submittal requirements set forth in the LEED Rating System from which the credit has been drawn. To demonstrate

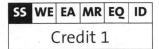
that the credit requirements have been satisfied, follow the submittal process that is outlined in this Guide and in the LEED for Commercial Interiors Submittal Templates.

In their original version in the other LEED Rating Systems, credit requirements and submittal criteria generally relate to whole building projects. The submittal requirements have been developed based on an expectation that design documentation is readily available. Due to the varied nature of LEED for Commercial Interiors projects, it is possible that a considerable period of time may have elapsed between the construction of the base building and the LEED for Commercial Interiors project submittal. Recognizing this fact, project teams that cannot document base building credits in the prescribed manner may propose alternative documentation strategies provided the project team successfully demonstrates credit compliance. For example, photographs showing the area of parking shaded by trees, or building permit documents depicting parking garage floor plans could be used to document Option D, Heat Island Effcct, Non-Roof. Project teams are encouraged to verify that alternative documentation strategies are valid using the CIR process.

Considerations

The requirements established in SS Credit 1 are intended to encourage selection of appropriate base buildings for tenant fit out projects. These points are awarded primarily in recognition of the positive environmental impacts encouraged through sustainable sites and water efficiency strategies. Each Option includes considerations relevant to its associated environmental performance characteristic.

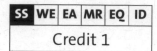

SS	WE	EA	MR	EQ	ID
Credit 1					

Select a LEED Certified Building

3 points

Submittals

- Provide the LEED for Commercial Interiors Submittal Template, signed by the responsible party, declaring that the commercial interiors project is located in a LEED certified building.

- Provide a copy of the core building LEED certification document.

Potential Technologies & Strategies

During the building selection process, give preference to properties that have achieved LEED Certification. Buildings that apply for achievement of this credit may be certified at any level using any LEED Rating System.

Approach and Implementation

Review the Timing on Credit Decisions and Actions tables at the start of each credit section to identify those credits that are impacted by the building selection. Many credits in the LEED for Commercial Interiors Rating System build off the capabilities of systems and attributes of the base building. Where possible, obtain the base building LEED certification review documents early in project development. The certification documents from the base building can serve as a resource for identification of credits and base building systems making achievement of some LEED for Commercial Interiors credits significantly easier.

Early establishment of project goals that maximize use of base building systems is a key to successful project delivery. Develop criteria for use by real estate and leasing agents. Consult the USGBC Web site for completed LEED certified projects. Local USGBC Chapters can serve as valuable resources for identification of leaseable space in LEED certified buildings and in-process buildings that are seeking LEED certification upon project completion.

Submittal Documentation

Complete the declaration included in the LEED for Commercial Interiors Submittal Template, and include a copy of the LEED certification document for the base building.

Additional Documentation

No additional documentation should be required during submittal review.

Exemplary Performance

No exemplary performance criteria exist.

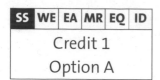

Option A. Brownfield Redevelopment

Intent

Rehabilitate damaged sites where development is complicated by real or perceived environmental contamination, reducing pressure on undeveloped land.

Requirements

- A building developed on a site documented (by means of an ASTM E1903-97 Phase II Environmental Site Assessment)

OR

- A building on a site that has been classified as a Brownfield by a local, state or federal government agency. Effective remediation of site contamination must have been completed.

Submittals

- Provide a copy of the pertinent sections of the ASTM E1903-97 Phase II Environmental Site Assessment documenting the site contamination OR provide a letter from a local, state or federal regulatory agency confirming that the site is classified as a Brownfield by that agency.

- Provide the LEED Submittal Template, signed by the civil engineer or responsible party, declaring the type of damage that existed on the site and describing the remediation performed.

Potential Technologies & Strategies

During the site selection process, give preference to Brownfield sites. Identify tax incentives and property cost savings. Develop and implement a site remediation plan using strategies such as pump-and-treat, bioreactors, land farming, and in-situ remediation.

Summary of Referenced Standards

ASTM E1903-97 Phase II Environmental Site Assessment

ASTM International

www.astm.org

This guide covers a framework for employing good commercial and customary practices in conducting a Phase II environmental site assessment of a parcel of commercial property. It covers the potential presence of a range of contaminants that are within the scope of CERCLA, as well as petroleum products.

EPA Brownfields Definition

EPA Sustainable Redevelopment of Brownfields Program

www.epa.gov/Brownfields

With certain legal exclusions and additions, the term "Brownfield site" means real property, the expansion, redevelopment, or reuse of which may be complicated by the presence or potential presence of a hazardous substance, pollutant or contaminant (source: Public Law 107-118, H.R. 2869–"Small Business Liability Relief and Brownfields Revitalization Act"). See the Web site for additional information and resources.

Credit Interpretation Rulings

Review LEED for New Construction v2.1 CIRs for SS Credit 3.

Approach and Implementation

Select a base building that was constructed on a site formerly classified as a Brownfield. Establish selection of a base building constructed on a remediated Brownfield as a requirement in the project location selection criteria and work with real estate brokers to help identify buildings which comply. Former Brownfield sites and remediation activities may be cataloged by federal, state or local authorities having jurisdiction.

Submittal Documentation

In addition to completing the declaration included in the LEED for Commercial Interiors Submittal Template, provide a copy of the pertinent sections of the ASTM E1903-97 Phase II Environmental Site Assessment documenting the site contamination or provide a letter from a local, state or federal regulatory agency confirming that the site was previously classified as a Brownfield by that agency. This supporting documentation should be available in the title work of existing buildings.

Additional Documentation

No additional documentation should be necessary if the initial submittal is complete.

Exemplary Performance

No exemplary performance criteria exist for Option A.

Considerations

Remediation and reclamation of contaminated sites can contribute to social and economic revitalization of depressed or disadvantaged neighborhoods. Local liabilities can be turned into valuable community assets and catalyze increased community investment. Clean up of contaminated properties can renew and augment a sense of community pride in local residents. Leasing from a developer who has successfully completed a Brownfield remediation initiative demonstrates that a market for these actions exists, as does the potential for return on the developers' past investment. Market reinforcement may provide the necessary support for developers to consider future Brownfield redevelopment projects.

Resources

Please see the USGBC Web site at www. usgbc.org/resources for more specific resources on materials sources and other technical information.

Web Sites

Brownfields Cleanup and Redevelopment U.S. Environmental Protection Agency

www.epa.gov/brownfields

(202) 566-2777

A comprehensive site on Brownfields that includes projects, initiatives, tools, tax incentives and other resources to address Brownfield remediation and redevelopment. For information by phone, contact your regional EPA office.

Definitions

Remediation is the process of cleaning up a contaminated site by physical, chemical or biological means. Remediation processes are typically applied to contaminated soil and groundwater.

A **Site Assessment** is an evaluation of above-ground (including facilities) and subsurface characteristics, including the geology and hydrology of the site, to determine if a release has occurred, as well as the extent and concentration of the release. Information generated during a site assessment is used to support remedial action decisions.

Please see the "Referenced Standards" section above for a definition of a Brownfield.

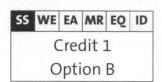
Option B. Stormwater Management: Rate and Quantity

Intent

Limit disruption and pollution of natural water flows by managing stormwater runoff.

Requirements

- A building that prior to development had:

  Less than or equal to 50% imperviousness and has implemented a stormwater management plan that equals or is less than the pre-developed 1.5-year/24-hour rate and quantity discharge.

  OR

- If greater than 50% imperviousness has implemented a stormwater management plan that reduced pre-developed 1.5-year/24-hour rate and quantity discharge by 25% of the annual stormwater load falling on the site. (This is based on actual local rainfall unless the actual exceeds the 10-year annual average local rainfall–then use the 10-year annual average.) This mitigation can be through a variety of measures including perviousness of site, stormwater retention ponds, capture of rainwater for reuse or other measures.

Submittals

- Provide the LEED Submittal Template, signed by the civil engineer or responsible party, declaring that the post-development 1.5-year/24-hour peak discharge rate and quantity does not exceed the pre-development 1.5-year/24-hour peak discharge rate and quantity. Include calculations demonstrating that existing site imperviousness is less than or equal to 50%.

  OR

- Provide the LEED Submittal Template, signed by the civil engineer or responsible party, declaring and demonstrating that the stormwater management strategies result in at least a 25% decrease in the rate and quantity of stormwater runoff. Include calculations demonstrating that existing site imperviousness exceeds 50%.

Potential Technologies & Strategies

Design the project site to maintain natural stormwater flows by promoting infiltration. Specify garden roofs and pervious paving to minimize impervious surfaces. Reuse stormwater volume generated for non-potable uses such as landscape irrigation, toilet and urinal flushing, and custodial uses.

Credit Interpretation Rulings

Credit Interpretation Rulings concerning this credit made for LEED for Commercial Interiors v2.0 project requests and as applicable for LEED for New Construction v2.1 project requests apply to LEED for Commercial Interiors projects. Review LEED for New Construction v2.1 CIRs for SS Credit 6.1.

Approach and Implementation

Locate the project in a building that has implemented one of the two compliance paths or can demonstrate performance equivalent to the requirements. Include this requirement in base building selection criteria. Local permitting agencies may have detailed information on the stormwater control techniques implemented or in use at the base building. A review of the application for the stormwater management permit may provide the required information.

Submittal Documentation

In addition to completing the declaration as required on the LEED for Commercial Interiors Submittal Template, provide the supporting documentation by either completing the calculation tables in the Submittal Templates or providing a narrative and calculations that demonstrate the requirements are satisfied at the time the project was constructed.

Calculations

The following calculation methodology is used to support the credit submittals. Stormwater runoff volumes are affected by surface characteristics on the site as well as rainfall intensity over a specified time period. To simplify stormwater calculations, consider only the surface characteristics of the project site. Stormwater volumes generated are directly related to the net imperviousness of the project site.

By reducing the amount of impervious surface on the site, stormwater volumes are reduced. The calculation methodology to estimate the imperviousness of the project site is as follows:

1. Identify the different surface types on the site: roof areas, paved areas (e.g., roads and sidewalks), landscaped areas, and other areas.

2. Calculate the total area for each of these surface types using site drawings. Use **Table 1** to assign a runoff coefficient to each surface type. If a surface type is not included in the table, use a "best estimate" or manufacturer information. For instance, if pervious paving is used, consult the manufacturer to determine the imperviousness or percentage of the surface that does not allow infiltration.

3. Create a spreadsheet to summarize the area and runoff coefficient for each surface type. Multiply the runoff coefficient by the area to obtain an impervious area for each surface type. This figure represents the square footage of each surface area that is 100% impervious (see **Equation 1**).

4. Add the impervious areas for each surface type to obtain a total impervious area for the site.

5. Divide the total impervious area by the total site area to obtain the imperviousness of the site (see **Equation 2**). Credit requirements state that for sites with im-

<table>
<tr><td>SS</td><td>WE</td><td>EA</td><td>MR</td><td>EQ</td><td>ID</td></tr>
<tr><td colspan="6">Credit 1
Option B</td></tr>
</table>

Table 1: Typical Runoff Coefficients

Surface Type	Runoff Coefficient	Surface Type	Runoff Coefficient
Pavement, Asphalt	0.95	Turf, Flat (0 - 1% slope)	0.25
Pavement, Concrete	0.95	Turf, Average (1 - 3% slope)	0.35
Pavement, Brick	0.85	Turf, Hilly (3 - 10% slope)	0.40
Pavement, Gravel	0.75	Turf, Steep (> 10% slope)	0.45
Roofs, Conventional	0.95	Vegetation, Flat (0 - 1% slope)	0.10
Roof, Garden Roof (< 4 in)	0.50	Vegetation, Average (1 - 3% slope)	0.20
Roof, Garden Roof (4 - 8 in)	0.30	Vegetation, Hilly (3 - 10% slope)	0.25
Roof, Garden Roof (9 - 20 in)	0.20	Vegetation, Steep (> 10% slope)	0.30
Roof, Garden Roof (> 20 in)	0.10		

Equation 1

$$\text{Impervious Area [SF]} = \text{Surface Area [SF]} \times \text{Runoff Coefficient}$$

Equation 2

$$\text{Imperviousness [\%]} = \frac{\text{Total Pervious Area [SF]}}{\text{Total Site Area [SF]}}$$

perviousness less than or equal to 50%, imperviousness must not increase from pre-development to post-development conditions. For previously developed sites with imperviousness greater than 50%, imperviousness must be reduced by 25% from pre-development to post-development conditions.

The following example describes the calculation method for site imperviousness. The example project is an office renovation and site improvements to an existing concrete parking lot of average slope. Surface types include sidewalks, parking areas, landscaping and the roof. The roof area is assumed to be equal to the building footprint as determined from site drawings. **Table 2** shows calculations for the design case. To reduce imperviousness, concrete sidewalks and asphalt parking lots can be substituted with pervious paving and vegetation in some areas. The building footprint is reduced and garden roofs are applied to reduce roof runoff. Next, calculations are done for the baseline case or the existing site conditions (see **Table 3**). The original use of the site was for parking and, thus, the entire site was paved with concrete pavement. The calculations demonstrate that the design case has an imperviousness of 47% and the baseline case has an imperviousness of 95%—a 50% reduction that exceeds the 25% required, thus earning one point.

Additional Documentation

No additional documentation should be necessary if the initial submittal is complete.

Exemplary Performance

No exemplary performance criteria exist for Option B.

Considerations

The volume of stormwater generated from a site depends on a number of factors including impervious surface area and rate of stormwater flows over pervious surfaces. On undeveloped sites, the majority of precipitation infiltrates into the ground while a small portion runs off on the surface and into receiving waters. This surface runoff water is classified as stormwater runoff. As areas are constructed and urbanized, surface permeability is reduced, resulting in increased stormwater runoff volumes that are transported via urban infrastructure (e.g., gutters, pipes and sewers) to receiving waters.

These stormwater volumes contain sediment and other contaminants that have a negative impact on water quality, navigation and recreation. Furthermore, conveyance and treatment of stormwater volumes require significant municipal infrastructure and maintenance. Reducing the generation of stormwater runoff maintains the natural aquifer recharge cycle. In addition, stormwater volumes do not have to be conveyed to receiving waters by the municipality, and receiving waters are not impacted.

Environmental Issues

Reduction of runoff volumes decreases or eliminates contaminants that pollute receiving water bodies. For instance, parking areas contribute to stormwater runoff that is contaminated with oil, fuel, lubricants, combustion byproducts, material from tire wear, and deicing salts. Minimizing the need for stormwater infrastructure also reduces construction impacts and the overall ecological "footprint" of the building. Finally, infiltration of stormwater on-site can recharge local aquifers, mimicking the natural water cycle.

Table 2: Design Case Imperviousness

Surface Type	Runoff Coefficient	Area [SF]	Impervious Area [SF]
Pavement, Asphalt	0.95	5,075	4,821
Pavement, Pervious	0.60	1,345	807
Roof, Garden Roof (4 - 8 in)	0.30	8,240	2,472
Vegetation, Average (1 -3% slope)	0.20	4,506	901
	TOTAL AREA	**14,660**	
	TOTAL IMPERVIOUS AREA		**8,100**
	IMPERVIOUSNESS		**55%**

Table 3: Baseline Case Imperviousness

Surface Type	Runoff Coefficient	Area [SF]	Impervious Area [SF]
Pavement, Concrete	0.95	19,166	18,208
	TOTAL AREA	**19,166**	
	TOTAL IMPERVIOUS AREA		**18,208**
	IMPERVIOUSNESS		**95%**

Community Issues

By locating the commercial interiors project in a community with progressive stormwater management, and by selecting a building that has met the requirements of SS Credit 1 Option B, the project team is recognizing the importance of stormwater volume reduction. This act leads to improved watershed quality that benefits the community through improved water quality, navigation and recreation activities. Reduced stormwater collection and treatment systems lessen the burden on municipalities for maintenance and repair, resulting in a more affordable and stable tax base.

Resources

Please see the USGBC Web site at www. usgbc.org/resources for more specific resources on materials sources and other technical information.

Web Sites

Wetlands, Oceans & Watersheds

U.S. Environmental Protection Agency

www.epa.gov/owow

(202) 566-1300

This Web site offers general information about watersheds, and information about protecting water resources, water conservation, landscaping practices, water pollution reduction, and more.

Post-Construction Storm Water Management in New Development & Redevelopment

U.S. Environmental Protection Agency

http://cfpub.epa.gov/npdes/stormwater/menuofbmps/post_7.cfm

(202) 564-9545

Information from the U.S. EPA about catch basins as a tool for sediment control.

The Stormwater Manager's Resource Center

www.stormwatercenter.net

Site for stormwater practitioners, local government officials, and others in need of technical assistance on stormwater management issues.

Center for Watershed Protection

www.cwp.org

(410) 461-8323

Non-profit dedicated to the dissemination of watershed protection information to community leaders and watershed managers via online resources, training seminars, and the publication of Watershed Protection Techniques.

Definitions

A **Constructed Wetland** is an engineered system designed to simulate natural wetland functions for water purification. Constructed wetlands are essentially treatment systems that remove contaminants from wastewaters.

Impervious Surfaces promote runoff of precipitation volumes instead of infiltration into the subsurface. The imperviousness or degree of runoff potential can be estimated for different surface materials.

Stormwater Runoff consists of water volumes that are created during precipitation events and flow over surfaces into sewer systems or receiving waters. All precipitation waters that leave project site boundaries on the surface are considered to be stormwater runoff volumes.

Total Phosphorous (TP) consists of organically bound phosphates, poly-phosphates and orthophosphates in stormwater, the majority of which originates from fertilizer application. Chemical precipitation is the typical removal mechanism for phosphorous.

Total Suspended Solids (TSS) are particles or flocs that are too small or light to be removed from stormwater via gravity settling. Suspended solid concentrations are typically removed via filtration.

Infiltration Basins and Trenches are devices used to encourage subsurface infiltration of runoff volumes through temporary surface storage. Basins are ponds that can store large volumes of stormwater. They need to drain within 72 hours to maintain aerobic conditions and to be available for the next storm event. Trenches are similar to infiltration basins except that they are shallower and function as a subsurface reservoir for stormwater volumes. Pretreatment to remove sediment and oil may be necessary to avoid clogging of infiltration devices. Infiltration trenches are more common in areas where infiltration basins are not possible.

Porous Pavement and Permeable Surfaces are used to create permeable surfaces that allow runoff to infiltrate into the subsurface. These surfaces are typically maintained with a vacuuming regime to avoid potential clogging and failure problems.

Vegetated Filter Strips and Grassed Swales utilize vegetation to filter sediment and pollutants from stormwater. Strips are appropriate for treating low-velocity surface sheet flows in areas where runoff is not concentrated. They are often used as pretreatment for other stormwater measures such as infiltration basins and trenches. Swales consist of a trench or ditch with vegetation and require occasional mowing. They also encourage subsurface infiltration, similar to infiltration basins and trenches.

Filtration Basins remove sediment and pollutants from stormwater runoff using a filter media such as sand or gravel. A sediment trap is usually included to remove sediment from stormwater before filtering to avoid clogging.

Constructed Wetlands are engineered systems that are designed to mimic natural wetland treatment properties.

Advanced designs incorporate a wide variety of wetland trees, shrubs, and plants while basic systems only include a limited number of vegetation types.

Detention Ponds capture stormwater runoff and allow pollutants to drop out before release to a stormwater or water body. A variety of detention pond designs are available, with some utilizing only gravity while others use mechanical equipment such as pipes and pumps to facilitate transport. Some ponds are dry except during storm events; others permanently store water volumes.

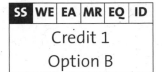

SS	WE	EA	MR	EQ	ID

Credit 1
Option B

Option C. Stormwater Management, Treatment

Intent

Limit disruption of natural water flows by eliminating stormwater runoff, increasing on-site infiltration and eliminating contaminants.

Requirements

- A building that has in place site stormwater treatment systems designed to remove 80% of the average annual site area Total Suspended Solids (TSS) and 40% of the average annual site area Total Phosphorous (TP).

- These values are based on the average annual loadings from all storms less than or equal to the 2-year/24-hour storm. The building must implement and maintain Best Management Practices (BMPs) outlined in Chapter 4, Part II (Urban Runoff), of the United States Environmental Protection Agency's Guidance Specifying Management Measures for Sources of Nonpoint Pollution in Coastal Waters, January 1993 (Document No. EPA 840B92002), or the local government's BMP document, whichever is more stringent.

Submittals

- Provide the LEED Submittal Template, signed by the civil engineer or responsible party, declaring that the design complies with or exceeds EPA or local government Best Management Practices (whichever set is more stringent) for removal of Total Suspended Solids and Total Phosphorous.

Potential Technologies & Strategies

Design mechanical or natural treatment systems such as constructed wetlands, vegetated filter strips, and bioswales to treat the site's stormwater.

Summary of Referenced Standard

Guidance Specifying Management Measures for Sources of Non-Point Pollution in Coastal Waters, January 1993 (Document No. EPA 840B92002)

www.epa.gov/owow/nps/MMGI

Hardcopy or microfiche (entire document, 836 pages): National Technical Information Service (order # PB93-234672), www.ntis.gov, (800) 553-6847

U.S. Environmental Protection Agency Office of Water, www.epa.gov/OW

This document discusses a variety of management practices that can be incorporated to remove pollutants from stormwater volumes. Chapter 4, Part II addresses urban runoff and suggests a variety of strategies for treating and infiltrating stormwater volumes after construction is completed.

Credit Interpretation Rulings

Credit Interpretation Rulings concerning this credit made for LEED for Commercial Interiors v2.0 project requests and as applicable for LEED for New Construction v2.1 project requests apply to LEED for Commercial Interiors v2.0 projects. Review LEED for New Construction v2.1 CIRs for SS Credit 6.2.

Approach and Implementation

Locate the project in a building that has in place a stormwater treatment system that meets the requirements of SS Credit 1, Option C. Determination that the existing stormwater system complies with the treatment requirements in the credit may require some investigation of the building history since underground systems are often not visible.

Project teams should consult facilities personnel, design documents, manufacturer information and code officials as possible sources for information on base building stormwater treatment systems. Building management and permitting authority may have the information needed to demonstrate that the credit requirements are being satisfied. For physical components, such as extractors, manufacturer cut sheets may confirm that the installed system has the capability to remove suspended solids and phosphorous as required by the referenced standard.

For that portion of stormwater that cannot be contained or reused on-site, facilities can be constructed to remove contaminants. The strategies include constructed wetlands, stormwater filtering systems, bio-swales, bio-retention basins and vegetated filter strips. While evaluating potential buildings for commercial interior projects, see if the base building site design incorporates compliant systems.

Submittal Documentation

In addition to completing the declaration included in the LEED for Commercial Interiors Submittal Template, provide a narrative and calculations demonstrating that the building stormwater management system was designed to remove 80% of the average annual site area total suspended solids and 40% of the average annual site area total phosphorous.

Calculations

In most cases where buildings implemented standard EPA or local BMPs, no calculations are required to demonstrate compliance with the requirements of Option C. In instances where designs far different than accepted BMPs have been developed and implemented, detailed engineering calculations may be required to demonstrate the TSS and phosphorus reductions that will be achieved.

Additional Documentation

No additional documentation should be necessary if the initial submittal is complete.

Exemplary Performance

No exemplary performance criteria exist for Option C.

Considerations

See considerations for SS Credit 1 Option B

Definitions

See definitions for SS Credit 1 Option B.

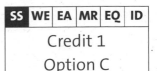

SS	WE	EA	MR	EQ	ID

Credit 1
Option C

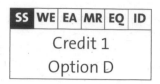
Option D. Heat Island Reduction, Non-Roof

Intent

Reduce heat islands (thermal gradient differences between developed and undeveloped areas) to minimize impact on microclimate and human and wildlife habitat.

Requirements

- A building that provides shade (or will have within 5 years of construction) and/or uses light-colored/high-albedo materials with a Solar Reflectance Index (SRI) of at least 30, and/or open grid pavement, that individually or in total equals at least 30% of the site's non-roof impervious surfaces, which include parking areas, walkways, plazas, fire lanes, etc.,

OR

- Has placed a minimum of 50% of parking spaces underground or covered by structured parking

OR

- Used an open-grid pavement system (less than 50% impervious) for 50% of the parking lot area.

Submittals

Provide the LEED Submittal Template, signed by the civil engineer or responsible party, referencing the site plan to demonstrate areas of paving, landscaping (list species) and building footprint, and declaring that—

- A minimum of 30% of non-roof impervious surfaces areas are constructed with high-albedo materials and/or open grid pavement and/or will be shaded within five years

- OR a minimum of 50% of parking spaces have been placed underground or are covered by structured parking

- OR an open-grid pavement system (less than 50% impervious) has been used for a minimum of 50% of the parking lot area.

Potential Technologies & Strategies

Shade constructed surfaces on the site with landscape features and minimize the overall building footprint. Consider replacing constructed surfaces (i.e. roof, roads, sidewalks, etc.) with vegetated surfaces such as open grid paving or specify high-albedo materials to reduce the heat absorption.

Credit Interpretation Rulings

Credit Interpretation Rulings concerning this credit made for LEED for Commercial Interiors v2.0 project requests and as applicable for LEED for New Construction v2.1 project requests apply to LEED for Commercial Interiors v2.0 projects. Review LEED for New Construction v2.1 CIRs for SS Credit 7.1.

Approach and Implementation

Locate the project in a building that has physical characteristics that reduce its contribution to heat island effect. LEED for Commercial Interiors SS Credit 1 Option D has three compliance paths. All three compliance paths seek to reduce the potential for non-roof building surfaces to absorb and retain heat.

Submittal Documentation

Provide the LEED Submittal Template, signed by the civil engineer or responsible party, identifying the compliance path or paths being followed to satisfy the requirements. In addition provide a site plan that supports each declaration.

Shaded Paving

Identify all non-roof impervious surfaces on a site plan. Include sidewalks, parking lots, entrance drives, plazas, fire lanes, etc. Cross-hatch these surfaces on the plan and label the cross-hatched section as "Paved Area." Sum total the square footage of cross-hatched/paved non-pervious surface.

Determine the portion of "paved area" shaded by trees at 12:00 PM June 21 (solar noon–sun directly overhead). If the trees on site are less than five years old, assume reasonable growth curve to project canopy shading with five-year old trees. Consult with Regional Landscape Architects, Nurseries or Landscaping Firms to determine projected tree canopy growth.

High Albedo Paving

Determine the unshaded paved area with a Solar Reflectance Index (SRI) value of at least 30. SRI is determined using the calulator in the Submittal Template for credit option E. The calculation for paving materials is based on tested values for reflectivity and reference values for emissivity, as provided in ASHRAE Handbook of Fundamentals and other sources. If 30% or more of the paved area has an SRI of at least 30, 1/2 point is awarded.

The area of shaded pavement and unshaded highly reflective pavement can be combined to demonstrate credit achievement. Note that these surfaces cannot be double-counted. For example if a surface is both reflective and shaded, the area of this surface can only be counted once

toward the 30% threshold. Both shaded and total paved area should be reported in identical units (e.g. square feet or acres).

If the total non-roof compliant surface is 60% or more based on the above calculations, the requirements for exemplary performance have been met earning an additional 1/2 point for Option D.

Underground Parking

1/2 point is awarded when at least 50% of the base building parking is located underground or is shaded.

An additional 1/2 point is awarded for exemplary performance if 100% of the building's parking is underground or shaded for Option L.

Open-Grid Pavement

Cross-hatch and sum all "surface pavement" utilized by vehicles (parking spaces, driving lanes, entrance driveways and fire lanes). It is not necessary to include underground parking areas.

Identify the portion of the surface pavement that meets the requirement for open-grid pavement systems. For purposes of this credit, open grid paving must include planting in the pervious portions of the paving system. Divide the total compliant open grid pavement (square feet) by total surface pavement area. 1/2 point is awarded for project teams with 50% open-grid pavement.

An additional 1/2 point is awarded for exemplary performance if 95% of the building's "surface pavement" meets open-grid requirements.

Additional Documentation

If the site plan provided does not clearly indicate the basis of the calculations for this credit, additional calculations may be necessary during the review process. Manufacturer's information, test results, or other data may be necessary to support solar reflectance characteristics and/or permeability of paving materials used.

Exemplary Performance

Up to two half points may be earned by meeting the requirements of two of the compliance paths under SS Credit 1 Option D or for exemplary performance as noted for Option L.

Calculations

The following calculations are used to support the credit submittals listed on the first page of this credit.

Shading of Non-Roof Impervious Surfaces

1. Identify all non-roof impervious surfaces on the project site and sum the total area.

2. Identify all trees that contribute shade to non-roof impervious surfaces. Calculate the shade coverage provided by these trees after five years on the non-roof impervious surfaces on June 21 at noon solar time to determine the maximum shading effect. Add the total area of shade provided for non-roof impervious surfaces.

3. Shade must be provided for at least 30% of non-roof impervious surfaces to earn this point (see **Equation 1**).

Highly Reflective Pavement

1. Identify all non-roof impervious surfaces on the project site and sum the total area.

2. Calculate the area of all paving materials with a Solar Reflectance Index of at least 30.

3. At least 30% of the non-roof impervious surface must have a Reflectance Index of at least 30 to earn this point.

Equation 1

$$\text{Shade [\%]} = \frac{\text{Shaded Impervious Area [SF]}}{\text{Total Impervious Area [SF]}}$$

Permeable Pavement

1. Identify all non-roof impervious surfaces on the project site and sum the total area.

2. Calculate the area of all paving materials with a permeability of at least 50%.

3. At least 30% of the non-roof paved surfaces must have a permeability of 50% to earn this point.

Note that the three calculation strategies above may be combined to demonstrate that at least 30% of the site paved surfaces are shaded, reflective, or permeable to earn this point. If the strategies are combined, paving with one or more of the above characteristics should not be double-counted (for example, shaded paving should not also be counted as reflective).

Covered Parking

1. Calculate the number of total parking spaces provided and demonstrate that at least 50% of the spaces are located underground or covered by "stacked" parking to reduce the overall parking footprint.

Open-Grid Parking Areas

(This strategy is distinct from the permeable pavement strategy above in that it addresses ONLY the parking lot area of the project.)

1. Calculate the total parking lot area of the project. Parking lots include parking spaces and driving lanes. Exclude parking spaces that do not receive direct sun (e.g., underground parking and stacked parking spaces), sidewalks, and other impervious surfaces that cannot support vehicle loads.

2. Calculate the parking area that is designed with open-grid paving with a permeability of at least 50% and vegetated in the open cavities.

3. A minimum of 50% of the total parking area must be comprised of paving materials that meet these characteristics.

Resources

Please see the USGBC Web site at www.usgbc.org/resources for more specific resources on materials sources and other technical information.

Web Sites

American Concrete Pavement Assn.

www.pavement.com

(847) 966-2272

National association representing concrete pavement contractors, cement companies, equipment and material manufacturers, and suppliers. See the R&T Update #3.05, June 2002, "Albedo: A measure of Pavement Surface Reflectance" (www.pavement.com/techserv/RT3.05.pdf).

Heat Island Group

Lawrence Berkeley National Laboratory

http://eetd.lbl.gov/HeatIsland/

LBL conducts heat island research to find, analyze, and implement solutions to minimizing heat island effect, with current research efforts focusing on the study and development of more reflective surfaces for roadways and buildings.

Heat Island Effect

U.S. Environmental Protection Agency

www.epa.gov/heatisland

(202) 343-9299

Basic information about heat island effect, its social and environmental costs, and strategies to minimize its prevalence.

Definitions

Heat Island Effects occur when warmer temperatures are experienced in urban landscapes compared to adjacent rural areas as a result of solar energy retention on constructed surfaces. Principal surfaces that contribute to the heat island effect include streets, sidewalks, parking lots and buildings.

Open-Grid Pavement is defined for LEED purposes as pavement that is less than 50% impervious and contains vegetation in the open cells.

Solar Reflectance Index (SRI) SRI is a yardstick that compares different materials based on their reflectance and emissivity characteristics. The Solar Reflectance Index (SRI) calculation is based on the relative temperature (Ts) of a surface of a specific material with respect to the standard white (SRI = 100) and standard black (SRI =0) under standard solar and ambient conditions. The SRI calculation allows equivalent comparison of materials having a lower reflectivity but higher emissivity with materials having a high reflectivity but lower emissivity. Higher SRIs are "cooler" than lower SRIs. SRI can be determined using ASTM Standard E1980-01 Standard Practice for Calculating Solar Reflectance Index of Horizontal and Low-Sloped Opaque Surfaces. (More information about SRI is also provided in the next sub-credit; Option E. Roof Heat Island Reduction.)

Emissivity is the ratio of the radiation emitted by a surface to the radiation emitted by a blackbody at the same temperature.

Infrared Emittance is a parameter between 0 and 1 that indicates the ability of a material to shed infrared radiation. The wavelength of this radiant energy is roughly 5 to 40 micrometers. Most building materials (including glass) are opaque in this part of the spectrum, and have an emittance of roughly 0.9. Materials such as clean, bare metals are the most important exceptions to the 0.9 rule. Thus clean, untarnished galvanized steel has low emittance, and aluminum roof coatings have intermediate emittance levels.

Non-Roof Impervious Surfaces include all surfaces on the site with a perviousness of less than 50%, not including the roof of the building. Examples of typically impervious surfaces include parking lots, roads, sidewalks and plazas.

Perviousness is the percent of the surface area of a paving material that is open and allows moisture to pass through the material and soak into the earth below the paving system.

Solar Reflectance is the ratio of the reflected electromagnetic energy to the incoming electromagnetic energy. A reflectance of 100% means that all of the energy striking a reflecting surface is reflected back into the atmosphere and none of the energy is absorbed by the surface.

Underground Parking is a "tuck-under" or stacked parking structure that reduces the exposed parking surface area.

Table 1: Typical Solar Reflectance Index (SRI) for Paving Materials*

Material	Solar Reflectance	Emissivity	Solar Reflectance Index
Asphalt Paving	0.05	0.9	8.7
Chip-Seal (w 0.28 albedo aggregate)	0.28[a]	0.9	29
Ordinary (grey or buff) Portland Cement Concrete	0.35[b]	0.88	37
White Portland Cement Concrete	0.7[b]	0.88	85

a. Reflectance must be laboratory verified using ASTM C1549.

b. American Concrete Pavement Association, "Concrete Pavement Research & Technology Update." Number 3.05 June 2002. These values are from the conservative end of the range reported.

*Project teams may use these values to determine compliance when no specific manufacturer's data is available for existing installed materials.

Option E. Heat Island Reduction, Roof

Intent

Reduce heat islands (thermal gradient differences between developed and undeveloped areas) to minimize impact on microclimate and human and wildlife habitat.

Requirements

A building with roofing having a Solar Reflectance Index (SRI) greater than or equal to the value in Table 1 for a minimum of 75% of the roof surface;

OR

A building that has installed a "green" (vegetated) roof for at least 50% of the roof area.

OR

A building having in combination high SRI roofs and vegetated roofs that satisfy the following area requirement:

Total Roof Area ≤ [(Area of SRI roof x 1.33) + (Area of vegetated roof x 2)]

Submittals

Provide the LEED Submittal Template, signed by the architect, civil engineer or responsible party, referencing the building plan and declaring that 75% the roofing materials have a Solar Reflectance Index (SRI) of at least the values indicated in **Table 1**.

Table 1: EPA ENERGY STAR Roof Criteria

Roof Type	Slope	SRI
Low-Sloped Roof	≤ 2:12	78
Steep-Sloped Roof	> 2:12	29

OR

Provide the LEED Submittal Template, signed by the architect, civil engineer or responsible party, referencing the building plan and demonstrating that vegetated roof areas constitute at least 50% of the total roof area.

Potential Technologies & Strategies

Visit the ENERGY STAR® Web site, www.energystar.gov, to look for compliant products. Consider installing high-albedo and vegetative roofs to reduce heat absorption. Note that ENERGY STAR® roofs do not automatically achieve this credit, as LEED applies additional standards which exceed ENERGY STAR® requirements.

Summary of Referenced Standards

ASTM Standard E1980-01 Standard Practice for Calculating Solar Reflectance Index of Horizontal and Low-Sloped Opaque Surfaces.

This standard describes how surface reflectivity and emissivity are combined to calculate a Solar Refelctance Index (SRI) for a roofing material or other surface. The standard also describes a laboratory and field testing protocol that can be used to determine SRI.

ASTM E408-71(1996)e1—Standard Test Methods for Total Normal Emittance of Surfaces Using Inspection-Meter Techniques

www.astm.org

(610) 832-9585

This standard describes how to measure total normal emittance of surfaces using a portable inspection-meter instrument. The test methods are intended for large surfaces where non-destructive testing is required. See the standard for testing steps and a discussion of thermal emittance theory.

ASTM E903-96—Standard Test Method for Solar Absorptance, Reflectance, and Transmittance of Materials Using Integrating Spheres

www.astm.org

(610) 832-9585

Referenced in the ENERGY STAR® roofing standard, this test method uses spectrophotometers and need only be applied for initial reflectance measurement. Methods of computing solar-weighted properties from the measured spectral values are specified. This test method is applicable to materials having both specular and diffuse optical properties. Except for transmitting sheet materials that are inhomogeneous, patterned, or corrugated, this test method is preferred over Test Method E1084.

The ENERGY STAR® roofing standard also allows the use of reflectometers to measure solar reflectance of roofing materials. See the roofing standard for more details.

EPA Energy Star Roofing Guidelines

U.S. Environmental Protection Agency ENERGY STAR® Program

www.energystar.gov

(888) 782-7937

The EPA's ENERGY STAR® program allows for voluntary partnerships between the U.S. Department of Energy, the U.S. Environmental Protection Agency, product manufacturers, local utilities and retailers. ENERGY STAR® is dedicated to promoting energy efficiency, reducing air pollution, and saving money for businesses and residences through decreased energy use. In addition to several other building product categories, the ENERGY STAR® program identifies roofing products that reduce the amount of air conditioning needed in buildings, and can reduce energy bills. Roofing products with the ENERGY STAR® logo meet the EPA criteria for reflectivity and reliability. Roofing products that meet ENERGY STAR® criteria are a good starting point for achievement of this credit, but note that ENERGY STAR® requirements are not as stringent as LEED credit requirements; LEED also accounts for roof emissivity in the SRI calculation. An ENERGY STAR® Rating alone does not necessarily meet LEED credit requirements.

See the ENERGY STAR® Roofing Web site for technical criteria, a list of qualifying products and additional information. Roof solar reflectance requirements for ENERGY STAR® roofing products are summarized in **Table 2**.

Credit Interpretation Rulings

Credit Interpretation Rulings concerning this credit made for LEED for Commercial Interiors v2.0 project requests and as applicable for LEED for New Construction v2.1 project requests apply to LEED for Commercial Interiors v2.0 projects. Review LEED for New Construction v2.1 CIRs for SS Credit 7.2.

Approach and Implementation

Locate the project in a building that has incorporated roof surfaces that reduce heat island effect. This may be accomplished through the use of highly reflective or vegetated roofs. Project teams should use the LEED certified buildings database to identify local projects which have achieved LEED credit for Roof Heat Island Reduction. Include this requirement in base building selection criteria. Local roofing product representatives may have detailed information on where their compliant products have been installed. Members of local USGBC chapters may have detailed information on projects that have achieved Roof Heat Island Reduction requirements.

Submittal Documentation

Complete the LEED for Commercial Interiors Submittal Template making the declaration that the requirements have been met. Provide a roof plan that clearly indicates roofing material in place and the compliance path selected. Provide product manufacturer information on material reflectance and emissivity to support the calculation protocol for SRI incorporated into the Submittal Template for non-vegetated roofing material.

Additional Documentation

Original contract documents or purchase orders for more recently installed roofing material may also be used to demonstrate compliance. Manufacturer's information or test data describing roof reflectance characteristics may be necessary to support credit achievement.

Calculations

The following calculation methodology is used to support the credit submittals for option E:

Vegetated Roof Calculations

1. Calculate the total roof area of the project. Deduct areas with equipment and accessories.

2. Calculate the area of roof that is surfaced with a vegetated roof system.

3. Calculate the percentage of the total roof area that is covered with a green vegetated roof system (see **Equation 3**).

Reflective Roof Calculations

1. Calculate the total roof area of the project. Deduct areas with equipment and appurtenances.

2. Calculate the area of roof that is covered with a roof system that meets the SRI requirements.

3. Calculate the percentage of the total roof area that is covered with a reflective roof system.

SRI is calculated within the LEED Submittal Template by inputing information about the roofing material reflectance and emissivity. The values used in this calculation must be based on manufacturer's test data. In the case where a painted top coating is used, the emissivity data should be based on test results for the roof assembly. ASTM Standard E1980-01 also describes a test protocol for determining SRI that may be implemented in the field.

The strategies above may be combined using a weighted average as indicated in the following equation:

Total Roof Area ≤ [(Area of SRI roof x 1.33) + (Area of vegetated roof x 2)]

Exemplary Performance

Project teams may earn an additional half point for exemplary performance for Option E if 100% of the roof area of is vegetated.

Considerations

The use of dark, non-reflective surfaces for parking, roofs, walkways and other surfaces contributes to heat island effect. Heat islands are created when heat from the sun is absorbed by buildings and paved surfaces and radiated back to surrounding areas. As a result of heat island effects, ambient temperatures in urban areas can be artificially elevated by more than 10°F when compared with surrounding suburban and undeveloped areas. This increase results in disproportionately greater cooling loads in the summer, requiring larger HVAC equipment and power consumption.

Environmental Issues

Heat island effects are detrimental to site habitat, wildlife and migration corridors. Plants and animals are sensitive to higher temperatures and may not thrive in areas that are unnaturally hot.

Vegetated roofs not only reduce heat island effect, but can also serve as stormwater runoff control structures.

Resources

Please see the USGBC Web site at www. usgbc.org/resources for more specific resources on materials sources and other technical information.

Web Sites

Cool Roof Rating Council

www.coolroofs.org (866) 465-2523

A nonprofit organization dedicated to implementing and communicating fair, accurate, and credible radiative energy performance rating systems for roof surfaces, supporting research into energy-related radiative properties of roofing surfaces, including durability of those properties, and providing education and objective support to parties interested in understanding and comparing various roofing options.

ENERGY STAR® Reflective Roofing Products

www.energystar.gov/index.cfm?c=roof_prods.pr_roof_products

(888) 782-7937

Provides solar reflectance levels required to meet ENERGY STAR® labeling requirements.

Extensive Green Roofs

Whole Building Design Guide

http://www.wbdg.org/design/greenroofs.php

This "Whole Building Design Guide" article by Charlie Miller, PE details the features and benefits of constructing green roofs.

Greenroofs.com

www.greenroofs.com

The green roof industry resource portal offers basic information, product and service directory, and research links.

Heat Island Group–Cool Roofs

Lawrence Berkeley National Laboratory

http://eetd.lbl.gov/HeatIsland/CoolRoofs/

This site offers a wealth of information about cool roof research and technology, including links to the Cool Roofing Materials Database.

Penn State Center for Green Roof Research

http://hortWeb.cas.psu.edu/research/greenroofcenter/

The Center has the mission of demonstrating and promoting green roof research, education, and technology transfer in the Northeastern US.

Definitions

Solar Reflectance is the ratio of the reflected electromagnetic energy to the incoming electromagnetic energy. A reflectance of 100% means that all of the energy striking a reflecting surface is reflected back into the atmosphere and none of the energy is absorbed by the surface.

Solar Reflectance Index (SRI) SRI is a yardstick that compares different materials based on their reflectance and emissivity characteristics. The Solar Reflectance

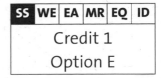

Index (SRI) calculation is based on the relative temperature (Ts) of a surface of a specific material with respect to standard white (SRI = 100) and standard black (SRI = 0) under standard solar and ambient conditions. The SRI calculation allows equivalent comparison of materials having a lower reflectivity but higher emissivity with materials having a high reflectivity but lower emissivity. Higher SRIs are "cooler" than lower SRIs. SRI can also be determined by laboratory testing, using ASTM Standard E1980-01 Standard Practice for Calculating Solar Reflectance Index of Horizontal and Low-Sloped Opaque Surfaces.

Thermal Emittance is the ratio of the radiant heat flux emitted by a sample to that emitted by a blackbody radiator at the same temperature.

Weathered Radiative Properties refer to the solar reflectance and thermal emittance of a roofing product after three years of exposure to the weather.

Table 2: Typical SRI for Roofing Materials

Source: Lawerence Berkely National Laboratory Cool Roofs Website

Roofing Material	SRI	Solar Reflectance	Infrared Emittance
White EPDM	84	0.69	0.87
Gray EPDM	21	0.23	0.87
Black EPDM	-1	0.06	0.86
White Granular Surface Bitumen	28	0.26	0.92
Light Gravel on Built Up Roof	37	0.34	0.9
Dark Gravel on Built Up Roof	9	0.12	0.9
White Elastomeric Coating (1 Coat / 8 Mils)	100	0.80	0.91

* Project teams may use these values to determine compliance when no specific manufacturer's data is available for existing installed materials.

Option F. Light Pollution Reduction

Intent

Eliminate light trespass from the building and site, improve night sky access and reduce development impact on nocturnal environments.

Requirements

A building that meets or provides lower light levels and uniformity ratios than those recommended by the Illuminating Engineering Society of North America (IESNA) *Recommended Practice Manual: Lighting for Exterior Environments* (RP-33-99). The building must have designed the exterior lighting such that all exterior luminaires with more than 1000 initial lamp lumens are shielded and all luminaires with more than 3500 initial lamp lumens meet the Full Cutoff IESNA Classification. The maximum candela value of all interior lighting shall fall within the property. Any luminaire within a distance of 2.5 times its mounting height from the property boundary shall have shielding such that no light from that luminaire crosses the property boundary.

Submittals

Provide the LEED for Commercial Interiors Submittal Template, signed by a lighting designer or an appropriate party, declaring that the credit requirements have been met.

Potential Technologies & Strategies

- Adopt site lighting criteria to maintain safe lighting levels as prescribed in IESNA RP-33-99 while avoiding off-site lighting and night sky pollution.

- Minimize site lighting where possible minimizing or eliminating façade and landscape lighting

- Model the site lighting using a computer model to predict impacts when changing the lighting. Calculate lighting power densities not to exceed ANSI/ASHRAE/IESNA 90.1-2004 Exterior lighting standards.

- Techniques to reduce light pollution and light trespass include –
  - using cutoff and full cutoff luminaires,
  - using low-reflectance surfaces in some locations,
  - minimizing uplighting,
  - shielding adjustable spotlights, and
  - using controls to turn off lighting after normal operating hours.

Summary of Referenced Standards

IESNA Recommended Practice Manual: Lighting for Exterior Environments (IESNA RP-33-99) Illuminating Engineering Society of North America

www.iesna.org

(212) 248-5000

This standard provides general exterior lighting design guidance and acts as a link to other IESNA outdoor lighting Recommended Practices (RPs). IESNA RP documents address the lighting of

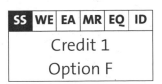
different types of environments. RP-33 was developed to augment other RPs with subjects not otherwise covered and is especially helpful in the establishment of community lighting themes and in defining appropriate light trespass limitations based on environmental area classifications. RP-33 addresses visual issues such as glare, luminance, visual acuity and illuminance. Also covered are exterior lighting design issues including community-responsive design, lighting ordinances, luminaire classification, structure lighting, and hardscape and softscape lighting. Light level recommendations in RP-33 are lower than in many other RPs, since RP-33 was written to address environmentally sensitive lighting.

Another useful Recommended Practice is RP-20-98, "Lighting for Parking Facilities." RP-20 discusses lighting design issues and makes light level recommendations for open and covered parking facilities. Not all the light level recommendations in the RP-20, or in any of the RPs, are appropriate for lighting in environmentally sensitive areas, so it is important to try to use the lowest recommended values. It is also important to recognize that, as a whole, different IESNA RP documents are not in agreement on all lighting issues and many of the RPs will be revised to include recommendations based on environmental zones. The designer must interpret related documents to find a recommendation that uses the lowest light levels while still addressing specific project issues. **Table 1** provides required light trespass limitations based on different types of environmental zones. Illuminance values are measured at the eye on a plane perpendicular to the line-of-sight.

Credit Interpretation Rulings

Credit Interpretation Rulings concerning this credit made for LEED for Commercial Interiors v2.0 project requests and as applicable for LEED for New Construction v2.1 project requests apply to LEED

Table 1: Light Trespass Limitations

Environmental Zone	Description	Recommended Maximum Illuminance Levels [fc]
E1: Intrinsically Dark	Parks and residential areas where controlling light pollution is a high priority	0.1
E2: Low Ambient Brightness	Outer urban and rural residential areas	0.1
E3: Medium Ambient Brightness	Urban residential areas	0.2
E4: High Ambient Brightness	Urban areas having both residential and commercial use and experiencing high levels of nighttime activity	0,6

Note: Table 1 has been adapted from IESNA RP-33-99. "Post Curfew" recommendations have been used for all values to ensure that light trespass is minimized for each environmental zone. It is recognized that in situations where the property line is very close to the area of development (commonly referred to as "zero property line"), and where lighting is required for emergency egress purposes, it may not be possible to meet the Table 1 recommendations. These situations should be carefully explained and documented.

for Commercial Interiors v2.0 projects. Also review LEED for New Construction v2.1 CIRs for SS Credit 8.

Approach and Implementation

Locate the project in a building with interior and exterior lighting equipment designed to eliminate light trespass from the building and site.

Include this requirement in base building selection criteria. Members of local USGBC chapters or the Illuminating Engineering Society of North America (IESNA) may have detailed information on projects that have achieved light pollution reduction requirements. Computer simulations of site lighting should be conducted to determine if the site lighting complies with the requirements of this option.

Submittal Documentation

Complete the LEED for Commercial Interiors Submittal Template making the declaration that the requirements have been met. Include a photometric site plan that indicates the location of all exterior fixtures and demonstrates the illuminance levels and uniformity ratios across the site, as required by the Submittal Template.

Additional Documentation

For potential use during submittal review, it is suggested that the project team obtain the following documents confirming the design requirements have been met:

1. An exterior site plan showing all buildings, parking and pedestrian areas, trees and landscape features and a luminaire schedule summary (plus a separate complete schedule showing the type, style, location, height, orientation, shielding and aiming of all light sources and all lighting control devices).

2. A computer-generated lighting calculation indicating horizontal illuminance on a 10'x10' minimum grid and a minimum of 10 feet beyond the lot or property boundary for areas that are representative of each design condition. See **Figure 1**.

Exemplary Performance

No exemplary performance criteria exists for Option F.

Considerations

Outdoor lighting is necessary for illuminating certain support facilities such as sidewalks, parking lots, roads and community gathering places. Through thoughtful planning, outdoor lighting can provide for the illumination needs of the site, including visibility, safety and security, while creating a low lighting profile for the building exterior, thereby minimizing negative impacts on neighboring properties.

Light pollution from poorly designed outdoor lighting affects the nocturnal ecosystem on the site and hinders enjoyment of the night sky by building occupants and neighbors. Reduction of light pollution encourages nocturnal life to thrive on and near the building site.

By not exceeding ANSI/ASHRAE/IESNA 90.1-2004 exterior lighting standards and avoiding unnecessary outdoor lighting, infrastructure costs and energy use over the lifetime of the building can be reduced.

Resources

Please see the USGBC Web site at www. usgbc.org/resources for more specific resources on materials sources and other technical information.

Web Sites

Illuminating Engineering Society of North America

www.iesna.org

A nonprofit organization advancing knowledge and disseminating informa-

Figure 1: Example of a Site Lighting Plan

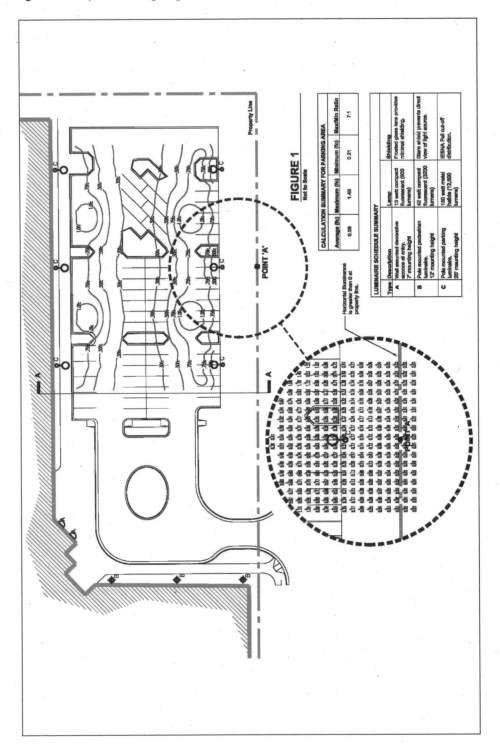

FIGURE 1
Not to Scale

POINT 'A'

Horizontal illuminance
is greater than 0 at
property line.

Property Line

CALCULATION SUMMARY FOR PARKING AREA

Average (fc)	Maximum (fc)	Minimum (fc)	Max/Min Ratio
0.58	1.48	0.21	7:1

LUMINAIRE SCHEDULE SUMMARY

Type	Description	Lamp	Shielding
A	Wall mounted decorative sconce at entry, 7' mounting height	13 watt compact fluorescent (900 lumens)	Frosted glass lens provides minimal shielding.
B	Pole mounted pedestrian luminaire, 12' mounting height	42 watt compact fluorescent (3200 lumens)	Glare shield prevents direct view of light source.
C	Pole mounted parking luminaire, 20' mounting height	150 watt metal halide (12,500 lumens)	IESNA Full cut-off distribution.

tion for the improvement of the lighted environment. See RP-33-99 Lighting for Exterior Environments, G-1-03 Guideline for Security Lighting for People, Property, and Public Spaces, and ANSI/ASHRAE/IESNA Standard 90.1-2004.

The International Dark-Sky Association

www.darksky.org/ida/ida_2/index_html

A nonprofit agency dedicated to educating and providing solutions to light pollution.

Lighting Research Center

www.lrc.rpi.edu

A leading university-based research center devoted to providing objective information about lighting technologies, applications and products.

The New England Light Pollution Advisory Group

http://cfa-www.harvard.edu/cfa/ps/nelpag_html

A volunteer group to educate the public on the virtues of efficient, glare-free outdoor night lighting as well as the benefits of no lighting for many outdoor applications.

Sky & Telescope

http://skyandtelescope.com/resources/darksky/default.asp

Includes facts on light pollution and its impact on astronomy, and information about purchasing light fixtures that minimize light pollution.

Print Media

Concepts in Practice Lighting: Lighting Design in Architecture, by Torquil Barker, B.T. Batsford Ltd., 1997.

The Design of Lighting, by Peter Tregenza and David Loe, E & F N Spon, 1998.

Definitions

Curfew Hours are locally determined times when greater lighting restrictions are imposed.

Cutoff Angle is the angle between the vertical axis of a luminaire and the first line of sight (of a luminaire) at which the light source is no longer visible.

Illuminance is the amount of light falling on a surface, measured in units of footcandles (fc) or lux (lx).

A **Footcandle (fc)** is a measure of light falling on a given surface. One footcandle is equal to the quantity of light falling on a one-square-foot area from a one candela light source at a distance of one foot (which equals one lumen per square foot). Footcandles can be measured both horizontally and vertically by a footcandle or "light meter."

A **Full Cutoff** luminaire has zero candela intensity at an angle of 90 degrees above the vertical axis (nadir or straight down) and at all angles greater than 90 degrees from straight down. Additionally, the candela per 1000 lamp lumens does not numerically exceed 100 (10%) at an angle of 80 degrees above nadir. This applies to all lateral angles around the luminaire.

Glare is the sensation produced by luminance within the visual field that is significantly greater than the luminance to which the eyes are adapted, which causes annoyance, discomfort or loss in visual performance and visibility.

Light Pollution is typically made up of three different types of errant light: Glare, Light Trespass and/or Sky Glow.

Light Trespass is commonly thought of as "the light shining in my window." It is defined as obtrusive light that is unwanted, because of quantitative, directional or spectral attributes. Light trespass can cause annoyance, discomfort, distraction or a loss of visibility

Luminance is what we commonly call brightness or the light coming from a surface or light source. Luminance is composed of the intensity of light striking an object or surface and the amount of that light reflected back toward the eye. Lumi-

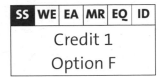

nance is measured in candela per square meter (cd/m2) or footlamberts (fl).

Shielding is a non-technical term that describes devices or techniques that are used as part of a luminaire or lamp to limit glare, light trespass and/or sky glow.

Sky Glow is caused by stray light from unshielded light sources and light reflecting off surfaces that enters the atmosphere where it illuminates and reflects off dust, debris and water vapor. Sky glow can substantially limit visual access to the night sky, compromise astronomical research, and adversely affect nocturnal environments. Stray light that enters the atmosphere does not increase nighttime safety or security and needlessly consumes energy and natural resources.

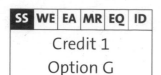

Credit 1
Option G

1/2 point

Option G. Water Efficient Irrigation, Reduced Potable Water Consumption

Intent

Limit or eliminate the use of potable water for landscape irrigation.

Requirements

A building that employs high-efficiency irrigation technology, OR uses captured rain or recycled site water to reduce potable water consumption for irrigation by 50% over conventional means.

Submittals

Provide the LEED Submittal Template, signed by the architect, engineer or responsible party, declaring that potable water consumption for site irrigation has been reduced by 50%. Include a brief narrative of the equipment used and/or the use of drought-tolerant or native plants. Include calculations demonstrating that irrigation requirements for potable water have been reduced by at least 50%. Calculations should be based on July conditions. See the calculation protocol below.

Potential Technologies & Strategies

Perform a soil/climate analysis to determine appropriate landscape types and design the landscape with indigenous plants to reduce or eliminate irrigation requirements. Use efficient irrigation systems and controllers to improve the distribution efficiency of the irrigation system. Consider using stormwater or graywater collection systems to offset potable water use for irrigation.

Option H. Water Efficient Irrigation, No Potable Water Use or No Irrigation

**1/2 point
in addition to
prior requirement**

Intent

Limit or eliminate the use of potable water for landscape irrigation.

Requirements

A building that uses only captured rain or recycled site water to eliminate all potable water use for site irrigation (except for initial watering to establish plants), OR does not have permanent landscaping irrigation systems.

Submittals

Provide the LEED Submittal Template, signed by the responsible architect and/or engineer, declaring that the project site will not use potable water for irrigation. Include a narrative describing the plant species used and how the plantings will tolerate lack of irrigation. If a water recycling strategy is used, describe the rain collection or recycled site water system, including capacity and anticipated refill frequency. Include calculations demonstrating that irrigation requirements can be met from captured rain or recycled site water. Calculations should be based on July conditions.

OR

Provide the LEED Submittal Template, signed by the landscape architect or responsible party, declaring that the project site does not have a permanent landscape irrigation system. Include a narrative describing how the landscape design allows for this.

Potential Technologies & Strategies

Perform a soil/climate analysis to determine appropriate landscape types and design the landscape with indigenous plants to reduce or eliminate irrigation requirements. Use efficient irrigation systems and controllers to improve the distribution efficiency of the irrigation system. Consider using stormwater or graywater collection systems to offset potable water use for irrigation

---

Credit Interpretation Rulings

Credit Interpretation Rulings concerning this credit made for LEED for Commercial Interiors v2.0 project requests and as applicable for LEED for New Construction v2.1 project requests apply to LEED for Commercial Interiors 2.0 projects. Review LEED for New Construction v2.1 CIRs also for WE Credit 1.1 and WE Credit 1.2.

Approach and Implementation

Locate the project in a building with water efficient landscape irrigation designed to reduce or eliminate the use of potable water with features such as—

- Landscaping with indigenous plants
- Rain-water collection systems
- High efficiency irrigation strategies including micro-irrigation systems, moisture sensors, clock timers, and weather database controllers
- Graywater systems used for site irrigation

Note that the use of groundwater does not meet the requirements of this credit for offsetting potable water use. Also if the project site has no landscaping these credits do not apply.

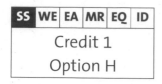

SS	WE	EA	MR	EQ	ID

Credit 1
Option H

SS	WE	EA	MR	EQ	ID

Option G

Submittal Documentation

Complete the LEED for Commercial Interiors Submittal Template making the declaration that the requirements have been met and provide a brief narrative and calculations as described in the submittal requirement for each credit.

The following calculation identifies how irrigation demand should be compared to a baseline for any project attempting to demonstrate reduced irrigation demand (Option G) or to quantify irrigation demand for any project offsetting irrigation demand with reclaimed site water. (Option H, where an irrigation system is installed.)

Calculations

The following calculation methodology is used to support the credit submittals for options G and H. In order to quantify water-efficient landscaping measures, it is necessary to calculate irrigation volumes for the designed landscape irrigation system for the month of July and compare this with irrigation volumes required for a baseline landscape irrigation system. The resulting water savings is the difference between the two systems. The factors that must be calculated to determine irrigation volumes are explained in detail in the following paragraphs and summarized in **Table 1**.

The **Landscape Coefficient** (K_L) indicates the volume of water lost via evapotranspiration and is dependent on the landscape species, the microclimate and the planting density. The formula for determining the landscape coefficient is given in **Equation 1**.

The **Species Factor** (k_s) accounts for variation of water needs by different plant species. The species factor can be divided into three categories (high, average and low) depending on the plant species considered. To determine the appropriate category for a plant species, use plant manuals and professional experience. This factor is somewhat subjective but landscape professionals should have a general idea of the water needs of particular plant species. Landscapes can be maintained in acceptable condition at about 50% of the reference evapotranspiration (ET0) value and thus, the average value of ks is 0.5. (Note: If a species does not require irrigation once it is established, then the effective k_s = 0 and the resulting K_L = 0.)

The **Density Factor** (k_d) accounts for the number of plants and the total leaf area of a landscape. Sparsely planted areas will have lower evapotranspiration rates than densely planted areas. An average kd is applied to areas where ground shading from trees is in the range of 60–100%. This is also equivalent to shrubs and

Table 1: Landscape Factors

Vegetation Type	Species Factor (k_s)			Density Factor (k_d)			Microclimate Factor (k_{mc})		
	low	average	high	low	average	high	low	average	high
Trees	0.2	0.5	0.9	0.5	1.0	1.3	0.5	1.0	1.4
Shrubs	0.2	0.5	0.7	0.5	1.0	1.1	0.5	1.0	1.3
Groundcovers	0.2	0.5	0.7	0.5	1.0	1.1	0.5	1.0	1.2
Mixed: trees, shrubs, groundcovers	0.2	0.5	0.9	0.6	1.1	1.3	0.5	1.0	1.4
Turfgrass	0.6	0.7	0.8	0.6	1.0	1.0	0.8	1.0	1.2

Equation 1

$$K_L = k_s \times k_d \times k_{mc}$$

ground cover shading 90–100% of the landscape area. Low kd values are found where ground shading from trees is less than 60% or shrub and groundcover is less than 90%. For instance, a 25% ground shading from trees results in a kd value of 0.5. In mixed landscape plantings where trees cover understory groundcover and shrubs, evapotranspiration increases. This represents the highest level of landscape density and the kd value should be between 1.0 and 1.3.

The **Microclimate Factor** (k_{mc}) accounts for environmental conditions specific to the landscape, including temperature, wind and humidity. For instance, parking lot areas increase wind and temperature effects on adjacent landscapes. The average kmc is 1.0 and this refers to conditions where the landscape evapotranspiration rate is unaffected by buildings, pavements, reflective surfaces and slopes. Higher kmc conditions occur where evaporative potential is increased due to landscapes surrounded by heat-absorbing and reflective surfaces or are exposed to particularly windy conditions. Examples of high kmc areas include parking lots, west sides of buildings, west and south sides of slopes, medians, and areas experiencing wind tunnel effects. Low microclimate areas include shaded areas and areas protected from wind. North sides of buildings, courtyards, areas under wide building overhangs, and north sides of slopes are low microclimate areas. **Table 1** provides suggested values for k_s, k_{mc}, and k_d.

Once KL is determined, the evapotranspiration (ET) rate of the specific landscape (ETL) can be calculated. K_L is multiplied by the reference evapotranspiration (ET0) to obtain ETL as shown in Equation 2. The evapotranspiration rate is a measure-

ment of the total amount of water needed to grow plants and crops. Different plants have different water needs, and thus different ET rates. Irrigation calculations are simplified by using ET0, which is an average rate for a known surface, such as grass or alfalfa, used as a reference point and expressed in millimeters or inches.

The values for ET0 in various regions throughout the United States can be found in regional agricultural data (see Resources section). The ET0 for July is used in the LEED calculation because this is typically the month with the greatest evapotranspiration effects and, therefore, the greatest irrigation demands.

To calculate irrigation volumes, apply the irrigation efficiency (IE). **Table 2** lists irrigation efficiencies for sprinkler and drip irrigation systems.

The Total Potable Water Applied (TPWA) to a given area (A) is calculated in **Equation 3**.

This equation indicates that a smaller landscape area, a smaller ETL value, and a larger IE value result in a lower TPWA value. This is sensible because smaller landscape areas require less water to irrigate, a smaller ETL value means less water loss due to evapotranspiration, and a higher IE means that irrigation water is being used more efficiently.

To determine the water savings for the designed landscaping irrigation system, perform the above calculations for the design case as well as a baseline case.

1. Use **Table 1** to determine the appropriate landscape factors for each specific landscape area in the design case (e.g., k_s, k_{mc}, and k_d). Use a spreadsheet to sum-

SS	WE	EA	MR	EQ	ID
Credit 1					
Option H					

SS	WE	EA	MR	EQ	ID
Option G					

Table 2: Irrigation Types

Irrigation Type	IE
Sprinkler	0.625
Drip	0.90

Equation 2

$$ET_L \, [\text{in}] = ET_0 \, [\text{in}] \times K_L$$

marize the different landscape areas and the associated factors.

2. Calculate the landscape coefficient (K_L) for each landscape area using the appropriate landscape factors and **Equation 1**.

3. Calculate the specific landscape evapotranspiration rate (ET_L) of each landscape area using the corresponding landscape coefficient (K_L) and the ET_L formula in **Equation 2**.

4. Calculate the TPWA to each landscape area using **Equation 3** and the applicable surface area, specific landscape evapotranspiration rate and irrigation efficiency data.

Repeat the above steps for the **baseline case** using conventional plant species and plant densities as determined by the project's landscape consultant. Differences between the two cases result from plant species choices, plant densities and irrigation system choices. Planting types should approximately correspond in both the baseline and design cases (i.e., it is unreasonable to assume that the baseline is 100% turfgrass if a project clearly intends to include trees, shrubs and planting beds). Do not change the landscape areas, microclimate factors or reference evapotranspiration rates.

An **example** of irrigation calculations is presented below. An office building in Austin, Texas, has a total site area of 6,000 square feet. The site consists of three landscape types: groundcover, mixed vegetation and turf grass. All of the site areas are irrigated with a combination of potable water and graywater harvested from the building. The reference evapotranspiration rate (ET_0) for Austin in July was obtained from the local agricultural data service and is equal to 8.12.

The high-efficiency landscape irrigation case utilizes drip irrigation with an efficiency of 90% and reuses an estimated 9,000 gallons of graywater during the month of July. **Table 3** shows the calculations to determine potable water use for the design case.

The baseline case uses the same reference evapotranspiration rate and total site area. However, the baseline case uses sprinklers for irrigation (IE = 0.625), does not take advantage of graywater harvesting, and uses only shrubs and turf grass. Calculations to determine potable water use for the baseline case are presented in **Table 4**.

The example illustrates that the design case has an irrigation water demand of 23,474 gallons. Graywater reuse provides 4,200 gallons towards the demand, and this volume is treated as a credit in the

Table 3: Design Case (July)

Landscape Type	Area	Species Factor		Density Factor		Microclimate Factor		K_L	ET_L	IE	TPWA
	[SF]	(k_s)		(k_d)		(k_{mc})					[gal]
Shrubs	1,200	Low	0.2	Avg	1.0	High	1.3	**0.3**	2.11	Drip	2,815
Mixed	3,900	Low	0.2	Avg	1.1	High	1.4	**0.3**	2.50	Drip	10,837
Turfgrass	900	Avg	0.7	Avg	1.0	High	1.2	**0.8**	6.82	Sprinkler	9,822
									Subtotal [gal]		23,474
									July Graywater Harvest [gal]		(4,200)
									Net GPWA [gal]		**19,274**

water calculation. Thus, the total potable water applied to the design case in July is 19,274 gallons. The baseline case has an irrigation demand of 62,518 gallons and reuses no graywater. The difference between the two cases results in potable water savings of 69% for the design case.

It is important to note that the LEED calculation provides an indication of the general efficiency gains provided by the green design. For more accurate understanding of water use and efficiency opportunities, an annual water balance is required. For example, graywater volumes may or may not be consistently available throughout the year because these volumes are dependent on building occupant activities.

In a typical office building, graywater volumes will change slightly due to vacation schedules and holidays but should be relatively consistent over the year. In contrast, graywater volumes in a school building will substantially decrease in summer months as a result of reduced building occupancy, and, therefore, graywater volumes may not be available for irrigation. Graywater systems should be modeled to predict graywater volumes generated on a monthly basis as well as optimal storage capacity of the graywater system. It is also important to address possible treatment processes needed for reuse and design of a makeup water system if graywater volume is not sufficient to satisfy reuse demands.

Rain harvest volume depends on the amount of precipitation that the project site experiences and the rainwater col-lection surface's area and efficiency. See **Equation 4** and consult a rainwater harvesting guide for more detailed instruction. Rainfall data is available from the local weather service (see the Resources section). Within the credit calculations, project teams may either use the collected rainwater total for July based on historical average precipitation, or use the historical data for each month in order to model collection and reuse throughout the year. The latter method allows the project team to determine what volume of water is expected to be in the storage cistern at the beginning of July and add it to the expected rainwater volume collected during the month. This approach also allows the project team to determine the optimal size of the rainwater cistern.

Additional Documentation

No additional documentation should be required during submittal review.

Exemplary Performance

No exemplary performance criteria exists for Options G and H.

Considerations

Landscape irrigation practices in the United States consume large quantities of potable water. For example, in urban areas of Texas, residential and commercial landscape irrigation accounts for an estimated 25% of total water consumption. Irrigation typically uses potable water, although water volumes of lower quality (i.e., non-potable water) are equally ef-

SS	WE	EA	MR	EQ	ID

Credit 1
Option H

SS	WE	EA	MR	EQ	ID

Option G

Table 4: Baseline Case (July)

Landscape Type	Area	Species Factor		Density Factor		Microclimate Factor		K_L	ET_L	IE	TPWA
	[SF]		(k_s)		(k_d)		(k_{mc})				[gal]
Shrubs	1,200	Avg	0.5	Avg	1.0	High	1.3	**0.7**	5.28	Sprinkler	10,134
Turfgrass	4,800	Avg	0.7	Avg	1.0	High	1.2	**0.8**	6.82	Sprinkler	52,384

Net GPWA [gal] **62,518**

SS	WE	EA	MR	EQ	ID
Credit 1					
Option H					

SS	WE	EA	MR	EQ	ID
Option G					

fective for irrigating landscapes. Sources of non-potable water volumes include captured rainwater from roof runoff as well as graywater from building systems (e.g., sinks and showers) or a municipal recycled water supply system. High-efficiency irrigation systems are another method to reduce potable water use for irrigation. These systems deliver up to 95% of the water supplied versus conventional irrigation systems that are as little as 60% efficient.

Environmental Issues

Native landscapes that have lower irrigation requirements tend to attract native wildlife, including birds, mammals and insects, creating a building site that is integrated with the natural surroundings. In addition, native plantings require less fertilizer and fewer pesticides and, thus, reduce water quality impacts.

Community Issues

Water-efficient landscaping helps to conserve local and regional potable water resources. Maintaining natural aquifer conditions is important to providing reliable water sources for future generations. Consideration of water issues during planning can encourage development when resources can support it and prevent development if it exceeds the resource capacity.

Resources

Please see the USGBC Web site at www.usgbc.org/resources for more specific resources on materials sources and other technical information.

Web Sites

The Irrigation Association

www.irrigation.org

A nonprofit organization focused on promoting products for the efficient use of water for irrigation applications.

Texas Evapotranspiration Network

http://texaset.tamu.edu

An evapotranspiration data Web site for the state of Texas with a discussion of crop water use and sprinkler efficiencies.

Water Efficient Gardening and Landscaping

University of Missouri Extension

http://muextension.missouri.edu/xplor/agguides/hort/g06912.htm

A Web site that has general descriptions and strategies for water efficiency in gardens and landscapes.

Water Wiser

The Water Efficiency Clearinghouse

www.awwa.org/waterwiser/

A Web clearinghouse with articles, reference materials and papers on all forms of water efficiency.

Print Media

ASCE Manuals and Reports on Engineering Practice No. 70, "Evapotranspiration and Irrigation Water Requirements," ASCE, 1990.

Estimating Irrigation Water Needs of Landscape Plantings in California

A guide to the landscaping coefficient method established by the University of California. www.owue.water.ca.gov/docs/wucols00.pdf

Landscape Irrigation: Design and Management, Stephen W. Smith, John Wiley and Sons, 1996.

Turf Irrigation Manual, Fifth Edition, Richard B. Choate, Telsco Industries, 1994.

Water-Efficient Landscaping: Preventing Pollution and Using Resources Wisely

A manual from the Environmental Protection Agency on reducing water consumption through creative landscaping techniques. www.epa.gov/owm/water-efficiency/final_final.pdf

Definitions

There is not a national definition for **blackwater**. Wastewater from toilets and urinals is always considered blackwater. Wastewater from kitchen sinks (perhaps differentiated by the use of a garbage disposal), showers, or bathtubs may be considered blackwater by state or local codes. Project teams should comply with blackwater definition as established by the authority having jurisdiction in their areas.

Drip Irrigation is a high-efficiency irrigation method in which water drips to the soil from perforated tubes or emitters.

Evapotranspiration is the loss of water by evaporation from the soil and transpiration from plants.

Graywater is defined by the Uniform Plumbing Code (UPC) in its Appendix G, titled "Gray Water Systems for Single-Family Dwellings" as "untreated household waste water which has not come into contact with toilet waste. Grey water includes used water from bathtubs, showers, bathroom wash basins, and water from clothes-washer and laundry tubs. It shall not include waste water from kitchen sinks or dishwashers."

The International Plumbing Code (IPC) defines graywater in its Appendix C, titled "Gray Water Recycling Systems" as "waste water discharged from lavatories, bathtubs, showers, clothes washers, and laundry sinks."

Some states and local authorities allow kitchen sink wastewater to be included in graywater. Other differences with the UPC and IPC definitions can probably be found in state and local codes. Project teams should comply with graywater definitions as established by the authority having jurisdiction in their areas.

Potable Water is water that is suitable for drinking and is supplied from wells or municipal water systems.

Xeriscape or "dry landscape" designs adopt water conservation as the primary objective. Xeriscape landscapes are based on sound horticultural practices and incorporate native plant species that are adapted to local climate conditions.

SS	WE	EA	MR	EQ	ID
	Credit 1				
	Option H				

SS	WE	EA	MR	EQ	ID
	Option G				

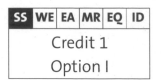
Option I. Innovative Wastewater Technologies

Intent

Reduce generation of wastewater and potable water demand, while increasing the local aquifer recharge.

Requirements

A building that reduces the use of municipally provided potable water for building sewage conveyance by a minimum of 50%, OR treats 100% of wastewater on-site to tertiary standards.

Submittals

Provide the LEED Submittal Template, signed by the architect, MEP engineer or responsible party, declaring that water for building sewage conveyance will be reduced by at least 50%. Include the spreadsheet calculation and a narrative demonstrating the measures used to reduce wastewater by at least 50% from baseline conditions.

OR

Provide the LEED Submittal Template, signed by the civil engineer or responsible party, declaring that 100% of wastewater will be treated to tertiary standards on site. Include a narrative describing the on-site wastewater treatment system.

Potential Technologies & Strategies

Specify high-efficiency fixtures and dry fixtures such as composting toilets and waterless urinals to reduce wastewater volumes. Consider reusing stormwater or graywater for sewage conveyance or on-site wastewater treatment systems (mechanical and/or natural).

Credit Interpretation Rulings

Credit Interpretation Rulings concerning this credit made for LEED for Commercial Interiors v2.0 project requests and as applicable for LEED for New Construction v2.1 project requests apply to LEED for Commercial Interiors v2.0 projects. Review LEED for New Construction v2.1 CIRs for WE Credit 2.

Approach and Implementation

Locate the project in a building with waste water technologies designed to reduce the use of municipal potable water. The project team must demonstrate that either the municipal potable water used for sewage conveyance has been reduced by 50% or that 100% of the on-site waste water is treated to tertiary standards. Include this requirement in base building selection criteria.

The necessity and availability of wastewater reuse and treatment strategies is often closely related to building location. In remote locations, it may be cost-effective to implement on-site wastewater treatment systems. Conversely, a project located in a dense area with limited site area for treatment or graywater storage may not be able to economically achieve this credit utilizing the on-site wastewater treatment option.

Wastewater generation and building water use are often closely linked in commercial interiors projects. Initiatives undertaken to reduce the amount of potable water used in a project often result in corresponding savings associated with generation of wastewater. Water efficient water closet and urinal fixtures not only reduce potable water demand but also reduce generation of waste/blackwater. This credit often has synergistic effects with SS Credit 1 Option J and WE Credits 1.1 and 1.2.

Submittal Documentation

Complete the LEED for Commercial Interiors Submittal Template making the declaration that the requirements have been met. In addition provide a brief narrative and calculations as described in the submittal requirement for this credit.

Additional Documentation

Fixture cut sheets may be necessary to support credit achievement. For on-site treatment systems, a narrative or other supporting documentation may be useful to support the documentation provided.

Exemplary Performance

No exemplary performance criteria exists for Option I.

Calculations

The following calculation methodology is used to support achievement of Option I. Wastewater calculations are based on the annual generation of blackwater volumes from plumbing fixtures such as water closets and urinals. The calculations compare the design case with a baseline case. The steps to calculate the **design case** are as follows:

1. Create a spreadsheet listing each type of blackwater-generating fixture and frequency of use data. Frequency-of-use data includes the number of female and male daily uses, and the sewage generated per use. Use the daily use assumptions shown in **Table 1** as the basis for the calculations, unless alternate assumptions on daily use

Table 1: Design Case

Fixture Type	Daily Uses	Flowrate [GPF]	Occupants	Sewage Generation [gal]
Low-Flow Water Closet (Male)	0	1.1	150	0
Low-Flow Water Closet (Female)	3	1.1	150	495
Composting Toilet (Male)	1	0.0	150	0
Composting Toilet (Female)	0	0.0	150	0
Waterless Urinal (Male)	2	0.0	150	0
Waterless Urinal (Female)	0	0.0	150	0

Total Daily Volume [gal]	495
Annual Work Days	260
Annual Volume [gal]	128,700
Rainwater or Graywater Reuse Volume [gal]	(36,000)
TOTAL ANNUAL VOLUME [gal]	**92,700**

Equation 1

$$\text{Sewage Volume [gal]} = \text{Uses} \times \text{Duration [mins or flushes]} \times \frac{\text{Water Volume [gal]}}{\text{Use [min or flush]}}$$

can be supported by specific back-up documentation. Using these values, calculate the total sewage generated for each fixture type and gender (see **Equation 1**).

2. Sum all of the sewage generation volumes used for each fixture type to obtain male and female daily sewage generation volumes.

3. Multiply the male and female sewage generation volumes by the number of male and female building occupants and sum these volumes to obtain the daily total sewage generation volume (see **Equation 2**).

4. Multiply the total daily sewage volume by the number of workdays in a typical year to obtain the total annual sewage generation volume for the building (see **Equation 3**).

5. If rainwater harvest or graywater reuse strategies are employed in the building, subtract these annual volumes from the annual sewage generation volume. The result shows how much potable water is used for sewage conveyance annually.

Repeat the above calculation methodology for the **baseline case**. Use Energy Policy Act of 1992 fixture flow rates for the baseline case (see WE Credit 3, **Table 1**). Do not change the number of building occupants, the number of workdays, or the frequency data. Do not include graywater or rainwater harvest volumes.

Table 1 shows **example** potable water calculations for sewage conveyance for a

two-story office building with a capacity of 300 occupants. The calculations are based on a typical 8-hour workday. It is assumed that building occupants are 50% male and 50% female. Male occupants are assumed to use water closets once and urinals twice in a typical work day. Female occupants are assumed to use water closets three times.

First, the design case is considered to determine annual potable water usage for sewage conveyance. The designed building has fixtures that use non-potable water for sewage conveyance (i.e., rainwater) or no water for sewage conveyance (i.e., waterless urinals and composting toilets). **Table 1** summarizes the sewage generation rates and indicates that 92,700 gallons of potable water are used annually for sewage conveyance.

When using graywater and rainwater volumes, calculations are required to demonstrate that these reuse volumes are sufficient to meet water closet demands. These quantities are then subtracted from the gross daily total because they reduce potable water usage. In the example, 36,000 gallons of rainwater are harvested and directed to water closets for flushing.

Next, the baseline potable water usage for sewage conveyance is developed using conventional fixtures that comply with the Energy Policy Act of 1992. Toilets are 1.6 gallons per flush (GPF) and urinals are 1.0 GPF. All fixtures drain to the existing municipal sewer system.

Equation 2

$$\text{Daily Sewage Generation [gal]} = \text{Male Occupants} \times \text{Male Sewage Generation [gal]} + \text{Female Occupants} \times \text{Female Sewage Generation [gal]}$$

Equation 3

$$\text{Annual Sewage Generation [gal]} = \text{Total Sewage Generation} \left[\frac{\text{gal}}{\text{day}}\right] \times \text{Workdays [days]}$$

Equation 4

$$\text{Rainwater Volume [gal]} = \text{collection area [SF]} \times \text{collection efficiency [\%]} \times \text{average rainfall [in]} \times 0.6233 \text{ gal/in}$$

Table 2: Baseline Case

Fixture Type	Daily Uses	Flowrate [GPF]	Occupants	Sewage Generation [gal]
Water Closet (Male)	1	1.6	150	240
Water Closet (Female)	3	1.6	150	720
Urinal (Male)	2	1.0	150	300
Urinal (Female)	0	1.0	150	0
			Total Daily Volume [gal]	1,260
			Annual Work Days	260
			TOTAL ANNUAL VOLUME [gal]	**327,600**

Table 3: Sample Fixture Types and GPFs

Fixture Type	[GPF]
Conventional Water Closet	1.6
Low-Flow Water Closet	1.1
Ultra Low-Flow Water Closet	0.8
Composting Toilet	0.0
Conventional Urinal	1.0
Waterless Urinal	0.0

Table 2 provides a summary of baseline calculations. The baseline case estimates that 327,600 gallons of potable water per year are used for sewage conveyance.

Comparison of the baseline to the designed building indicates that a 72% reduction in potable water volumes used for sewage conveyance is realized (1 − 92,700/327,600). Thus, this strategy earns one point for this credit. When developing the baseline, only the fixtures, sewage generation rates and the water reuse credit are different from the designed building. Usage rates, occupancy and number of workdays are identical for the designed case and the baseline case. See **Table 3** for sample fixture flow rates.

When reusing graywater volumes from the building, it is necessary to model the system on an annual basis to determine graywater volumes, generated storage capacity of the system and any neces-sary treatment processes before reusing the water volumes. Graywater volumes may or may not be consistently available throughout the year because these volumes are dependent on building occupant activities. For instance, in a typical office building, graywater volumes will change slightly due to vacation schedules and holidays but should be relatively consistent over the year.

In contrast, graywater volumes in a school building will substantially decrease in summer months due to the school calendar, and, therefore, graywater volumes may not be available for irrigation.

If the project uses rainwater volume as a substitute for potable volumes in water closets or urinals, it is necessary to calculate water savings over a time period of one year. Rain harvest volume depends on the amount of precipitation that the project site experiences, the rainwater collection surface's area and efficiency, and storage tank capacity. See **Equation 4** and consult a rainwater harvesting guide for more detailed instruction. Rainfall data is available from the local weather service (see the Resources section). Rainwater volume depends on variations in precipitation, and thus, it is necessary to model the reuse strategy on an annual basis. A model of rainwater capture based on daily precipitation and occupant demand is helpful to determine the rainwater volumes captured and storage tank size. Subtract annual rainwater use for sewage conveyance in the design case calculations.

Considerations

Conventional wastewater systems require significant volumes of potable water to convey waste to municipal wastewater treatment facilities. However, graywater volumes from sinks, showers and other sources can be substituted for potable water to flush toilets and urinals. Water can also be harvested from roof runoff volumes that would otherwise be absorbed into the ground or released to local water bodies. Low-flow fixtures, automatic controls, and dry fixtures such as composting toilets and waterless urinals can be used to reduce sewage volume generation.

Once wastewater has been conveyed to treatment facilities, extensive treatment is required to remove contaminants before discharging to a receiving water body. A more efficient method for handling wastewater is to treat it on-site. On-site wastewater strategies reduce regional wastewater infrastructure costs as well as provide autonomy from the public treatment works. A variety of on-site wastewater treatment options are available including conventional biological treatment facilities similar to regional treatment plants and organic systems that mimic natural processes to treat wastewater.

Environmental Issues

On-site wastewater treatment systems transform perceived "wastes" into resources that can be used on the building site. These resources include treated water volumes for potable and non-potable use, as well as nutrients that can be applied to the site to improve soil conditions. Reducing wastewater treatment at the local wastewater treatment works minimizes public infrastructure, energy use

and chemical use. In rural areas, on-site wastewater treatment systems avoid aquifer contamination problems prevalent in current septic system technology.

Community Benefits

By reducing potable water use, the local aquifer is conserved as a water resource for future generations. In areas where aquifers cannot meet the needs of the population economically, rainwater and other recovered water is the least expensive alternative source of water. Reserving potable water only for specific applications benefits the entire community through lower utility rates and taxes.

Resources

Please see the USGBC Web site at www. usgbc.org/resources for more specific resources on materials sources and other technical information.

Web Sites

American Rainwater Catchment Systems Association

www.arcsa-usa.org

Includes a compilation of publications, such as the Texas Guide to Rainwater Harvesting.

How to Conserve Water and Use it Wisely

U.S. Environmental Protection Agency

www.epa.gov/OW/you/chap3_html

A U.S. EPA document that provides guidance for commercial, industrial and residential water users on saving water and reducing sewage volumes.

National Climatic Data Center

www.ncdc.noaa.gov/oa/climate/stateclimatologists_html

Useful for researching local climate data, such as rainfall data for rainwater harvesting calculations. Includes links to state climate offices.

How to Conserve Water and Use it Effectively

U.S. Environmental Protection Agency

www.epa.gov/OW/you/chap3_html

A Web site that provides guidance for commercial, industrial, and residential water users on saving water and reducing sewage volumes.

Print Media

Constructed Wetlands for Wastewater Treatment and Wildlife Habitat: 17 Case Studies, EPA 832/B-93-005, 1993.

Mechanical & Electrical Equipment for Buildings, Eighth Edition, Benjamin Stein and John Reynolds, John Wiley and Sons, 1992.

Sustainable Building Technical Manual, Public Technology, Inc., 1996 (www.pti.org).

On-site Wastewater Treatment Systems Manual

Provides a focused and performance-based approach to on-site wastewater treatment and system management. This document provides valuable information on a variety of on-site sewage treatment options. www.epa.gov/owm/septic/pubs/septic_2002_osdm_all.pdf

Definitions

Potable Water is defined as water that meets drinking water quality standards and is approved for human consumption by the state or local authorities having jurisdiction.

There is not a national definition for **blackwater**. Wastewater from toilets and urinals is always considered blackwater. Wastewater from kitchen sinks (perhaps differentiated by the use of a garbage disposal), showers, or bathtubs may be considered blackwater by state or local codes. Project teams should comply with blackwater definition as established by the authority having jurisdiction in their areas.

Graywater is defined by the Uniform Plumbing Code (UPC) in its Appendix G, titled "Gray Water Systems for Single-Family Dwellings" as "untreated household waste water which has not come into contact with toilet waste. Grey water includes used water from bathtubs, showers, bathroom wash basins, and water from clothes-washer and laundry tubs. It shall not include waste water from kitchen sinks or dishwashers."

The International Plumbing Code (IPC) defines graywater in its Appendix C, titled "Gray Water Recycling Systems" as "waste water discharged from lavatories, bathtubs, showers, clothes washers, and laundry sinks."

Some states and local authorities allow kitchen sink wastewater to be included in graywater. Other differences with the UPC and IPC definitions can probably be found in state and local codes. Project teams should comply with graywater definitions as established by the authority having jurisdiction in their areas.

Tertiary Treatment is the highest form of wastewater treatment and includes removal of organics, solids and nutrients as well as biological or chemical polishing, generally to effluent limits of 10 mg/L BOD5 and 10 mg/L TSS.

Aquatic Systems are ecologically designed treatment systems that utilize a diverse community of biological organisms (e.g., bacteria, plants and fish) to treat wastewater to advanced levels.

On-Site Wastewater Treatment uses localized treatment systems to transport, store, treat and dispose of wastewater volumes generated on the project site.

Composting Toilets are dry plumbing fixtures that contain and treat human waste via microbiological processes.

Non-Water Using Urinals are dry plumbing fixtures that use advanced hydraulic design and a buoyant fluid to maintain sanitary conditions.

Option J. Water Use Reduction, 20% Reduction

Intent

Maximize water efficiency within buildings to reduce the burden on municipal water supply and wastewater systems.

Requirements

A building that meets the 20% reduction in water use requirement for the entire building and has an on-going plan to require future occupants to comply.

Submittals

Provide the LEED Submittal Template, signed by the MEP engineer or responsible party, declaring that the project uses 20% less water than the baseline fixture performance requirements of the Energy Policy Act of 1992.

Provide the spreadsheet calculation demonstrating that water-consuming fixtures specified for the stated occupancy and use of the building reduce occupancy-based potable water consumption by 20% compared to baseline conditions.

Potential Technologies & Strategies

Estimate the potable and non-potable water needs for the building. Use high-efficiency fixtures, dry fixtures such as composting toilets and waterless urinals, and occupant sensors to reduce the potable water demand. Consider reuse of stormwater and graywater for non-potable applications such as toilet and urinal flushing, mechanical systems and custodial uses.

Summary of Referenced Standards

The Energy Policy Act (EPAct) of 1992

This Act was promulgated by the U.S. government and addresses energy and water use in commercial, institutional and residential facilities. The water usage requirements of the Energy Policy Act of 1992 (EPAct) are provided in **Table 1**.

Credit Interpretation Rulings

Credit Interpretation Rulings concerning this credit made for LEED for Commercial Interiors v2.0 project requests and as applicable for LEED for New Construction v2.1 project requests apply to LEED for Commercial Interiors v2.0 projects. Review LEED for New Construction v2.1 CIRs for WE Credit 3.

Approach and Implementation

Select a tenant space in a building equipped with water-conserving plumbing fixtures for the entire building. The building owner is required to demonstrate that these fixtures use 20% less water than the baseline fixture performance requirements of EPAct. This credit applies to those tenants who occupy 50% or less of the entire building square footage.

Submittal Documentation

Complete the LEED for Commercial Interiors Submittal Template making the declaration that the requirements have been met along with calculations as described in the submittal requirement.

Provide a copy of the building owner's on-going plan that requires future occupants to comply with the 20% reduc-

Table 1: EPACT Fixture Ratings

Fixture	Energy Policy Act of 1992 Flow Requirement
Water Closets [GPF]	1.6
Urinals [GPF]	1.0
Showerheads [GPM]*	2.5
Faucets [GPF]*	2.2
Replacement Aerators [GPM]*	2.2
Metering Faucets [gal/CY]	0.25

*At flowing water pressure of 80 pounds per square inch (psi)

tion in water use requirement for their tenant space.

Additional Documentation

For potential use during submittal review, it is suggested that the project team compile and maintain the manufacturers' information indicating the flush/flow rates of the plumbing fixtures installed.

Exemplary Performance

One additional half point may be earned by demonstrating 30% reduction in water use for entire building for Option J.

Calculation Methodology

The following calculation methodology is used to support the credit submittals listed above. To calculate the potable water savings for a building, the design case must be compared with a baseline case. The steps to calculate the **design case** are as follows:

1. Utilizing the calculation spreadsheet entries in the LEED for Commercial Interiors Submittal Template, list each water-using fixture and frequency-of-use data for the building's design case and baseline case. Frequency-of-use data includes the number of female and male daily uses, the duration of use, and the water volume per use. Use the same daily use assumptions indicated in the example calculations unless specific conditions can be documented to support

alternate assumptions. The Submittal Template Calculator utilizes the fixture flow/flush rate along with the estimated daily uses and duration to determine the average daily water use for the project. (Note: this calculation methodology differs from traditional plumbing design calculations that are based on fixture units.) **Tables 2 and 3** provide samples of design case and baseline calculations.

2. In the calculation spreadsheet include the volume of graywater or stormwater reuse for the project in the design case table.

3. Project teams may modify or add to the flow and flush fixture tables as needed to provide an accurate representation of installed fixture types and flow/flush rates. A sample of the fixture tables is provided in **Tables 4 and 5**.

Option J is awarded for specification of water using fixtures regulated by the Energy Policy Act of 1992. EPAct covers the following fixture types: lavatories, kitchen sinks, showers, hand wash fountains, janitor sinks, water closets and urinals.

An example potable water use calculation is included for a two-story office building with a capacity of 300 persons: Occupant fixtures that use potable water include water closets, urinals, lavatories, kitchen sinks and showers. Calculations are based on a typical 8-hour workday and 260 workdays per year.

It is assumed that building occupants are 50% male and 50% female. Male occupants are assumed to use water closets once and urinals twice in a typical work day.

Female occupants are assumed to use water closets three times. All occupants in this example are assumed to use lavatories for each restroom use for 15 seconds and kitchen sinks once for 15 seconds. An estimated 10% of the building occupants use showering facilities on a typical day.

Water closets use graywater volumes captured from showers, sinks and lavatories in the building. Waterless urinals are used in male restrooms and these fixtures use no water. Showers, lavatories and kitchen sinks are conventional fixtures and use 2.5 GPM. Motion sensors and electronic controls are used on lavatories, sinks and water closets. These devices are estimated to reduce lavatory and sink use duration by 20% but do not reduce the flow of water closets. These fixtures' duration data have been correspondingly adjusted from 15 seconds to 12 seconds. All of the above data is specific to the design case.

Table 2 provides a summary of the design case. The calculations indicate annual potable water use of 311,100 gallons.

The baseline case is calculated in the same manner as the design case except that ALL fixtures are assumed to be standard fixtures that comply with EPAct. Also, automatic sensors are not used on any fixtures and there is no graywater reuse. Usage rates, occupancy and annual workdays are identical for the baseline and the designed building. **Table 3** provides a summary of the baseline case. The calculations estimate an annual potable water use of 620,100 gallons.

Table 2: Design Case

Flush Fixture	Daily Uses	Flowrate	Duration	Occupants	Water Use
		[GPF]	[flush]		[gal]
Ultra Low-Flow Water Closet (Male)	0	0.8	1	150	0
Ultra Low-Flow Water Closet (Female)	3	0.8	1	150	360
Composting Toilet (Male)	1	0.0	1	150	0
Composting Toilet (Female)	0	0.0	1	150	0
Waterless Urinal (Male)	2	0.0	1	150	0
Waterless Urinal (Female)	0	0.0	1	150	0

Flow Fixture	Daily Uses	Flowrate	Duration	Occupants	Water Use
		[GPM]	[sec]		[gal]
Conventional Lavatory	3	2.5	12	300	450
Kitchen Sink	1	2.5	12	300	150
Shower	0.1	2.5	300	300	375

Total Daily Volume [gal]	1,335
Annual Work Days	260
Annual Volume [gal]	347,100
Graywater Reuse Volume [gal]	(36,000)
TOTAL ANNUAL VOLUME [gal]	**311,100**

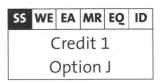

Comparison of the design case to the baseline case indicates that a potable water savings of 309,000 gallons is realized by using low-flow water closets, waterless urinals, auto controls on lavatories and sinks, and graywater reuse. This equates to a savings of 50% over the baseline case.

When reusing graywater volumes from the building, it is necessary to model the system on an annual basis to determine graywater volumes generated, storage capacity of the system and any necessary treatment processes before reusing the water volumes. Graywater volumes may or may not be consistently available throughout the year because these volumes are dependent on building occupant activities.

For instance, in a typical office building, graywater volumes will change slightly due to vacation schedules and holidays but should be relatively consistent over the year. In contrast, graywater volumes in a school building will substantially decrease in summer months due to the school calendar, and therefore, graywater volumes may not be available for non-potable applications.

Table 3: Baseline Case

Flush Fixture	Daily Uses	Flowrate	Duration	Auto Controls	Occupants	Water Use
		[GPF]	[flush]	N/A		[gal]
Conventional Water Closet (Male)	1	1.6	1		150	240
Conventional Water Closet (Female)	3	1.6	1		150	720
Conventional Urinal (Male)	2	1.0	1		150	300
Conventional Urinal (Female)	0	1.0	1		150	0

Flow Fixture	Daily Uses	Flowrate	Duration	Auto Controls	Occupants	Water Use
		[GPM]	[second]	N/A		[gal]
Conventional Lavatory	3	2.5	15		300	563
Kitchen Sink	1	2.5	15		300	188
Shower	0.1	2.5	300		300	375

Total Daily Volume [gal]	2,385
Annual Work Days	260
TOTAL ANNUAL VOLUME [gal]	**620,100**

Table 4: Sample Flush Fixture Types

Flush Fixture Type	Water Use
	[GPF]
Conventional Water Closet	1.6
Low-Flow Water Closet	1.1
Ultra Low-Flow Water Closet	0.8
Composting Toilet	0.0
Conventional Urinal	1.0
Waterless Urinal	0.0

Table 5: Sample Flow Fixture Types

Flow Fixture Type	Water Use
	[GPM]
Conventional Lavatory	2.5
Low-Flow Lavatory	1.8
Kitchen Sink	2.5
Low-Flow Kitchen Sink	1.8
Shower	2.5
Low-Flow Shower	1.8

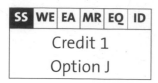
If the project uses rainwater volume for non-potable uses, it is necessary to calculate water savings over a time period of one year. Rain harvest volume depends on the amount of precipitation that the project site experiences, the rainwater collection surface's area and efficiency, and available storage capacity. See **Equation 1** and consult a rainwater harvesting guide for more detailed instruction. Rainfall data is available from the local weather service (see the Resources section). Rainwater volume depends on variations in precipitation, and thus, it is necessary to model the reuse strategy on an annual basis. A model of rainwater capture based on daily or monthly precipitation and occupant demand is helpful to determine the rainwater volumes captured and storage tank size. Subtract annual rainwater use as budgeted for flush and flow fixtures in the design case calculations.

Considerations

See LEED for Commercial Interiors v2.0 WE Credit 1.

Resources and Definitions

See LEED for Commercial Interiors v2.0 WE Credit 1.

Equation 1

$$\text{Rainwater volume [gal]} = \text{collection area [SF]} \times \text{collection efficiency [\%]} \times \text{Average rainfall [in]} \times 0.6233 \text{ gal/in}$$

Option K. Onsite Renewable Energy

Intent

Encourage and recognize increasing levels of on-site renewable energy self-supply in order to reduce environmental impacts associated with fossil fuel energy use.

Requirements

A building which supplies at least 5% of the building's total energy use (expressed as a fraction of annual energy cost) through the use of on-site renewable energy systems.

Submittals

Provide the LEED Submittal Template, signed by the architect, owner or responsible party, declaring that at least 5% of the building's energy is provided by on-site renewable energy. Include a narrative describing on-site renewable energy systems installed in the building and calculations demonstrating that at least 5% of total energy costs are supplied by the renewable energy system(s).

Potential Technologies & Strategies

Assess the project for non-polluting renewable energy potential including solar, wind, geothermal, low-impact hydro, biomass, and bio-gas strategies. When applying these strategies, take advantage of net metering with the local utility.

Summary of Referenced Standards

ANSI/ASHRAE/IESNA 90.1 – 1999: Energy Standard For Buildings Except Low-Rise Residential

American Society of Heating, Refrigerating and Air-Conditioning Engineers

www.ashrae.org

(800) 527-4723

On-site renewable or site-recovered energy that might be used to capture EA Credit 2 is handled as a special case in the modeling process. If either renewable or recovered energy is produced at the site, the ECB Method considers it free energy and it is not included in the Design Energy Cost. See the Calculation section for details.

Credit Interpretation Rulings

Credit Interpretation Rulings concerning this credit made for LEED for Commercial Interiors v2.0 project requests and as applicable for LEED for New Construction v2.1 project requests apply to LEED for Commercial Interiors v2.0 projects.

Table 1: Photovoltaic Economic Trends

Photovoltaic Data	1991	1995	2000	2010 - 2030
Electricity Price [¢/kWh]	40 - 75	25 - 50	12 - 20	<6
Module Efficiency [%]	5 - 14	7 - 17	10 - 20	15 - 25
System Cost [$/W]	10 - 20	7 - 15	3 - 7	1 - 1.50
System Lifetime [years]	5 - 10	10 - 20	>20	>30
U.S. Cumulative Sales [MW]	75	175	400 - 600	>10,000

Source: U.S. Department of Energy Photovoltaics Program

Review LEED for New Construction v2.1 CIRs for EA Credit 2.

Approach and Implementation

Locate the tenant space in a building that is equipped with on-site renewable energy systems. The project team is required to demonstrate that these technologies contribute at least 5% to the total energy requirements of the building. Project teams should use the LEED certified buildings database to identify local projects which have achieved LEED credit for on-site renewable energy. Include this requirement in base building selection criteria. Members of local USGBC chapters may have detailed information on projects that have achieved on-site renewable energy requirements.

Technologies Synergies and Trade-Offs

Renewable energy equipment typically impacts the project site. Some project sites are more compatible with renewable strategies than others. The magnitude of the impact of renewable energy generation equipment is usually small. Renewable energy equipment will impact energy performance of the building and requires commissioning and Measurement & Verification attention. Building-integrated PV systems should be integrated with daylighting strategies.

Geothermal energy is electricity generated from steam or hot water that is released from the Earth, and is captured by sizable power plants rather than small on-site systems. This is not to be confused with geothermal heat exchange, which is an energy-efficient heating and cooling strategy, the benefits of which are applicable to EA Credit 1 (Optimize Energy Performance).

Submittal Documentation

Complete the LEED for Commercial Interiors Submittal Template making the declaration that the requirements have been met along with a narrative and the calculations as described in the submittal requirement.

Exemplary Performance for Option K

An additional half point for Option K may be earned by demonstrating exemplary performance of 10%.

Calculations

New Buildings with no utility history or Existing Buildings with no Renewable Energy Submetering

The following calculation methodology supports the submittals as listed for Option K. The fraction of energy cost supplied by the renewable energy features is calculated against the DEC determined in EA Credit 1. An energy simulation of the base project is required to capture the Renewable Energy Credit. The quantity of energy generated on-site may be estimated outside of the simulation tool.

The following example illustrates how to calculate the renewable energy credit achievement levels.

Performance of the renewable source may be predicted using a bin type calculation. This requires the applicant to account for the contribution of variables associated with the renewable source. For example,

Table 2: BIPV Renewable Energy Calculation

BIPV system design	
Number of stories	5
Length of south facade	525 LF
Depth of awning	2 LF
Gross area of awning	5,250 SF
Shading effects	85%
Net area of awning =	4,463 SF
PV capacity	5.5 w/SF
Awning peak capacity	25 kW
Average daily output	4.03 kWh/100 SF
Average annual output	65,641 kWh

Table 3: Commercial Sector Average Energy Costs by State

State	Electricity [$/kWh]	Natural Gas [$/mcf]	No. 2 Fuel Oil [$/MMBtu]	No. 6 Fuel Oil [$/MMBtu]
Alabama	$0.066	$6.98	$4.07	$2.40
Alaska	$0.094	$2.44	$5.92	n/a
Arizona	$0.076	$5.31	$5.06	n/a
Arkansas	$0.057	$5.23	$4.09	n/a
California	$0.091	$6.41	$5.11	$2.70
Colorado	$0.057	$4.06	$4.70	n/a
Connecticut	$0.101	$7.23	$4.94	$3.38
Delaware	$0.069	$6.70	$4.06	$2.62
District of Columbia	$0.071	$7.37	$4.60	$3.16
Florida	$0.065	$6.85	$4.36	$2.71
Georgia	$0.071	$6.43	$4.27	$2.76
Hawaii	$0.126	$15.77	$5.01	$2.93
Idaho	$0.043	$4.49	$5.25	$2.31
Illinois	$0.078	$5.43	$4.55	$2.78
Indiana	$0.062	$5.44	$4.20	$2.49
Iowa	$0.066	$5.18	$4.30	n/a
Kansas	$0.063	$5.38	$4.30	$2.51
Kentucky	$0.052	$5.79	$4.34	n/a
Louisiana	$0.066	$6.22	$4.07	n/a
Maine	$0.110	$7.70	$5.15	$2.75
Maryland	$0.065	$6.52	$4.39	$2.74
Massachusetts	$0.092	$7.34	$4.90	$2.86
Michigan	$0.080	$5.00	$4.48	$2.57
Minnesota	$0.061	$4.80	$4.39	$2.41
Mississippi	$0.067	$5.26	$4.19	n/a
Missouri	$0.058	$5.88	$4.27	$2.36
Montana	$0.061	$4.83	$4.56	$2.20
Nebraska	$0.053	$4.88	$4.30	$2.38
Nevada	$0.066	$5.08	$5.13	n/a
New Hampshire	$0.115	$7.63	$4.68	$2.55
New Jersey	$0.099	$5.88	$4.40	$2.92
New Mexico	$0.080	$4.01	$4.11	n/a
New York	$0.115	$6.49	$5.06	$3.34
North Carolina	$0.063	$7.00	$4.27	$2.81
North Dakota	$0.059	$4.35	$4.30	$2.38
Ohio	$0.076	$6.23	$4.30	$2.69
Oklahoma	$0.053	$5.34	$4.28	$2.37
Oregon	$0.051	$4.63	$4.54	$2.74
Pennsylvania	$0.082	$7.35	$4.62	$2.80
Rhode Island	$0.099	$8.21	$5.49	$3.00
South Carolina	$0.063	$6.74	$4.32	$2.72
South Dakota	$0.065	$4.71	$4.26	$2.36
Tennessee	$0.064	$6.11	$4.34	$2.40
Texas	$0.067	$4.91	$4.16	$2.46
Utah	$0.057	$3.92	$4.79	$1.86
Vermont	$0.104	$5.18	$5.22	$2.90
Virginia	$0.057	$6.45	$4.48	$2.68
Washington	$0.048	$4.73	$4.91	$2.75
West Virginia	$0.056	$6.34	$4.43	n/a
Wisconsin	$0.059	$5.35	$4.59	$2.38
Wyoming	$0.053	$3.93	$4.75	$2.29
U.S. Average	**$0.074**	**$5.79**	**$4.69**	**$3.14**

Source: ASHRAE/IESNA Standard 90.1-1999 User's Manual

LEED for Commercial Interiors v2.0 Reference Guide

Credit 1

Option K

a BIPV design would include the effects of sunny, cloudy and overcast conditions, the orientation and altitude of the array, and system losses. **Table 2** shows the factors that affect a calculation of the energy generated by a BIPV array installed on a building.

Once the amount of energy generated by the renewable system is calculated, an energy cost must be computed to establish the LEED level of achievement. The dollar value of the renewable energy must be derived from the simulation results of the energy model by determining a "virtual" energy rate for the renewable system.

As in the Calculations section of EA Credit 1, there are three options to compute the project energy costs, from which the "virtual" rate is derived. First, the LEED Energy Modeling Protocol (EMP) allows the use of a rate schedule available for the project location from local utility companies. The second option is to compute the energy cost using a proposed energy rate schedule, preferably approved by the local ASHRAE/IESNA 90.1–1999 adopting authority. In the absence of these approved rates, a third option is to follow the rates as shown in **Table 3**. This table is based on Table 11-K from ASHRAE/IESNA 90.1–1999 User's Manual, and the data published periodically in the document DOE/EIA-0380 (2000/03).

The value of the on-site production of energy is a simplified calculation. To assign a dollar value to the on-site energy, determine the "virtual" energy rate by dividing the total energy cost (regulated and unregulated) by the total energy use. Multiply the predicted on-site energy produced by the "virtual rate" for the value of this type of energy. **Table 4** shows the calculation for the renewable energy "virtual" rate of electricity and gas used by the sample building described in Credit 1.

When calculating the total energy cost using the LEED Energy Modeling Protocol, the contribution of any on-site renewable or recovered energy is accounted for by deducting the "virtual" utility costs. In other words, the Renewable Energy Cost (REC) is deducted from the DEC, as the ECB method is based on energy that crosses the property line. This net regulated energy cost is designated as the DEC in the calculation method. The DEC is used as the denominator of the achievement calculation, which in turn increases the percent improvement over the reference standard (see **Equation 1**).

In the example, the project described in EA Credit 1 is modified to include BIPVs as part of the design. The energy-modeling simulation is not changed for this credit. A bin analysis is used to predict that ~65,000 kWh are generated and fed into the grid through net metering. To calculate the value of this energy, a virtual rate is established from the existing simulation and then used to determine the dollar value used in the LEED savings calculation. **Table 5** shows how to incorporate the renewable energy cost into the calculations.

Table 4: Renewable Energy Rate Calculation

Utility Rate	Resource	Energy Use	Energy Cost
E -19 -Office	Electricity	540,675 kWh	$ 37,800
E -19 -Rtl	Electricity	180,225 kWh	$ 12,600
		720,900 kWh	$ 50,400
		Virtual Electricity Rate	$ 0.07 /kWh
G - NR1- Office	Natural Gas	12,000 CCF	$ 8,500
G - NR1- Rtl	Natural Gas	-	$ -
		12,000 CCF	$ 8,500
		Virtual Natural Gas Rate	$ 0.71 /CCF

The example also shows how the renewable energy can change the overall energy savings calculation used to determine the points achieved. Compare **Table 6** with **Table 5** of this credit. Note that the Energy Cost Budget (ECB) is the same in both examples. There are no default values for renewable energy, so there is no change to the ECB.

The total percent reduction in energy use changes, however. This is because Credit 1 is based on grid energy that crosses the property line. When part of the building energy load is handled from an on-site generation source, it is deducted from the numerator in the calculation. The final LEED point tallies are shown in **Table 6**.

Existing buildings with a utility history may use recent annual utility bills as a basis for the calculation of renewable energy contribution. Renewable Energy Submetering

Equation 1: Renewable Energy Calculation

$$\% \text{ Renewable Energy} = 100 \times \frac{REC'}{DEC''}$$

Table 5: Proposed Case Processed Data

End Use	Energy Type	Electric [kWh]	Gas [CCF]	Energy Use [10³ Btu]	Cost [$]
Regulated					
Lighting	Electric	160,200		546,602	$11,200
Space Heating	Natural gas		4,550	455,000	$3,223
Space Cooling	Electric	240,300		819,904	$16,800
Fans/Pumps	Electric	120,150		409,952	$8,400
Hot Water (1)	Natural gas		1,750	175,000	$1,240
Hot Water (2)	Natural gas		700	70,000	$496
Subtotal Regulated (DEC')		520,650	7,000	2,476,458	$41,358
Nonregulated/ Process					
Lighting	Electric	80,100		273,301	$5,600
Space Heating	Natural gas		4,000	400,000	$2,833
Space Cooling	Electric	40,050		136,651	$2,800
Fans/Pumps	Electric	80,100		273,301	$5,600
Hot Water	Natural gas		1,000	100,000	$708
Subtotal Non-Regulated		200,250	5,000	1,183,253	$17,542
Total Building		**720,900**	**12,000**	**3,659,711**	**$58,900**
Subtotal Regulated (DEC')		520,650	7,000	2,476,458	$41,358
Subtotal Renewable (REC')		(65,641)		(223,968)	-$4,589
DEC"				2,252,489	**$36,769**

data may also be used in this calculation. Calculate renewable energy contribution based on the total building energy cost by dividing submetered renewable energy cost (renewable energy generated multiplied by utility purchase rate) generated over a 12-month period, by the 12-month total utility costs for the building.

Considerations

Renewable energy can be generated on a building site by using technologies that convert energy from the sun, wind and biomass into usable energy. On-site renewable energy is superior to conventional energy sources such as coal, nuclear, oil, natural gas and hydropower generation, because of its negligible transportation costs and impacts. In addition to preventing environmental degradation, on-site use of renewable power can improve power reliability and reduce reliance on the local power distribution grid. In the 1990s, renewable energy applications were the fastest growing new sources of energy. Opportunities for renewable energy vary by location and climate.

Environmental Issues

Use of renewable energy reduces environmental impacts associated with utility energy production and use. These impacts include natural resource destruction, air

Table 6: LEED Energy Cost Budget Compliance Table

Regulated Energy Summary by End Use	Energy Type	Proposed Building		Budget Building		Proposed/ Budget Energy
		Energy	Peak	Energy	Peak	
		[10^3 Btu]	[10^3 Btu]	[10^3 Btu]	[10^3 Btu]	[%]
Lighting - Conditioned	Electricity	491,942	163,981	1,074,780	346,703	46%
Lighting - Unconditioned	Electricity	54,660	5,466	119,420	12,571	46%
Space Heating	Gas	455,000	1,365,000	900,000	4,320,000	51%
Space Cooling	Electricity	819,904	273,301	853,000	304,643	96%
Pumps	Electricity	40,995	7,884	51,180	10,236	80%
Fans - Interior Ventilation	Electricity	360,758	649,364	450,384	150,128	80%
Fans - Interior Exhaust	Electricity	8,199	8,199	10,236	10,236	80%
Service Water Heating	Gas	245,000	81,667	600,000	214,286	41%

Energy & Cost Summary by Fuel	DEC" Use	DEC" Cost	ECB' Use	ECB' Cost	DEC" / ECB'	
	[10^3 Btu]	[$]	[10^3 Btu]	[$]	Energy %	Cost %
Electricity	1,776,458	$36,400	2,559,000	$75,000	69%	49%
Natural Gas	700,000	$4,958	1,500,000	$9,750	47%	51%
Other Fossil Fuel	-	$0	-	$0	-	-
Subtotal Non-Renewable (DEC')	2,476,458	$41,358	4,059,000	$84,750		
Subtotal Renewable (REC')	(223,968)	-$4,589	-	$0	-	-
Total	2,252,489	$36,769	4,059,000	$84,750		

Percent Savings = 100 x (ECB' $ -DEC" $)/ECB' $ =   56.6%

Credit 1 Points Awarded =   9

Percent Renewable = 100 x (REC' $)/DEC' $ =   11.1%

Credit 2 Points Awarded =   2

pollution and water pollution. Utilization of biomass can divert an estimated 350 million tons of woody construction, demolition, and land-clearing waste from landfills each year. Conversely, air pollution will occur due to incomplete combustion if these wastes are not processed properly.

Economic Issues

Use of on-site renewable energy technologies can result in energy cost savings, particularly if peak-hour demand charges are high. Utility rebates are often available to reduce first costs of renewable energy equipment. In some states, first costs can be offset by net metering, where excess electricity is sold back to the utility. Despite their long-term economic and environmental advantages, renewable energy systems can have a very high first cost.

Community Issues

Renewable energy has a dramatic impact on outdoor environmental quality. Reductions in air and water pollution are beneficial to all community members. Renewable energy has a positive impact on rural communities. Economic development in these communities can be enhanced by siting and operating wind farms and biomass conversion facilities. Wind Powering America is an initiative by the DOE to dramatically increase the use of wind energy in the United States.

Rural wind generation is providing new sources of income for American farmers, Native Americans and other rural landowners while meeting the growing demand for clean sources of electricity. However, care must be taken to minimize undesirable noise from wind farms and suboptimal combustion at biomass conversion facilities.

Resources

Please see the USGBC Web site at www.usgbc.org/resources for more specific resources on materials sources and other technical information.

Web Sites
ENERGY Guide

www.energyguide.com

Includes information on different power types, including green power, as well as general information on energy efficiency and tools for selecting power providers based on various economic, environmental and other criteria.

National Center for Photovoltaics (NCPV)

www.nrel.gov/ncpv/

Provides clearinghouse information on all aspects of PV systems.

National Renewable Energy Laboratory

www.nrel.gov

The National Renewable Energy Laboratory (NREL) is a leader in the U.S. Department of Energy's effort to secure an energy future for the nation that is environmentally and economically sustainable.

The Office of Energy Efficiency and Renewable Energy (EERE)
U.S. Department of Energy

www.eere.energy.gov

This Web site includes information on all types of renewable energy technologies and energy efficiency.

Green Power Partnership
U.S. Environmental Protection Agency

www.epa.gov/greenpower/index.htm

EPA's Green Power Partnership provides assistance and recognition to organizations that demonstrate environmental leadership by choosing green power. It includes a buyers guide with listings of providers of green power in each state.

Print Media

Wind and Solar Power Systems, Mukund Patel, CRC Press 1999.

SS	WE	EA	MR	EQ	ID
Credit 1					
Option K					

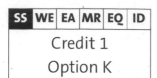
Wind Energy Comes of Age, Paul Gipe, John Wiley & Sons 1995.

Definitions

Biomass is plant material such as trees, grasses and crops, which can be converted to heat energy to produce electricity.

The **Environmental Attributes of Green Power** include emission reduction benefits that result from green power being used instead of conventional power sources.

Photovoltaic Energy is electricity from photovoltaic cells that convert the energy in sunlight into electricity.

Renewable Energy is energy from sources that are renewed on an ongoing basis. This includes energy from the sun, wind and small hydropower. Ways to capture energy from the sun include photovoltaic, thermal solar energy systems, and bio-energy. One issue with bioenergy is the amount of fossil fuel energy used to produce it.

Wind Energy is electricity generated by wind machines.

Option L. Other Quantifiable Environmental Performance

Requirements

A building that has in place at time of submittal other quantifiable environmental performance characteristics, for which the requirements may be found in other LEED Rating Systems.

Submittals

Provide the LEED for Commercial Interiors Submittal Template, signed by the architect, interior designer, building owner, engineer or other responsible party, declaring compliance with each claimed requirement based on the applicable standards as defined in applicable LEED Green Building Rating System.

OR

Provide the LEED for Commercial Interiors Submittal Template, signed by the architect, interior designer, building owner, engineer or other responsible party, declaring exemplary performance has been achieved for a LEED for Commercial Interiors SS Credit 1 Option.

Potential Technologies & Strategies

Refer to the appropriate Potential Technology and Strategy provided for the LEED Rating System and credit selected.

Credit Interpretation Rulings

Credit Interpretation Rulings concerning this credit made for LEED for Commercial Interiors v2.0 project requests and as applicable for other LEED Rating System project requests apply to LEED for Commercial Interiors v2.0 projects.

Approach and Implementation

Select a building that has achieved an environmental performance characteristic for at least one credit found in another LEED Rating System. Innovation in Design credits that are not addressed by existing LEED credits in other LEED Rating Systems will also be considered on their merit. A half point can be earned for each credit selection with an additional half point as appropriate for exemplary performance.

Project teams are advised to submit a CIR to confirm their credit selection unless precedence has been set by another LEED for Commercial Interiors certified project.

A second way to earn this credit is to achieve exemplary performance for eligible credits in Options A through K. A maximum of one additional half point can be awarded if the specified exemplary performance threshold is achieved.

Submittal Documentation

Complete the LEED for Commercial Interiors Submittal Template making the declaration that the requirements have been met for the credit selected from another LEED Rating System. In addition provide a brief narrative, calculations or other quantifiable environmental performance as described in the documentation requirement for this credit.

SS	WE	EA	MR	EQ	ID
Credit 1					
Option L					

OR

Complete the LEED for Commercial Interiors Submittal Template making the declaration that the level of exemplary performance associated with the appropriate credit requirement has been achieved. In addition provide the associated calculations or documentation necessary for the achievement for this credit.

Additional Documentation

No additional documentation should be required during submittal review.

Development Density and Community Connectivity

Intent

Channel development to urban areas with existing infrastructure, protect greenfields, and preserve habitat and natural resources.

Requirements

- Select space in a building that is located in an established, walkable community with a minimum density of 60,000 square feet per acre net (two-story downtown development),

OR

- Select space in a building that is located within 1/2 mile of a residential zone or neighborhood (with an average density of 10 units per acre net),

    AND

- The building has pedestrian access to at least 10 of the basic services below within 1/2 mile:

    1) Bank; 2) Place of Worship; 3) Convenience Grocery; 4) Day Care; 5) Cleaners; 6) Fire Station; 7) Hair Care; 8) Hardware; 9) Laundry; 10) Library; 11) Medical/Dental; 12) Senior Care Facility; 13) Park; 14) Pharmacy; 15) Post Office; 16) Restaurant; 17) School; 18) Supermarket; 19) Commercial Office; 20) Community Center, and other recognized services evaluated on their merit.

Greenfield developments and projects that do not use existing infrastructure are not eligible.

Submittals

- Provide the LEED for Commercial Interiors Submittal Template, signed by the civil engineer, architect or other responsible party, declaring that the project met the credit requirement.

- Provide density calculations for the building and surrounding area with an area plan, highlighting the building location.

OR

- Provide an area plan highlighting the building location, the residential zone or neighborhood, and 10 or more basic services located within 1/2 mile of the project space (inclusive of the building selected).

Potential Technologies and Strategies

During the site selection process, give preference to urban sites with pedestrian access to a variety of services.

Credit Interpretation Rulings

LEED for Commercial Interiors v2.0 SS Credit 2 has the same requirements as LEED for New Construction v2.1 SS Credit 2 for the first compliance option for this credit.

Credit Interpretation Rulings made under LEED for New Construction v2.1 (SSc 2) may apply only to the first option for this LEED for Commercial Interiors credit.

Approach and Implementation

The density criteria above is based on development within a downtown neighborhood in which the majority of buildings are at least two stories tall and cover 75% or more of any given property.

Option 1 (Density)

To determine the development density of a project, both the project density and the densities of surrounding developments must be considered. The calculations detailed below refer to the base building in which the LEED for Commercial Interiors project is located, the base building site area and the buildings surrounding the base building. Note: The LEED for Commercial Interiors Submittal Templates can be used to perform these calculations.

The density calculation process is described in the following steps:

1. Determine the total area of the project site and the total square footage of the building. For projects that are part of a larger property (such as a campus), define the project area as that which is defined in the project's scope. The project area must be defined consistently throughout LEED documentation.

2. Calculate the development density for the project by dividing the total square footage of the building by the total site area in acres. This development density must be equal to or greater than 60,000 square feet per acre (see **Equation 1**).

3. Convert the total site area from acres to square feet and calculate the square root of this number. Then multiply the square root by three to determine the appropriate density radius. (Note: the square root function is used to normalize the calculation by removing effects of site shape.) (see **Equation 2**).

4. Overlay the density radius on a map that includes the project site and surrounding areas, originating from the center of the site. This is the density boundary. Include a scale on the map.

5. For each property within the density boundary and for those properties that intersect the density boundary, create a table with the building square footage and site area of each property. Include all properties in the density calculations except for undeveloped public areas such as parks and water bodies. Do not include public roads and right-of-way areas. Information on neighboring properties can be obtained from your city or county zoning department.

6. Add all the square footage values and site areas. Divide the total square footage by the total site area to obtain the average property density within the density boundary. The average property density of the properties within the density

Equation 1

Development Density (SF / Acre) = Building Square Footage (SF) / Property Area (Acres)

Equation 2

Density Radius (LF) = 3 X $\sqrt{}$ (Property Area (acres) x 43,560 (SF/acre))

boundary must be equal to or greater than 60,000 square feet per acre.

The following example illustrates the property density calculations: A 30,000-square-foot building is located on a 0.44-acre urban site and the calculations are used to determine the building density. The building density is above the minimum density of 60,000 square feet per acre required by the credit (see **Table 1**).

Next, the density radius is calculated. A density radius of 415 feet is calculated (see **Table 2**).

The density radius is applied to an area plan of the project site and surrounding area. The plan identifies all properties that are within or are intersected by the density radius. The plan includes a scale and a north indicator.

Table 3 below summarizes the information about the properties identified on the map. The building space and site area are listed for each property. These values are summed and the average density is calculated by dividing the total building space by the total site area.

For this example, the average building density of the surrounding area is greater than 60,000 square feet per acre, and, thus, the example qualifies for one point under this credit.

OR

Option 2 (Community Connectivity)

To determine the connectivity of a project, both residential and commercial adjacencies must be considered. The calculation process is described in the

Figure 1: An Illustration of a Sample Area Plan

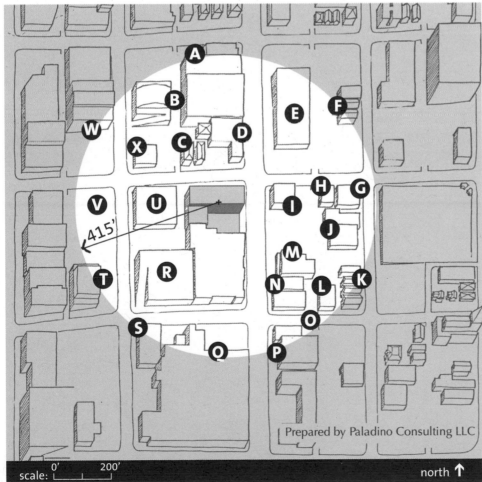

scale: 0' 200' north ↑

Prepared by Paladino Consulting LLC

Table 1: Property Density Calculations

Project Buildings	Building Space [SF]	Site Area [acres]
Project	30,000	0.44
Density [SF/acre]		**68,182**

Table 2: Density Radius Calculation

Density Radius Calculation	
Site Area [acres]	0.44
Density Radius [LF]	415

following steps:

Prepare a site map and draw a 1/2-mile radius around the center of the project. Note all residential developments within the radius. At least one area zoned for residential development of 10 units per acre or greater must be present within the radius for the project to earn this credit.

1. Note all commercial buildings within the radius. At least 10 community services

must be present within the radius for the project to earn this credit.

Services may include: Bank, Place of Worship, Convenience Grocery, Day Care, Cleaners, Fire Station, Hair Care, Hardware, Laundry, Library, Medical/Dental, Senior Care Facility, Park, Pharmacy, Post Office, Restaurant, School, Supermarket, Commercial Office, and Community Center.

Other services will be considered on their merit.

With the exception of restaurants, no service may be counted more than once in the calculation. Up to 3 restaurants may be counted towards achievement of this credit.

Submittal Documentation

This credit applies to the building in which the tenant space is located. Follow the submittal criteria included in the LEED for Commercial Interiors Submittal Template as follows:

Table 3: Sample Area Properties

Buildings within Density Radius	Building Space [SF]	Site Area [acres]	Buildings within Density Radius	Building Space [SF]	Site Area [acres]
A	33,425	0.39	N	28,740	0.30
B	87,500	1.58	O	6,690	0.15
C	6,350	0.26	P	39,000	0.39
D	27,560	0.32	Q	348,820	2.54
E	66,440	1.17	R	91,250	1.85
F	14,420	1.36	S	22,425	0.27
G	12,560	0.20	T	33,650	0.51
H	6,240	0.14	U	42,400	0.52
I	14,330	0.22	V	-	0.76
J	29,570	0.41	W	19,200	0.64
K	17,890	0.31	X	6,125	0.26
L	9,700	0.31	Y	5,000	0.30
M	24,080	0.64	Z	4,300	0.24
			Total Building Space [SF]	997,665	
			Total Site Area [acres]		16.04
			AVERAGE DENSITY [SF/acres]		**62,199**

For Option 1 (Density)

Provide the LEED for Commercial Interiors Submittal Template, signed by the civil engineer, architect or other responsible party, declaring that the project has met the credit requirements, and incorporating the density calculations.

AND

Provide an area plan, highlighting the building location and surrounding buildings within 1/2 mile of the project. Label all surrounding buildings within 1/2 mile for coordination with the information provided in the Submittal Template.

OR

For Option 2 (Connectivity)

Provide the LEED for Commercial Interiors Submittal Template, signed by the civil engineer, architect or other responsible party, declaring that the project has met the credit requirement.

AND

Provide an area plan, highlighting the building location, the residential zone or neighborhood, and 10 or more of the basic services located within 1/2 mile of the project space (inclusive of the building selected). Label all buildings within the 1/2-mile radius for clarity.

Additional Documentation

For Option 1

The Submittal Template includes the calculation demonstrating credit achievement. If the Submittal Template is filled out and the required site map is provided, no additional documentation will be necessary.

For Option 2

All of the information necessary for credit achievement is included or described on the Submittal Template.

Exemplary Performance

No exemplary performance criteria exist.

Considerations

Strategies

The general approach for achieving this credit is to give preference to sites within an existing urban fabric. Work with local jurisdictions and follow the urban development plan to meet or exceed density goals. Consider synergies with neighbors and choose sites based on infrastructure, transportation and quality-of-life considerations. Sites with redevelopment plans that will achieve the required development density by the completion of the project should not be excluded from consideration. This credit can be achieved by choosing to develop a site where community revitalization is occurring provided the required development density is achieved by the project's completion.

Consider the functional adjacencies of the site with respect to transportation and productivity. Community developments with at least 10 of the basic services listed in this credit within a 1/2-mile radius reduce transportation impacts. Making access to basic services walkable may improve productivity by reducing the time spent driving between services and accessing parking. In addition, occupant health can be improved by increased levels of physical activity.

Synergies and Trade-Offs

Urban redevelopment affects all areas of site design including site selection, transportation planning, building density and stormwater management. Urban sites often involve the rehabilitation of an existing building, with a reduction of construction waste and new material use.

The potential trade-offs of sites in dense areas are limited open space and possible negative IEQ aspects such as contaminated soils, undesirable air quality or limited daylighting applications.

SS | WE | EA | MR | EQ | ID

Credit 2

Resources

Please see the USGBC Web site at www. usgbc.org/resources for more specific resources on materials sources and other technical information.

Web Sites

Congress for New Urbanism

www.cnu.org

Urban Land Institute

ULI Washington

www.washington.uli.org

(703) 390-9217

The Urban Land Institute is a nonprofit organization based in Washington D.C. that promotes the responsible use of land in order to enhance the total environment.

The International Union for the Scientific Study of Population

www.iussp.org

33 1 56 06 21 73

The IUSSP promotes scientific studies of demography and population-related issues.

Print Media

Changing Places: Rebuilding Community in the Age of Sprawl, Richard Moe and Carter Wilkie, Henry Holt & Company, 1999.

Density by Design: New Directions in Residential Development, Steven Fader, Urban Land Institute, 2000.

Green Development: Integrating Ecology and Real Estate, Alex Wilson, et al., John Wiley & Sons, 1998.

Once There Were Greenfields: How Urban Sprawl Is Undermining America's Environment, Economy, and Social Fabric, F. Kaid Benfield, et al., Natural Resources Defense Council, 1999.

Suburban Nation: The Rise of Sprawl and the Decline of the American Dream, Andres Duany, et al., North Point Press, 2000.

Definitions

Building Density is the floor area of the building divided by the total area of the site (square feet per acre).

Property Area is the total area within the legal property boundaries of a site and encompasses all areas of the site including constructed areas and non-constructed areas. This is also called the "site area".

The **Building Footprint** is the portion of the property area covered by the building. It does not include constructed site elements such as parking lots, sidewalks and access roads.

The **Site Area** is the total area within the legal property boundaries of a building and encompasses all areas of the site including constructed areas and non-constructed areas. This is also called the "property area."

A **Greenfield** is undeveloped land or land that has not been impacted by human activity.

The **Square Footage** of a building is the total area in square feet of all rooms including corridors, elevators, stairwells and shaft spaces.

Connectivity is a measurement of the functional adjacencies within a reasonable walking distance of a project.

Alternative Transportation

Overview

Transportation accounts for 27.4% of energy use in the United States, the vast majority (96.4%) of which is powered by petroleum-based fuels.[1] Light vehicles, including automobiles, motorcycles, and light trucks, consume more energy than any other transportation mode.[2] In 2001, Americans were estimated to own more than 200 million private vehicles.[3] Along with steady increases in vehicle ownership, the number of miles traveled by Americans has also steadily increased over the past few decades. In 2001, on average each American (excluding persons ages 0 to 4) traveled 40.25 miles per day, with 88.2% of all daily travel attributed to private vehicles.[4] Travel to and from work makes up a significant portion (nearly 30%) of the vehicles miles traveled in personal vehicles, and the average length and duration of these commuting trips has steadily increased over the past few decades.[5]

As of the late 1990s, an estimated 200 million of the 520 million cars worldwide were located in the United States. The infrastructure (roadways and parking lots) used by automobiles dissects open expanses that wildlife relies on for migration and foraging. This impervious infrastructure also contributes to the erosion and pollution of receiving waters. The exhaust from automobiles pollutes the air and contributes to acid rain. Environmental impacts occur during extracting, refining and transporting crude oil for gasoline production. Reducing private automobile use saves energy and reduces associated environmental problems.

Fortunately, alternatives to conventional transportation methods exist. A surprisingly large number of people are willing to use alternative means of transportation such as bicycles, mass transit and car-pools if they are convenient and facilities are provided to encourage their use.

Parking facilities for automobiles also have negative impacts on the environment because asphalt surfaces increase stormwater runoff and contribute to urban heat island effects. By restricting the size of parking lots and promoting car-pooling activities, building occupants can benefit from increased green space.

Environmental Issues

Reduction of private automobile use reduces fuel consumption and the associated release of air and water pollutants in vehicle exhaust.

Parking lots produce stormwater runoff and contribute to the urban heat island effect. They also diminish green space on the project site. Minimizing parking lot size reduces the development footprint and sets aside more space for natural areas or greater development densities.

Economic Issues

Reducing the size of parking areas based on anticipated use of bicycles, car-pools and public transit by building occupants may lower initial project costs. If local utilities charge for stormwater runoff based on impervious surface area, minimization of these areas can result in lower stormwater charges.

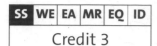
The initial cost to design and construct a project in proximity to mass transit varies widely. During the site selection process, project owners should compare the cost of building sites in different areas to determine if a reduction in automobile use is possible and economical. Many occupants view proximity to mass transit as a benefit and this can influence the value and marketability of the building. Parking infrastructure and transportation requirements, disturbance of existing habitats, resource consumption, and future fuel costs should also be assessed.

The initial project cost increase for bike storage areas and changing facilities is nominal relative to the overall project cost. Initial costs for alternative vehicles are higher than for conventional vehicles and this may delay their purchase, decreasing the necessity for refueling stations. Different alternative fuel vehicles need different refueling stations, and the costs associated with these stations vary.

Community Issues

Building occupants can realize health benefits through bicycle and walking commuting strategies. Bicycling and walking also expose people to the community, encouraging interaction among neighbors and allowing for enjoyment of the area in ways unavailable to automobile passengers.

Alternative Transportation
Public Transportation Access

Intent

Reduce pollution and land development impacts from automobile use.

Requirements

- Tenant to select building within 1/2 mile of a commuter rail, light rail or subway station or 1/4 mile of two or more public or campus bus lines usable by tenant occupants.

Submittals

- Provide the LEED for Commercial Interiors Submittal Template, signed by an appropriate party, declaring that the building in which the project is located is located within required proximity to mass transit.

- Provide an area drawing or transit map highlighting the building location, the fixed rail stations and bus lines, and indicate the distances between them. Include a scale bar for distance measurement.

Potential Technologies & Strategies

Perform a transportation survey of potential tenant occupants to identify transportation needs. Choose a building near mass transit.

Credit Interpretation Rulings

Credit Interpretation Rulings concerning this credit made for LEED for Commercial Interiors v2.0 project requests and as applicable for LEED for New Construction v2.1 project requests apply to LEED for Commercial Interiors v2.0 projects. Review LEED for New Construction v2.1 CIRs for SS Credit 4.1

If a light rail or subway station is sited and under construction at the time the tenant space was selected, it satisfies the intent of the credit.

Approach and Implementation

Select a tenant space in a building that has convenient access to existing transportation networks to minimize the need for new transportation lines. Local telephone books and community Web sites provide maps and directories that will be helpful in determining the transportation options available.

During the selection of tenant space, survey potential building occupants and determine if the available mass transportation options meet their needs. Look for functional and direct sidewalks, paths and walkways to existing mass transit stops.

Figure 1: Sample Area Drawing

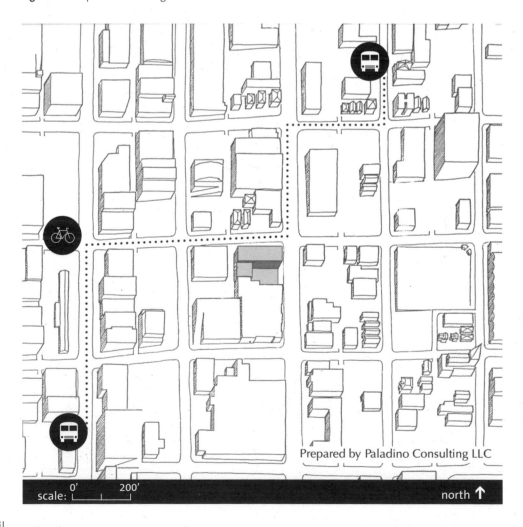

Prepared by Paladino Consulting LLC

scale: 0'   200'   north ↑

Provide incentives such as transit passes to encourage occupants to use mass transit. Encourage employees to work from home if practical and design the building to account for the needs of telecommuting.

Submittal Documentation

The criteria for this credit is based on the building in which the tenant space is located, not the project space. In determining the distance traveled to public facilities, do not include the distance within the building to the tenant space, but begin the measurements at any primary building entrance.

Additional Documentation

If achievement of this credit is based in part on the use of private shuttle busses, the project may need to provide documentation of shuttle capacity and schedule demonstrating that it is capable of serving commuting needs of the building population.

Calculations

Use an area drawing to indicate mass transit stops within 1/2 mile of the project. Remember that the project is required to be within a 1/2 mile pedestrian route to a commuter rail, light rail or subway station or within 1/4 mile of two or more bus lines. **Figure 1** shows two bus lines within ¼ mile of the project location. The map includes a scale bar and a north indicator. If private shuttle buses will be used to meet the requirements, they must connect to public transit and operate during the most frequent commuting hours.

Considerations

The extensive use of private automobiles and their heavy reliance on petroleum contributes to a number of environmental problems. Fortunately, alternatives to conventional transportation methods ex-

ist. A surprisingly large number of people are willing to use alternative means of transportation such as mass transit if it is convenient and facilities are provided to encourage their use. Encouraging the use of mass transit reduces the energy demand for transportation needs and affects building sites by reducing the space needed for parking lots, which encroach on green space on the building site. Minimizing parking lots reduces the building footprint and sets aside more space for natural areas or greater development densities.

Environmental Issues

The environmental effects of automobile use include vehicle emissions that contribute to smog and air pollution as well as environmental impacts from oil extraction and petroleum refining. Increased use of public transportation can improve air quality. For every passenger mile traveled, public transportation emits 95% less carbon monoxide, 92% fewer volatile organic compounds (VOCs), and almost 50% less carbon dioxide and nitrogen oxides than private vehicles.[6]

Reduction in private vehicle use reduces fuel consumption and air and water pollutants in vehicle exhaust. On the basis of passenger miles traveled, public transportation is twice as fuel efficient as private vehicles, and annually saves 45 million barrels of oil.[7] Another benefit of public transportation is the associated reduction in the need for infrastructure used by vehicles. Parking facilities and roadways for automobiles have negative impacts on the environment because impervious surfaces like asphalt increase stormwater runoff while contributing to urban heat island effects.

Economic Issues

Many occupants view proximity to mass transit as a benefit and this can influence the value and marketability of the building. For building occupants, costs associated with traveling to and from the

workplace can be significantly reduced if access to public transportation is available. For this reason, providing access to public transportation may provide an economic benefit associated with attracting and retaining employees. Existing building project teams have little to no control over their building's proximity to mass transit. If a building is not near mass transit, a shuttle can be provided to earn this credit, but this would be an added operating cost for the building.

Reducing the size of parking areas based on anticipated use of public transit by building occupants may alter operating costs associated with parking lot maintenance. If local utilities charge for stormwater based on impervious surface area, minimization of these areas can result in lower stormwater charges.

Resources

Please see the USGBC Web site at www.usgbc.org/resources for more specific resources on materials sources and other technical information.

Web Sites

Office of Transportation and Air Quality

U.S. Environmental Protection Agency

www.epa.gov/otaq/

U.S. EPA Web site provides information on the types and effects of air pollution associated with automobile use, information for consumers, and links to resources for organizations interested in promoting commuter choice programs.

Best Workplaces for Commuters

www.bestworkplacesforcommuters.gov/index.htm

(888) 856-3131

This program, established by the U.S. EPA and DOT, publicly recognizes employers for their exemplary commuter benefits programs. It provides tools, guid-ance and promotions to help employers incorporate commuter benefits into their employee benefits plan, reap financial benefits and gain national recognition.

Advanced Transportation Technology Institute

www.atti-info.org

A nonprofit organization that advances clean transportation technologies through research, education and technology transfer in order to promote a healthy environment and energy independence.

Definitions

Mass Transit includes transportation facilities designed to transport large groups of persons in a single vehicle such as buses or trains.

Public Transportation is bus, rail or other transportation service for the general public on a regular, continual basis that is publicly or privately owned.

Alternative Transportation
Bicycle Storage & Changing Rooms

Intent

Reduce pollution and land development impacts from automobile use.

Requirements

- Provide secure bicycle storage, with convenient changing/shower facilities (within 200 yards of the building) for 5% or more of tenant occupants.

Submittals

- Provide the LEED for Commercial Interiors Submittal Template, signed by the architect, interior designer or responsible party, declaring the distance to the cycle storage and showers from the building entrance, showing the number of regular tenant occupants and demonstrating that more than 5% of occupants have provision.

Potential Technologies & Strategies

Select a building with transportation amenities such as bicycle racks and showering/changing facilities or add them as part of the tenant fit-out.

Credit Interpretation Rulings

Credit Interpretation Rulings concerning this credit made for LEED for Commercial Interiors v2.0 project requests and as applicable for LEED for New Construction v2.1 project requests apply to LEED for Commercial Interiors v2.0 projects. Review LEED for New Construction v2.1 CIRs for SS Credit 4.2.

Access (provided within the lease agreement) to a health and fitness club on the property in which the project is located meets the credit intent as long as there is unlimited access to the showering facilities for the tenants. Credit compliance for bicycle storage also must be provided.

Approach and Implementation

Select a tenant space in a building that has convenient access to safe bicycle pathways and secure bicycle storage areas for cyclists. Provide shower and changing areas for cyclists that are easily accessible from bicycle storage areas. Local bike shops, telephone books and community Web sites provide maps and directories that will be helpful in determining the transportation options available.

During the selection of tenant space, survey potential building occupants and determine if the available bike routes and their compatibility with mass transit options meet their needs. Look for functional and direct paths that can be used by bicycle commuters.

Shower facilities may be either within the tenant's space, or in a common facility within 200 yards of the building.

If changing rooms and showers are not within the tenant space, the submittals must demonstrate that the required capacity will not be compromised by other users. Demonstrate that the arrangements are permanent and are not subject to lease revisions or other circumstances out of the control of the tenant.

If the required bike rack capacity cannot be reserved for the specific tenant space, the quantity then must be based on the entire building population.

Follow the submittal criteria included in the LEED for Commercial Interiors Submittal Template. Provide a narrative with the letter template explaining how alternative approaches to dedicated racks, changing facilities and showers meet the credit requirements.

Submittal Documentation

Complete the LEED for Commercial Interiors Submittal Template making the declaration that the requirements have been met.

Additional Documentation

Provide drawings and cut sheets or photos highlighting the bicycle securing apparatus and its location, along with floor plans and/or photos indicating the location of changing/shower faciliities. Provide calculations indicating that there is at least one shower for every 8 cyclists.

Exemplary Performance

There are no exemplary performance criteria for this credit.

Calculations

To determine the number of secure bicycle spaces and changing/showering facilities required for the building, follow the calculation methodology as follows:

1. Identify the total number of full-time and part-time building occupants.

2. Calculate the Full-Time Equivalent (FTE) building occupants based on a standard eight-hour workday. A full-time worker has an FTE value of 1.0 while a part-time worker has a FTE value of 0.5 (see **Equation 1**). Note that FTE calculations for the project must be used consistently for all LEED for Commercial Interiors credits.

3. Total the FTE values for each shift to obtain the total number of FTE building occupants. In buildings that house companies utilizing multiple shifts, select the shift with the greatest number of FTE building occupants.

4. The minimum number of **secure bicycle spaces** required is equal to 5% of the FTE building occupants during the maximum shift (see **Equation 2**). Secure bicycle spaces include bicycle racks, lockers and storage rooms. These spaces must be easily accessible by building occupants during all periods of the year, and free of charge.

5. The required number of **changing** and **showering facilities** for non-residential buildings is based on the number of bicycling occupants. A minimum of one shower for every eight bicycling occupants is required to earn this point. (This number is based on recommended showering facilities for institutional spaces). Showering facilities can be unit showers or group showering facilities (see **Equation 3**).

For example, a building houses a company with two shifts. The first shift includes 240 full-time workers and 90 part-time workers. The second shift includes 110 full-time workers and 60 part-time workers. Calculations to determine the total FTE building occupants for each shift are included in **Table 1**.

The first shift is used for determining the number of bicycling occupants because it has the greatest FTE building occupant total. Based on a total of 285 FTE building occupants, the estimated number of bicycling occupants is 15. Thus, 15 secure bicycle spaces are required for this example. The required number of changing and showering facilities is one facility for each eight bicycling occupants. Thus, total number of required showering facilities in this example is two. More showers may be necessary for the building based on the number of actual bicycling occupants.

Considerations

The extensive use of private automobiles and their heavy reliance on petroleum contributes to a number of environmental problems. Since the early 1990s, the U.S. Department of Transportation (DOT) has increasingly focused on studying and supporting bicycling as an environmentally responsible, cost effective, healthy transportation mode. This has led to better

Table 1: Sample FTE Calculation

Shift	Full-Time Occupants		Part-Time Occupants		Full-Time Equivalent (FTE) Occupants
	Occupants	[hr]	Occupants	[hr]	Occupants
First Shift	240	8	90	4	285
Second Shift	110	8	60	4	140

Equation 1

FTE = Worker Hours [hours] / 8 [hours]

Equation 2

Secure Bicycle Spaces (non-residential buildings) = FTE Building Occupants x 5%

Equation 3

Showering Facilities (non-residential buildings) = Bicycle Spaces/8

knowledge of bicycling rates and barriers to increased participation, increased funding for bicycling facilities, and the development of programs promoting bicycle use and safety.[8] Building owners can help promote the expansion of bicycling as a transportation mode for commuters by ensuring that building grounds offer the appropriate facilities for building occupants interesting in bicycle commuting.

Environmental Issues

Bicycling as an alternative to personal vehicle operation offers a number of environmental benefits. Bicycle commuting produces no emissions and has zero demand for petroleum-based fuels. Bicycle commuting also relieves traffic congestion, reduces noise pollution, and requires far less infrastructure for roadways and parking lots. Roadways and parking lots produce stormwater runoff, contribute to the urban heat island effect, and encroach on green space.

Bicycles are more likely to be used for relatively short commuting trips. Displacing vehicle miles with bicycling even for short trips carries a large environmental benefit, since a large portion of vehicle emissions occur in the first few minutes of driving following a cold start, as emissions control equipment is less effective at cool operating temperatures.[9]

Economic Issues

If local utilities charge for stormwater based on impervious surface area, minimization of these areas (like vehicle parking lots) can result in lower stormwater charges. The cost increase for bike storage areas is typically relatively small. Adding changing facilities and showers in existing buildings can be a more significant cost. Local and state governments may assist employees in meeting the cost of bicycle facilities through commuter choice incentive programs. Encouraging bicycle commuting among employees can improve employee health and reduce sick leave.

Resources

Please see the USGBC Web site at www.usgbc.org/resources for more specific resources on materials sources and other technical information.

Web Sites

Advanced Transportation Technology Institute

www.atti-info.org

A nonprofit organization that advances clean transportation technologies through research, education and technology transfer in order to promote a healthy environment and energy independence.

Transportation and Air Quality

U.S. Environmental Protection Agency

www.epa.gov/otaq/

U.S. EPA Web site provides information on the types and effects of air pollution associated with automobile use, information for consumers, and links to resources for organizations interested in promoting commuter choice programs.

Best Workplaces for Commuters

www.bestworkplacesforcommuters.gov/index.htm

(888) 856-3131

This program, established by the U.S. EPA and DOT, publicly recognizes employers for their exemplary commuter benefits programs. It provides tools, guidance, and promotion to help employers incorporate commuter benefits into their employee benefits plan, reap financial benefits and gain national recognition.

Bicyclinginfo.org

www.bicyclinginfo.org

This resource from the Pedestrian and Bicycle Information Center provides information and resources for a number of issues related to bicycle commuting, including health and safety, engineering, advocacy, education, facilities and more.

Information and links for bicycle parking issues can be found at www.bicyclinginfo.org/de/park.htm.

Bicycle & Pedestrian Program

U.S. Department of Transportation

www.fhwa.dot.gov/environment/bikeped/

(202) 366-5007

This program of the Federal Highway Administration's Office of Human and Natural Environment promotes bicycle and pedestrian transportation accessibility, use and safety.

Bike To Work

www.biketowork.com

This online resource for bicycle commuters provides a variety of links and information.

A Commuting Guide for Employers

www.self-propelled-city.com/employcomm_html

This Web site outlines strategies employers can use as they try to encourage employees to bicycle commute.

An Employer's Guide to Encouraging Bicycle Commuting

Bicycle Coalition of Maine

www.bikemaine.org/btwemployer.htm

(207) 623-4511

From the Bicycle Coalition of Maine, this site suggests ways to encourage and facilitate bike commuting among employees.

Definitions

Bicycle Racks include outdoor bicycle racks, bicycle lockers, or indoor bicycle storage rooms.

Full-Time Equivalent Building Occupants refers to the total number of hours all building occupants spend in the building during the peak 8-hour occupancy period divided by 8 hours. For buildings used for multiple shifts each day the shift with the greatest number of FTE building occupants set the overall FTE building occupants for the building.

SS	WE	EA	MR	EQ	ID
		Credit 3.2			

Alternative Transportation
Parking Availability

Intent

Reduce pollution and land development impacts from single occupancy vehicle use.

Requirements

CASE A: For projects occupying less than 75% of gross building square footage:

Parking spaces provided to tenant shall not exceed minimum number required by local zoning regulations.

AND

Priority parking for car-pools or van-pools will be provided for 5% or more of tenant occupants.

OR

No parking will be provided or subsidized for tenant occupants.

CASE B: For projects occupying 75% or over of gross building square footage:

Parking capacity of the building will not exceed minimum local zoning requirements.

AND

Priority parking for car-pools and van-pools will be provided capable of serving 5% of the building occupants.

OR

No new parking will be added for rehabilitation projects.

AND

Preferred parking for car-pools or van-pools will be provided capable of serving 5% of the building occupants.

Submittals

- Provide the LEED for Commercial Interiors Submittal Template, signed by the architect, interior designer or responsible party, stating any relevant section of local zoning regulation defining parking requirements for tenant's occupancy group and zone and priority parking accommodations

- Provide the LEED for Commercial Interiors Submittal Template, signed by the architect, interior designer or responsible party, showing the section of tenant's lease that indicates parking guarantees and preferred parking accommodations

Potential Technologies and Strategies

Select a building with minimized car parking capacity and include limited parking inclusions in the lease.

Credit Interpretation Rulings

Credit Interpretation Rulings concerning this credit made for LEED for Commercial Interiors v2.0 project requests and as applicable for LEED for New Construction v2.1 project requests apply to LEED for Commercial Interiors v2.0 projects. Review LEED for New Construction v2.1 CIRs for SS Credit 4.4.

Approach and Implementation

The intent of this credit is to limit availability of parking as a means of encouraging the use of alternative forms of transportation to and from the site. Project teams should work with real estate brokers to identify buildings with easy access to mass transit and construct lease agreements such that parking spaces guaranteed to tenant do not exceed minimums established by local zoning regulations.

Prior to completion of lease negotiations, obtain the parking requirements of the local zoning ordinances. Determine the minimum number of spaces required by the code for the project's actual area and use types (i.e., 20,000 sq.ft. of office require 100 spaces, 10,000 sq.ft. of warehouse require 10 spaces, etc.).

Confirm that the lease does not guarantee more spaces than the calculation requirement. The criteria for "guaranteed" includes the following –

- Assigned spaces reserved only for the tenant's use, including tenant's guests

- The portion of a restricted parking area reserved for the tenant's use (i.e., the number of access cards issued to tenant)

"Guaranteed" does not require that the payment for parking be included in the lease. When the tenant organization makes separate payments, as for parking that is a concession of the building or at another facility, the applicant must demonstrate that the spaces reserved for the project occupants are less than the calculated requirement.

This credit also requires the provision of preferred parking spaces for car-pools to serve 5% of the occupants.

Submittal Documentation

Provide the LEED for Commercial Interiors Submittal Template, signed by the responsible party, stating that the appropriate compliance requirements have been met. Complete the associated calculator if applicable and include a description (narrative and/or drawings) of parking amenities available to occupants of the project space.

This credit has two alternatives based on the portion of the building the tenant occupies with two compliance paths for each alternative.

Tenants that occupy less than 75% of gross building square footage must demonstrate that the parking spaces provided do not exceed the minimum number required by the local zoning regulations and priority parking for car-pools/van-pools is provided for 5% or more of the tenant occupants or that no parking is provided or subsidized for the tenant occupants.

To document the credit criteria follow the declarations in the LEED for Commercial Interiors v2.0 Submittal Template. A copy of local zoning requirements and the tenant's lease must be provided with information specific to this credit highlighted. Zoning calculations must also be included.

The first compliance path requires that the number of parking spaces guaranteed by the lease and the minimum number of parking spaces required by local zoning regulations are documented on the Submittal Template, and in addition includes priority parking for can-pools/van-pools.

The second compliance path requires that the responsible party declares that no parking availability has been provided.

Tenants that occupy 75% or more of gross building square footage must demonstrate that the parking spaces provided do not exceed the minimum number required by the local zoning regulations and priority parking for car/van pools is provided for 5% or more of the building occupants (note that this criterion relates to the building as a whole and not the tenant space). The second alternative applies to rehabilitation projects. In this scenario no new parking is added and priority parking for car-pools/van-pools is provided for 5% or more of the building occupants.

To document the credit criteria follow the declarations in the LEED for Commercial Interiors v2.0 Submittal Template. A copy of local zoning requirements and the tenant's lease must be provided with information specific to this credit highlighted. Zoning calculations must also be included.

The first compliance path requires that the number of parking spaces guaranteed by the lease and the minimum number of parking spaces required by local zoning regulations are documented including priority parking for car-pools/van-pools for the total number of building occupants.

The second compliance path for rehabilitation projects requires that the responsible party declares that no new parking availability has been provided for the building occupants and that priority parking for car-pools/van-pools for the building occupants is included in the Submittal Template.

Additional Documentation

It is suggested that the project team compile and maintain the following documentation as appropriate to the design: Calculations which illustrate the parking capacity determined to be required for the project, a car-pooling plan/policy and documentation of how the spaces are designated as reserved for car-pooling (photos, signage), and/or pre-rehabilitation and post-rehabilitation plans indicating the amount of parking on each, demonstrating that no new parking capacity has been added.

Exemplary Performance

No exemplary performance criteria exists.

Considerations

The space occupied by an office worker's vehicle is generally greater than their share of the gross space within the building where they are employed. In retail development, the parking is frequently designed to meet a peak demand and during the balance of the year, this paved area is underutilized.

The environmental impacts of parking lot development include, but are by no means limited to, increased heat gain and increased surface stormwater runoff. Parking lots sized to accommodate single occupant vehicles at peak times has changed the way community designs are developed and constructed.

Those involved in the planning and zoning of their communities are often required by code to design parking lots and roadways that preclude alternatives that would increase the use density of developed land. Opportunities to share existing parking areas often remain unexplored.

New urbanists are addressing these concerns with traditional neighborhood development concepts. Mixed-use development, urban redevelopment, and transit-oriented development all share the recognized benefits that result from higher land utilization. The emphasis in many of these neighborhood developments is on the individual's experience rather than on accommodation of automobiles.

Resources

Please see the USGBC Web site at www. usgbc.org/resources for more specific resources on materials sources and other technical information.

Web Sites

Advanced Transportation Technology Institute

www.atti-info.org

A nonprofit organization that advances clean transportation technologies through research, education and technology transfer in order to promote a healthy environment and energy independence.

Association for Commuter Transportation

http://tmi.cob.fsu.edu/act/

The ACT is an association of professionals who specialize in commute options and solutions and organizations interested in creating a more workable transportation system. ACT serves as an information resource, provides advocacy on transportation issues involving commute alternatives, and offers networking and professional development opportunities to its members.

Benefits of Using Alternative Transportation Costs Calculator

www.metrocommuterservices.org/cost.htm

This online calculator helps commuters estimate the costs associated with driving a single occupancy vehicle and the savings associated with car-pooling.

Online TDM Encyclopedia

www.vtpi.org/tdm

Transportation Demand Management (TDM) is a general term for strategies that result in more efficient use of transportation resources. This online encyclopedia from the Victoria Transport Policy Institute is a comprehensive source of information about innovative management solutions to transportation problems.

Smart Commute

www.smartcommute.org/

Smart Commute is a program of Research Triangle Park that has valuable information about telecommuting and car-pool programs that can be useful for any organization.

State of Arizona Telecommuting Program

www.teleworkarizona.com

This Web site provides background information on the significance of telecommuting and an example of the development, implementation and results of telecommuting program.

The Telework Collaborative

www.teleworkcollaborative.com

The Telework Collaborative combines the expertise and resources of five western states (Texas, Arizona, California, Oregon and Washington) to deliver some of the most respected telework program implementation materials in the field.

Teletrips

www.secure-teletrips.com

Teletrips helps create, implement and manage public-private partnership programs to reduce commuter congestion, improve air quality and reduce energy consumption.

Definitions

A **Car-pool** is an arrangement where two or more people share a vehicle together for transportation.

High Occupancy Vehicles are vehicles with more that one occupant.

Parking Subsidies are the costs of providing occupant parking that is not recovered in parking fees.

Preferred Parking is parking that is preferentially available to particular users, and usually located closer to the building.

Endnotes for SS Section

[1] United States Department of Energy. Energy Information Administration. Annual Energy Review 2003. Report No. DOE/EIA-0384(2003). 1 March 2005 <http://www.eia.doe.gov/emeu/aer/contents_html>.

[2] Davis, Stacy C. and Susan W. Diegel. Transportation Energy Data Book: Edition 24. Center for Transportation Analysis, Engineering Science & Technology Division, Oak Ridge National Laboratory. U.S. Department of Energy, 2004.

[3] Hu, Patricia S., and Timothy R Reuscher. Prepared for the U.S Department of Transportation, Federal Highway Administration. Summary of Travel Trends: 2001 National Household Travel Survey December 2004. 25 February 2005 <http://nhts.ornl.gov/2001/pub/STT.pdf>.

[4] Ibid.

[5] Ibid.

[6] Shapiro, Robert J., Kevin A. Hassett, and Frank S. Arnold. Prepared for the American Public Transportation Association. Conserving Energy and preserving the Environment: The Role of Public Transportation July 2002. 25 February 2005 <http://www.apta.com/research/info/online/documents/shapiro.pdf>.

[7] Ibid.

[8] U.S. Department of Transportation. Federal Highway Administration. National Bicycling and Walking Study: Ten Year Status Report October 2004. 28 February 2005 < http://www.fhwa.dot.gov/environment/bikeped/study/>.

[9] United States Department of Transportation. Federal Highway Administration. Transportation Air Quality – Selected Facts and Figures: Vehicle Emissions 2004. 28 February 2005 < http://www.fhwa.dot.gov/environment/aqfactbk/factbk13.htm>.

Water Efficiency

In the United States, approximately 340 billion gallons of fresh water are withdrawn per day from rivers, streams and reservoirs to support residential, commercial, industrial, agricultural and recreational activities. This accounts for about one-fourth of the nation's total supply of renewable fresh water. Almost 65% of this water is discharged to rivers, streams and other water bodies after use and, in some cases, treatment.

Additionally, water is withdrawn from underground aquifers. In some parts of the United States, water levels in these aquifers have dropped more than 100 feet since the 1940s. On an annual basis, the water deficit in the United States is currently estimated at about 3,700 billion gallons. In other words, Americans extract 3,700 billion gallons per year more than they return to the natural water system to recharge aquifers and other water sources.

On a positive note, U.S. industries today use 36% less water than they did in 1950 although industrial output has increased significantly. This reduction in water use is largely due to the rigorous water reuse strategies in industrial processes. In addition, the Energy Policy Act of 1992 mandated the use of water-conserving plumbing fixtures to reduce water use in residential, commercial and institutional buildings.

Using large volumes of water increases maintenance and lifecycle costs for building operations and increases consumer costs for additional municipal supply and treatment facilities. Conversely, facilities that use water efficiently can reduce costs through lower water use fees, lower sewage volumes to treat energy and chemical use reductions, and lower capacity charges and limits. Many water conservation strategies involve either no additional cost or rapid paybacks. Other water conservation strategies such as biological wastewater treatment, rainwater harvesting and graywater plumbing systems often involve more substantial investment.

Water efficiency measures in commercial buildings can easily reduce water usage by 30% or more. In a typical 100,000-square foot office building, low-flow fixtures coupled with sensors and automatic controls can save a minimum of 1 million gallons of water per year, based on 650 building occupants each using an average of 20 gallons per day. Non-potable water volumes can be used for landscape irrigation, toilet and urinal flushing, custodial purposes and building systems. Utility savings, though dependent on the local water costs, can save thousands of dollars per year, resulting in rapid payback on water conservation infrastructure.

Credit Timing

The water use reduction credit calculation is based on the occupancy use. When the restrooms are not a part of the project scope, it is important to evaluate the plumbing in common areas of the building. When the fixtures are not high performance, consider asking the building owner to make the upgrade. The request may be most effective if made during lease negotiations. See **Table 1**.

Overview of LEED® Credits

WE Credit 1
Water Use Reduction

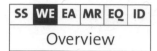
Table 1: Timing on Credit Decisions and Actions

Credit	Area Selection	Building Selection	Lease Negotiations	Schematic Design	Design Documentation	Construction	Prior to Occupancy	After Occupancy	Extended Commitment
WE 3.1 Water Use Reduction 20% Reduction		●------	●————	————	————	————			
WE 3.2 Water Use Reduction 30% Reduction		●------	●————	————	————	————			

Key to symbols

●   Critical decision point
———   Period of critical activity
———   Period of activity
- - - - -   Period of possible activity

Water Use Reduction

20% Reduction

Intent

Maximize water efficiency within tenant spaces to reduce the burden on municipal water supply and wastewater systems.

Requirements

Based on tenant occupancy requirements, employ strategies that in aggregate use 20% less water than the water use baseline calculated for the tenant space (not including irrigation) after meeting Energy Policy Act of 1992 fixture performance requirements.

Submittals

- Provide the LEED for Commercial Interiors Submittal Template, signed by the MEP Engineer or other responsible party, declaring that the project uses 20% less water, based on tenant occupancy requirements, than the baseline fixture performance requirements of the Energy Policy Act of 1992.

- Provide spreadsheet calculation demonstrating that the water-consuming fixtures identified for the stated occupancy and use of the tenant reduce occupancy-based potable water consumption by 20% compared to baseline conditions.

Potential Technologies and Strategies

Estimate potable water needs for the tenant space. Use high-efficiency fixtures such as composting toilet systems and non-water using urinals, and occupant sensors to reduce the potable water demand.

Water Use Reduction

30% Reduction

Intent

Maximize water efficiency within tenant spaces to reduce the burden on municipal water supply and wastewater systems.

Requirements

- Based on tenant occupancy requirements, employ strategies that in aggregate use 30% less water than the water use baseline calculated for the tenant space (not including irrigation) after meeting Energy Policy Act of 1992 fixture performance requirements.

Submittals

- Provide the LEED for Commercial Interiors Submittal Template, signed by the MEP Engineer or other responsible party, declaring that the project uses 30% less water, based on tenant occupancy requirements, than the baseline fixture performance requirements of the Energy Policy Act of 1992.

- Provide spreadsheet calculation demonstrating that the water-consuming fixtures identified for the stated occupancy and use of the tenant reduce occupancy-based potable water consumption by 30% compared to baseline conditions.

Potential Technologies & Strategies

Estimate potable water needs for the tenant space. Use high-efficiency fixtures such as composting toilets and non-water using urinals, and occupant sensors to reduce the potable water demand.

Summary of Referenced Standards

The Energy Policy Act (EPAct) of 1992

This Act was promulgated by the U.S. government and addresses energy and water use in commercial, institutional and residential facilities. The water usage requirements of the Energy Policy Act of 1992 are provided in **Table 1**.

Credit Interpretation Rulings

In addition to LEED for Commercial Interiors Credit Interpretation Rulings (CIRs), applicable LEED for New Construction CIRs concerning WE Credit 3.1 and 3.2 may also apply to LEED for Commercial Interiors projects.

Approach and Implementation

The Energy Policy Act of 1992 established water conservation standards for water closets, shower heads, faucets and other uses to save the United States an estimated 6.5 billion gallons of water per day. Toilet flushing uses the most water in residential and commercial buildings, accounting for approximately 4.8 billion gallons per day. Older toilets use 4 to 8 gallons of water per flush, while all new toilets must have a maximum flush volume of 1.6 gallons.

While the EPAct is a good starting point, there are many ways to exceed this standard and achieve even greater water savings. Effective methods to reduce potable water use include reusing roof runoff or collected graywater volumes for non-potable applications, installing and maintaining water fixture control sensors, installing flow restrictors on lavatory and sink fixtures, installing submeters, and installing dry fixtures such as composting toilet systems and non-water using urinals.

Strategies

Develop a water use inventory based on the occupancy of the tenant space that includes all water-consuming fixtures, equipment and seasonal conditions according to the methodology outlined in the Calculations section below. Use this to identify significant potable water demands and determine methods to minimize or eliminate these demands.

Document existing or specify water-conserving plumbing fixtures that exceed the fixture requirements stated in the Energy Policy Act of 1992. Consider ultra-high efficiency fixture and control technologies, including toilets, faucets, and showers. Although water efficient dishwashers, clothes washers and other water consuming fixtures are not counted in the calculations for this credit they may be included in exemplary performance calculations. (See Exemplary Performance for this credit) A variety of low-flow plumbing fixtures and appliances are currently available in the marketplace and can be installed in the same manner as conventional fixtures.

Synergies and Trade-Offs

Water use strategies depend on the site location and site design. Project sites with no access to municipal potable water service typically use groundwater wells to satisfy potable water demands. Site locations with significant precipitation volumes may de-

Table 1: EPACT Fixture Ratings

Fixture	Energy Policy Act of 1992 Flow Requirement
Water Closets [GPF]	1.6
Urinals [GPF]	1.0
Showerheads [GPM]*	2.5
Faucets [GPF]*	2.2
Replacement Aerators [GPM]*	2.2
Metering Faucets [gal/CY]	0.25

*At flowing water pressure of 80 pounds per square inch (psi)

termine that reuse of these volumes is more cost-effective than creating stormwater treatment facilities. Potable water use is significant for irrigation applications and is directly correlated with the amount of wastewater generated on-site.

Some water-saving technologies impact energy performance and require commissioning and Measurement & Verification (M&V) attention. Reuse of existing buildings may hinder water efficiency measures due to space constraints or characteristics of existing plumbing fixtures.

Planning Phase

While graywater collection and storage may not be a water reduction method that most commercial interior tenants have the opportunity to include in their projects, high-efficiency plumbing fixtures are. When the project is located in a leased space, early planning should focus on the building selection. Investigate code related issues associated with installation and use of water harvesting and collection systems and high-performance plumbing fixtures such as non-water using urinals.

Design Phase

The design team, possibly in conjunction with the building owner, should determine–

- which water saving strategies may exist or are appropriate and desired for the particular project;

Table 2: Sample Flush Fixture Types

Flush Fixture Type	Water Use [GPF]
Conventional Water Closet	1.6
Low-Flow Water Closet	1.1
Ultra Low-Flow Water Closet	0.8
Composting Toilet	0.0
Conventional Urinal	1.0
Waterless Urinal	0.0

- any special construction detailing or specifications needed to ensure proper fixture/equipment installation; and

- existing or targeted water saving percentages through preliminary calculations.

Construction Phase

Install appropriate water saving fixtures and equipment. Ensure that any specialized equipment that is within the scope of the commissioning agent is accounted for during building commissioning.

Operations Phase

Ensure that maintenance staff has been trained in the operations and maintenance of any specialized equipment. For example, non-water using urinals generally need to be cleaned according to manufacturer's specifications and their chemical traps appropriately maintained.

Calculations

The LEED for Commercial Interiors Submittal Templates include a calculator that covers most project situations. The reduction is the difference between the design case and a baseline case. The credit percentage is determined by dividing the reduction by the baseline usage.

Table 3: Sample Flow Fixture Types

Flow Fixture Type	Water Use [GPM]
Conventional Lavatory	2.5
Low-Flow Lavatory	1.8
Kitchen Sink	2.5
Low-Flow Kitchen Sink	1.8
Shower	2.5
Low-Flow Shower	1.8
Janitor Sink	2.5
Hand Wash Fountain	0.5

The methodology differs from traditional plumbing design where the calculations are based on fixture counts. In this credit, the calculation is based on occupant usage. The fixtures do not necessarily need to be within the project space or need to have been installed as part of the project scope of work. However, the design case rates and volumes should be for those fixtures that the occupants typically use.

The baseline case must use the flow rates and flush volumes established by EPAct. See **Table 1**. These values are the default settings in the calculator for the conventional fixtures and they should not be changed even when they were not the actual rates of the fixtures existing prior to retrofit.

In addition to the list of fixtures provided in the flow fixture chart and flush fixture chart, the project team may add others. These charts are located near the top of the Submittal Template page and are similar to **Tables 2 and 3**. For these added fixtures, the project team will need to include supporting documentation, such as cut sheets, with their submittal.

There are no prescribed daily uses, but **Table 4** includes representative counts. Note that flush fixtures, which include water closets and urinals, differentiate between females and males. The calculator expects both the male and female lines to be completed. Zeros may be used.

Table 4: Sample Design Case Water Use Calculation

Design Case					
Flush Fixture	**Daily Uses**	**Flow Rate [GPF]**	**Duration [flush]**	**Occupant users**	**Sewage Generation [gal]**
Conventional Water Closet ▾					
Male	1	1.6	1.0	8	12.8
Female	1	1.6	1.0	8	12.8
Ultra Low-Flow Water Closet ▾			·		
Male	2	0.8	1.0	8	12.8
Female	2	0.8	1.0	8	12.8
Conventional Water Closet ▾					
Male	3	1.6	1.0	8	38.4
Female	3	1.6	1.0	8	38.4
--- ▾					
Male		0.0	1.0		0
Female		0.0	1.0		0
--- ▾					
Male		0.0	1.0		0
Female		0.0	1.0		0
Flow Fixture	**Daily Uses**	**Flow Rate [GPM]**	**Duration [sec]**	**Occupant users**	**Sewage Generation [gal]**
Ultra Low-Flow Lavatory ▾	3	0.5	15	32	12
Low-Flow Kitchen Sink ▾	1	1.8	15	32	14.4
--- ▾		0.0	0		0
--- ▾		0.0	0		0
--- ▾		0.0	0		0
--- ▾		0.0	0		0
--- ▾		0.0	0		0
--- ▾		0.0	0		0
			Total uses by all occupants		224
			Total Daily Volume [gal]		154
			Annual Work Days		260
			Annual Volume [gal]		40,144
			Graywater or Stormwater Reuse Volume [gal]		0
			Total Annual Volume [gal]		**40,144**

For consistency across LEED projects, the calculations require the use of a balanced, one-to-one, gender ratio unless specific project conditions warrant an alternative. For these situations, the project team will need to provide supporting documentation.

A typical calculation may assume that male occupants use the water closet once and the urinal twice in a typical day. For female occupants, the water closet three times in a typical day. And all occupants use the lavatories for each restroom use for 15 seconds, and kitchen sinks, if available, once during the day for 15 seconds. If your project has bike riders, include the shower facility use as well; the count should be based on actual usage, with a typical duration being 300 seconds (5 minutes).

When the count of total uses by all occupants fails to match between the design and baseline cases, the calculator generates an error message. Remember to enter the volume of graywater and stormwater reuse in the design case chart.

WEc1 credits are awarded for specification of water using fixtures regulated by the Energy Policy Act of 1992. EPAct covers the following fixture types– lavatories, kitchen sinks, showers, hand wash fountains, janitor sinks, water closets and urinals. Project teams are encouraged to apply for Innovation in Design credits for reduction in non-EPAct regulated and process water consuming fixtures. Examples of non-regulated and process water use include but are not limited to dishwashers, clothes washers and cooling towers.

Submittal Documentation

The LEED for Commercial Interiors applicant should provide the LEED for Commercial Interiors Submittal Template, signed by the engineer or responsible party, declaring that the project uses 20% or 30% less water, based on the tenant occupancy requirements, than the baseline fixture performance requirements of the Energy Policy Act of 1992. Complete the calculation included in the Submittal Template.

Additional Documentation

Submitting a narrative, additional documentation, and/or other calculations as described below may be requested as part of the LEED for Commercial Interiors review process. These documents may include–

- a narrative describing the installed plumbing systems and any special water supply systems (i.e. graywater reclamation, etc.),

- contractor's submittals and manufacturer's product data for installed water use fixtures clearly showing the flow/flush rates for each,

- highlighted drawings showing any special water supply/collection systems that contribute to water use reduction, and

- documentation of daily use rates if they differ from standard LEED assumptions.

Exemplary Performance

In addition to earning WE credits 1.1 and 1.2, project teams that achieve a projected water savings of 40% are eligible for an exemplary performance ID credit.

Project teams may also achieve an ID credit for demonstrating potable water use reduction in process and non-regulated water consuming fixtures. The calculation methodology for demonstrating process and non-regulated water savings is similar to the calculation outlined above for regulated water use. Project teams define reasonable usage assumptions and calculate design and baseline water consumption based on high efficiency and standard water use fixtures. Process and non-regulated water use savings is then compared to regulated water use. If the process and non-regulated water use savings is at least

10% of the total design regulated water use, the project team is eligible for an Innovation in Design point.

Considerations

Cost

Water-conserving fixtures that use less water than requirements in the Energy Policy Act of 1992 may have higher initial costs. Additionally, there may be a longer lead time for delivery because of their limited availability. However, installation of water-efficient fixtures and equipment can result in significant, long-term financial and environmental savings.

For example, the first cost of non-water using urinals is marginally higher than conventional urinals and they initially require additional maintenance attention to ensure that staff understands their particular maintenance requirements. Nonetheless, significant construction savings may be realized through the reduction of required supply water piping within the building and long-term operational savings will be seen as a result of eliminated potable water use and reduced sewage generation.

Building Type

The above strategies can be effectively applied to most building types and occupancies.

Regional Considerations

Local weather conditions should be factored into determining the feasibility of rainwater harvesting systems for use in reduction of potable water for flushing. Local building and health codes/ordinances vary with regards to allowance of graywater or harvested rainwater for use in sewage conveyance. Additionally, codes differ in how alternative plumbing fixtures, such as dual-flush water closets, composting toilets and non-water using urinals are handled. It is critical to confirm acceptability of non-traditional approaches with code officials prior to commitment to specific water saving strategies.

Supply water quality from graywater and recycled water systems should also be considered in fixture selection. Project teams should identify if minimum supply water quality standards have been established for specific fixtures by manufacturers. When recycled graywater or collected stormwater is used with plumbing fixtures designed for use with municipally supplied potable water, it is good practice to verify that supply water quality is acceptable and will not compromise long-term fixture performance.

Environmental Issues

The reduction of potable water use in buildings for toilets, shower heads and faucets reduces the total amount withdrawn from rivers, streams, underground aquifers and other water bodies. Another benefit of potable water conservation is reduced energy use and chemical inputs at municipal water treatment works.

Economic Issues

Reductions in water consumption minimize overall building operating costs. Reductions can also lead to more stable municipal taxes and water rates. By handling reduced water volumes, water treatment facilities can delay expansion and maintain stable water prices.

Accelerated retrofits of high-efficiency plumbing fixtures, especially 1.6 gallon per flush (GPF) toilets, through incentive programs has become a cost-effective way for some municipalities to defer, reduce or avoid capital costs of needed water supply and wastewater facilities.

For example, New York City invested $393 million in a 1.6 GPF toilet rebate program that has reduced water demand and wastewater flow by 90.6 million gallons per day (MGD), equal to 7% of the city's total water consumption. The rebate program accomplished a net present value

savings of $605 million from a 20-year deferral of water supply and wastewater treatment expansion projects. Another successful water efficiency program was instituted in Santa Monica, where the toilet replacement program achieved permanent reductions in water usage and wastewater flows of over 1.9 MGD, representing a 15% reduction in average total water demand and a 20% reduction of average total wastewater flow. The cost of the rebate program was $5.4 million. The program will have a net savings of $6 million in the year 2002 due to avoided costs of water imports and wastewater treatment.

Community Issues

Water use reductions, in aggregate, allow municipalities to reduce or defer the capital investment needed for water supply and wastewater treatment infrastructure. These strategies protect the natural water cycle and save water resources for future generations.

Resources

Web Sites

Please see the USGBC Web site at www. usgbc.org/resources for more specific resources on materials sources and other technical information.

American Rainwater Catchment Systems Association

www.arcsa-usa.org

Includes a compilation of publications, such as the Texas Guide to Rainwater Harvesting.

Composting Toilet Reviews

www.buildinggreen.com/features/mr/waste.html

(802) 257-7300

An Environmental Building News article on commercial composting toilets.

National Climatic Data Center

www.ncdc.noaa.gov/oa/climate/stateclimatologists.html

Useful site for researching local climate data, such as rainfall data for rainwater harvesting calculations. Includes links to state climate offices.

Terry Love's Consumer Toilet Reports

www.terrylove.com/crtoilet.htm

This Web site offers a plumber's perspective on many of the major toilets used in commercial and residential applications.

WaterWiser: The Water Efficiency Clearinghouse

www.waterwiser.org

(800) 926-7337

The American Water Works Association's clearinghouse includes articles, reference materials and papers on all forms of water efficiency.

Choosing a Toilet

www.taunton.com/finehomebuilding/pages/h00042.asp

An article in Fine Homebuilding that includes several varieties of water efficient toilets.

Rocky Mountain Institute

www.rmi.org/sitepages/pid15.php

This portion of RMI's Web site is devoted to water conservation and efficiency. The site contains information on commercial, industrial and institutional water use, watershed management, and articles on policy and implementation.

Smart Communities Network

www.sustainable.doe.gov/efficiency/weinfo.shtml

A project of the U.S. Department of Energy concerning water efficiency and conservation.

Water Closet Performance Testing

www.ebmud.com/conserving_
&_recycling/toilet_test_report/
NAHBRC%20Toilet%20Report.pdf

NAHB Research Center conducted tests on the performance, reliability and water efficiency of a variety of different toilets. Report No.: P01-1660902. September 2002.

Water Efficiency Manual for Commercial, Industrial and Institutional Facilities

www.p2pays.org/ref/01/00692.pdf

A straightforward manual on water efficiency from a number of different North Carolina government departments.

U.S. EPA's Water Use Efficiency Program

www.epa.gov/owm/water-efficiency

An overview of the program and information about using water more efficiently.

Print Media

Water, Sanitary and Waste Services for Buildings, Fourth Edition, by A. Wise and J. Swaffield, Longman Scientific & Technical, 1995.

Definitions

There is not a national definition for **blackwater**. Wastewater from toilets and urinals is always considered blackwater. Wastewater from kitchen sinks (perhaps differentiated by the use of a garbage disposal), showers, or bathtubs may be considered blackwater by state or local codes. Project teams should comply with blackwater definition as established by the authority having jurisdiction in their areas.

Graywater is defined by the Uniform Plumbing Code (UPC) in its Appendix G, titled "Gray Water Systems for Single-Family Dwellings" as "untreated household waste water which has not come into contact with toilet waste. Grey water includes used water from bathtubs, showers, bathroom wash basins, and water from clothes-washer and laundry tubs. It shall not include waste water from kitchen sinks or dishwashers."

The International Plumbing Code (IPC) defines graywater in its Appendix C, titled "Gray Water Recycling Systems" as "waste water discharged from lavatories, bathtubs, showers, clothes washers, and laundry sinks."

Some states and local authorities allow kitchen sink wastewater to be included in graywater. Other differences with the UPC and IPC definitions can probably be found in state and local codes. Project teams should comply with graywater definitions as established by the authority having jurisdiction in their areas.

Fixture sensors are ultra-sonic or infrared sensors applied to lavatories, sinks, water closets and urinals to sense fixture use and automatically flush or turn on and off.

Potable water is water that is suitable for drinking and is supplied from wells or municipal water systems.

Process water is water used for industrial processes and building systems such as cooling towers, boilers and chillers.

Composting toilet is a dry plumbing fixture that contains and treats human waste via microbiological processes.

Non-water using urinal is a dry plumbing fixture that uses advanced hydraulic design and a buoyant fluid instead of water to maintain sanitary conditions.

SS	WE	EA	MR	EQ	ID
Credit 1					

Energy and Atmosphere

Overview

Buildings consume approximately 37% of the energy and 68% of the electricity produced in the United States annually, according to the U.S. Department of Energy.

Electricity generated from fossil fuels–oil and coal–impact the environment in a myriad of adverse ways, beginning with their extraction, transportation, refining and distribution. Coal mining disrupts habitat and can devastate landscapes. Acidic mine drainage further degrades regional ecosystems. Coal is rinsed with water, which results in billions of gallons of sludge stored in ponds. Mining is a dangerous occupation in which accidents and long-term effects of breathing coal dust result in shortened life spans of coal miners.

Conventional fossil-based generation of electricity releases carbon dioxide, which contributes to global climate change. Coal-fired electric utilities emit almost one-third of the country's anthropogenic nitrogen oxide, the key element in smog, and two-thirds the sulfur dioxide, a key element in acid rain. They also emit more fine particulate material than any other activity in the United States. Because the human body is incapable of clearing these fine particles from the lungs, they are contributing factors in tens of thousands of cancer and respiratory illness-related deaths annually.

Natural gas, nuclear fission and hydro-electric generators all have adverse environmental impacts as well. Natural gas is a major source of nitrogen oxide and greenhouse gas emissions. Nuclear power increases the potential for catastrophic accidents and raises significant waste transportation and disposal issues. Hydroelectric generating plants disrupt natural water flows, resulting in disturbance of habitat and depletion of fish populations.

Green buildings address these issues in two primary ways: by reducing the amount of energy required, and by using more benign forms. The better the energy performance of a project, the lower the operations costs. As world competition for the available supply of fuels heightens, the rate of return on energy-efficiency measures improves. Electrical generation using sources other than fossil fuels reduces environmental impacts.

LEED for Commercial Interiors Approach to E & A

Because most commercial interiors projects occupy only a portion of a larger building, where many of the energy-related decisions may have already been made, LEED for Commercial Interiors focuses on the individual aspects of energy efficiency, lighting, HVAC, and appliances and equipment. There are separate requirements for each. In addition, there is an incentive to purchase green power. **Table 1** relates the timing of credit decisions and actions to the overall project schedule.

Overview of LEED® Prerequisites and Credits

EA Prerequisite 1
Fundamental Commissioning

EA Prerequisite 2
Minimum Energy Performance

EA Prerequisite 3
CFC Reduction in HVAC&R Equipment

EA Credit 1.1
Optimize Energy Performance, Lighting Power

EA Credit 1.2
Optimize Energy Performance, Lighting Controls

EA Credit 1.3
Optimize Energy Performance, HVAC

EA Credit 1.4
Optimize Energy Performance, Equipment and Appliances

EA Credit 2
Enhanced Commissioning

EA Credit 3
Energy Use, Measurement & Payment Accountability

EA Credit 4
Green Power

Table 1: Timing on Credit Decisions and Actions

Credit	Area Selection	Building Selection	Lease Negotiations	Schematic Design	Design Documentation	Construction	Prior to Occupancy	After Occupancy	Extended Commitment
EA Prerequisite 1 Fundamental Commissioning			● ▬		● ▬ ▬		● ▬		
EA Prerequisite 2 Minimum Energy Performance				▬					
EA Prerequisite 3 CFC Reduction in HVAC&R Equipment				▬	─ ─				
EA 1.1 Optimize Energy Performance, Lighting Power				▬					
EA 1.2 Optimize Energy Performance, Lighting Controls				▬					
EA 1.3 Optimize Energy Performance, HVAC		⋯⋯		▬					
EA 1.4 Optimize Energy Performance, Equipment & Appliances				▬		▬			
EA 2 Enhanced Commissioning			●▬●▬●▬●▬●▬●▬●▬●▬●▬						
EA 3 Energy Use, Measurement & Payment Accountability		●─ ▬							
EA 4 Green Power		─ ─ ─				─ ─			

Key to symbols

●   Critical decision point
▬▬▬   Period of critical activity
─────   Period of activity
─ ─ ─ ─   Period of possible activity

Fundamental Commissioning

Required

Intent

Verify that the project's energy-related systems are installed, calibrated and perform as intended.

Requirements

The following commissioning process activities shall be completed by the commissioning team:

- Designate an individual as the Commissioning Authority to lead the commissioning process activities. This individual should not be directly responsible for project design or construction management.

- Clearly document the owner's project requirements and the basis of design for the project's energy related systems. Updates to these documents shall be made during design and construction by the design team.

- Develop and incorporate commissioning requirements into the construction documents.

- Develop and utilize a commissioning plan.

- Verify that the installation and performance of energy consuming systems meet the owner's project requirements and basis of design.

- Complete a commissioning report.

Commissioned Systems:

The energy related systems to be included in the commissioning process activities, if included in the tenant scope, include as a minimum

- Heating, ventilating, air conditioning and refrigeration (HVAC&R) systems (mechanical and passive) and associated controls

- Lighting controls, including day lighting

- Domestic hot water systems

- Renewable energy systems (PV, wind, solar, etc.)

Submittals

Provide the LEED for Commercial Interiors Submittal Template, signed by the commissioning authority and tenant, confirming that the commissioning requirements for the project's energy related systems have been successfully executed or will be provided under existing contract(s).

Provide a narrative and diagrams indicating how the HVAC system works, what portions are shared with other tenants in the building, what was included in the project scope of work, and if improvements were made in conjunction with the project by others to any common building systems supplying the tenant area.

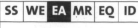

| SS | WE | **EA** | MR | EQ | ID |

Prerequisite 1

Potential Technologies & Strategies

Engage a Commissioning Authority prior to the start of design. Determine the owner's program and initial design intent. Develop and maintain a commissioning plan for use during design and construction. Incorporate commissioning requirements in bid documents. Assemble the commissioning team and, prior to occupancy, verify the performance of energy consuming systems. Complete the commissioning reports with recommendations prior to acceptance of the HVAC systems.

Credit Interpretation Rulings

Credit interpretation rulings concerning LEED for Commercial Interiors EA Prerequisite 1 and EA Credit 2 apply to LEED for Commercial Interiors projects. Where applicable, rulings made in other rating systems concerning Fundamental and Enhanced Commissioning also apply to LEED for Commercial Interiors projects.

Approach and Implementation

Relationship Between Fundamental and Enhanced Commissioning

LEED for Commercial Interiors addresses building commission in two places, EA Prerequisite 1 and EA Credit 2. **Table 1** and the discussion included here cover activities that are required in both. They are presented in the sequence that they generally occur over the duration of a commercial interior project.

SS	WE	**EA**	MR	EQ	ID
Prerequisite 1					

SS	WE	**EA**	MR	EQ	ID
Credit 2					

Table 1: Relationship between Fundamental Commissioning (EAp1) and Enhanced Commissioning (EAc2)

	EA p 1	EA c 2
Select Commissioning Authority	Not directly connected with the design or project management	Independent firms not involved in design or project management
Activities and Responsibilities		
Document owner's project requirements, and basis of design for energy-related systems.	Commissioning Authority, Project Team	Independent Commissioning Authority, Project Team
Update these documents during design and construction.	Commissioning Authority, Project Team	Independent Commissioning Authority, Project Team
Lead the commissioning design review activities prior to the end of Design Development.		Independent Commissioning Authority
Develop and incorporate Commissioning requirements into construction documents.	Commissioning Authority, Project Team	Independent Commissioning Authority, Project Team
Develop and utilize commissioning plan.	Commissioning Authority, Project Team	Independent Commissioning Authority, Project Team
Conduct review of tenant space's energy-related systems contractor submittals.		Independent Commissioning Authority
Verify that installation and performance of energy consuming systems meet owner's project requirements and basis of design.	Commissioning Authority, Project Team	Independent Commissioning Authority, Project Team
Develop a single manual containing information required for re-commissioning.		Independent Commissioning Authority
Verify that requirements for training operating personnel and tenant space occupants are completed.		Independent Commissioning Authority
Complete a commissioning report.	Commissioning Authority	Independent Commissioning Authority
Review tenant space operation with O&M staff and occupants, 8 to 10 months after final acceptance. Develop plan to resolve outstanding issues.		Independent Commissioning Authority, O& M Staff

SS	WE	EA	MR	EQ	ID
Prerequisite 1					

SS	WE	EA	MR	EQ	ID
Credit 2					

Scope of Work

Commissioning should be based on the owner's project requirements. At a minimum, to meet the requirements of this prerequisite, the commissioning process activities must cover all energy-related systems within the project scope. **Table 2** lists possible energy systems and highlights the relationship between the energy systems and other prerequisites and credits of the LEED for Commercial Interiors Rating System. For commercial interior projects, the scope can vary tremendously. Some may only include lighting systems, whereas others may include all HVAC, service water and lighting systems.

Strategies

The commissioning process is a planned,

Table 2: Potential Systems to be Commissioned

Systems
Prerequisites and Credits
Potential Commissioning Activities

Heating, ventilating, air conditioning and refrigeration systems, both mechanical and passive, and associated controls

> To the extent applicable based on project scope:
> EAp2—Mandatory provisions and prescriptive requirements of ASHRAE 90.1-2004 have been meet, as the standard applies to the scope of the project
> EAp3—No CFC in newly purchased equipment
> EAc1.3 Option 1—HVAC equipment sized on actual loads; mechanical equipment meet enhanced efficiency standards; use of variable speed controls; appropriate zoning and controls
> EAc1.3 Option 2—Same as EAp2
> EQp1—ASHRAE 62.1-2004
> EQp2 Option B—Designated smoking rooms ventilation requirements
> EQp2 Option C—Residential facilities: test results of air leakage and air sampling
> EQc1—Functioning outdoor air monitoring system
> EQc2—Mechanical systems: air testing and balance confirm increase ventilation rates; Passive systems: minimum flow rates set and met
> EQc3.1—Filter media replacement
> EQc5—Exhaust system in areas where hazardous gasses or chemicals are present; MERV 13 air filtration media
> EQc6.2—Functioning controllability for temperature and ventilation
> EQc7.1—HVAC system and control systems accomplish ASHRAE 55-2004 requirements
> EQc7.2—Monitoring system functioning
> ID credits, or SSc1 Option L—where applicable

Lighting controls, including day lighting

> To the extent applicable based on project scope:
> SSc1 Option F—Existing building, site and project lighting designs compliant with requirements
> EAp2—Mandatory provisions and prescriptive requirements of ASHRAE 90.1-2004 have been meet, as the standard applies to the scope of the project
> EAc1.1—ASHRAE 90.1-2004 compliance documentation
> EAc1.2—Functioning daylight responsive controls
> EQc8.1, 8.2—Daylighting requirements met
> ID credits, or SSc1 Option L—where applicable

Domestic hot water systems

> To the extent applicable based on project scope:
> EAp2—Mandatory provisions and prescriptive requirements of ASHRAE 90.1-2004 have been meet, as the standard applies to the scope of the project
> ID credits, or SSc1 Option L—where applicable

Renewable energy systems (PV, wind, solar, etc.)

> To the extent applicable based on project scope:
> SSc1 Option K—On-site renewable energy performance
> ID credits, or SSc1 Option L—where applicable

systematic quality-control based process that involves the owner, users, occupants, operations and maintenance staff, design professionals and contractors. It begins at project inception; has ongoing verification of achievement of the owner's project requirements; requires integration of contractor-completed commissioning process activities into the construction documents; aids in the coordination of static and dynamic testing that acceptance is based on; verifies staff training; and concludes with warranty verification and lessons-learned documentation and implementation. An explanation of the steps satisfying this LEED for Commercial Interiors prerequisite is summarized in the following sections.

Engage a Commissioning Authority

Designate a Commissioning Authority as early as possible in the project timeline, ideally at project inception. The Commissioning Authority serves as an objective advocate of the owner, directs the commissioning process, and presents final recommendations to the owner regarding the performance of commissioned systems and assemblies. The Commissioning Authority introduces standards and strategies early in the planning process and then verifies implementation of the commissioning process activities by clearly specifying the requirements in construction documents.

Ideally, a person on the owner's staff would be the Commissioning Authority. If this is not possible, a third-party firm is preferable. For the purposes of this LEED for Commercial Interiors prerequisite, the Commissioning Authority may be from a project team firm, as long as that person is not responsible for project design, construction management or supervision. In all scenarios, the reporting of all conditions and findings must be immediate and direct from the Commissioning Authority to the owner.

When the project team plans to include EA Credit 2 in its LEED for Commer-

cial Interiors submittal, a third-party, independent Commissioning Authority should be identified at the start of the project and must lead the commissioning design review activities prior to the end of design development.

Form the Commissioning Team

The Commissioning Team is led by the Commissioning Authority and is composed of the owner, users, occupants, operations and maintenance staff, design professionals and contractors. The Commissioning Team is responsible for accomplishing the commissioning process activities and provides leadership for identifying and resolving all commissioning process issues.

Document the Owner's Requirements

The Commissioning Team shall clearly document the owner's project requirements. The owner's project requirements are utilized throughout the Commissioning Process to provide focus on the key success criteria. These requirements typically address HVAC, lighting, indoor environment, energy efficiency, siting, water and environmental responsiveness of the facility. The document also addresses the ideas, objectives and criteria that the owner considers important. Any criteria listed in the owner's project requirements needs to be measurable, documentable and verifiable. Ideally, the owner's project requirements are developed upon project inception in tandem with LEED goals. However, if the commissioning process is not started until later in the project, the owner's project requirements must still be documented by the Commissioning Team.

Review the Basis of Design

The basis of design is developed by the design professionals as part of their normal design duties, but not often provided to the owner in a cohesive document. The basis of design includes how each

SS	WE	**EA**	MR	EQ	ID
Prerequisite 1					

SS	WE	**EA**	MR	EQ	ID
Credit 2					

Prerequisite 1

Credit 2

of the owner's project requirements has been met; primary design assumptions such as occupancy, space and process requirements; applicable codes, policies and standards; and load and climatic assumptions that influence design decisions. On projects with multiple phases, an updated basis of design and design narrative should accompany each design phase submission.

Create a Commissioning Plan

The Commissioning Authority develops a commissioning plan at the start of the commissioning process, preferably at project inception. The commissioning plan evolves with results added as the project progresses. In circumstances when the decision to pursue a LEED rating is made after the design phase, the commissioning plan, including the owner's project requirements and basis of design, should be completed prior to the installation of any commissioned elements. **Table 3** lists the components that are required in the commissioning plan to satisfy this LEED prerequisite.

Commission Design Review Prior to End of Design Development

When a project team plans to meet the requirements of EA Credit 2, Enhanced Commissioning, this valuable additional step must be performed. Under the lead-

ership of an independent Commissioning Authority, not employed by any other firm represented on the project team, a review of the design activities of the energy-related systems must be completed prior to the completion of design development. During this phase of a project, the design professionals determine how they will satisfy the program; the configuration of walls and ceilings are set, systems designed, and materials and equipment selected. It normally ends with a review by the owner. A third-party Commissioning Authority review that is completed prior to the end of this design phase serves as a peer review, providing an independent set of eyes to confirm assumptions and solutions. It identifies potential problems before the design is presented to the owner. Revisions to the design during the contract document phase or during construction are more costly.

Inclusion of Commissioning Requirements in Bid Documents

The contractor's commissioning process responsibilities must be integrated in the contract documents and must clearly describe the components listed in **Table 4**.

Submittal Review

When EA Credit 2 Enhanced Commissioning requirements are being followed, the Commissioning Authority conducts

Table 3: Required Commissioning Plan Components

Required Commissioning Plan Components
Brief overview of the commissioning process
List of all systems and assemblies included in the Commissioning Authority's scope of work
Identification of the Commissioning Team and its responsibilities
Description of the management, communication and reporting of the commissioning process
Overview of the commissioning process activities for the pre-design, design, construction, and occupancy and operations phases, including development of the owner's project requirements, review of the basis of design, schematic design, construction documents and submittals, construction phase verification, functional performance test development and implementation, and 10-month warranty review.
List of the expected work products.
List of key commissioning process milestones

Table 4: Commissioning Components in Construction Documents

Commissioning Components in Construction Documents
Commissioning Team involvement
Submittal review procedures
Operations and maintenance documentation requirements
Training plan development
Construction verification procedures
Start-up plan development and implementation
Functional performance testing
Milestones
Traning
Warranty review site visit

SS	WE	EA	MR	EQ	ID

Prerequisite 1

SS	WE	EA	MR	EQ	ID

Credit 2

a review of the energy-related systems contractor submittals for the tenant space. This review is in addition to the submittal approval procedure used by the contractor and design professional.

Installation Verification

The Commissioning Authority must accomplish ongoing site visits to verify that each commissioned system and assembly is being installed to achieve the owner's project requirements as detailed in the contract documents and manufacturer's instructions, and to verify that other building systems or assemblies are not compromising the performance of the feature. The Commissioning Authority should accomplish this through verification of the contractor's completed construction checklists.

Start-up and Checkout

The contractor completes the start-up and initial checkout of all items listed in the contract documents. The start-up and checkout results must be clearly documented according to the manufacturer's written instructions and the contract documents, typically the last section of the construction checklists.

Sampling

As the commissioning process is quality-based, the Commissioning Authority applies appropriate sampling techniques to verify that construction, startup and initial checkout of all commissioned systems and assemblies is successfully completed. For example, instead of checking 100% of the controls system, which is the contractor's responsibility, the Commissioning Authority utilizes sampling techniques to complete an in-depth periodic review of the control system installation, verifying that the components are calibrated; point-to-point checkouts are successful; and each control point is commanding, reporting and controlling according to the intended purpose. This ongoing sampling verification enables the Commissioning Authority to identify systemic issues early so they can be fixed and so that rework can be avoided at complete system checkout.

Functional Testing

The Commissioning Authority prepares written, repeatable test procedures, specifically for each project, which are used to functionally test systems and assemblies. These tests must be documented to clearly describe the individual systematic test procedures, the expected system response or acceptance criteria for each procedure, the actual response or findings and any pertinent discussion. The test procedures are reviewed and accepted by the contractor's test entity, who may choose to implement the tests under the direction of the Commissioning Authority.

After acceptance of the installation, startup and initial checkout (using the construction checklists), the following modes must be tested. Test each sequence in the sequence of operations and other significant modes. Sequences and control strategies include start-up, shutdown, unoccupied and manual modes, modulation up and down the unit's range of capacity, power failure, alarms, component staging and backup upon failure (unit and pump), interlocks with other equipment, and sensor and actuator calibrations. Test all larger equipment individually. Similar units that are numerous (e.g., many smaller rooftop packaged units, air terminal units and exhaust fans) may require a specific sampling strategy. Heating equipment must be tested during the winter and air-conditioning equipment must be tested during summer, as appropriate to demonstrate performance under near-design conditions.

Operation and Maintenance (O&M) Manuals

An area requiring careful coordination is the creation of operation and maintenance manuals. Depending on the owner's needs and relationship with the Commissioning Team members, the responsibility for this deliverable can reside with the Commissioning Authority, the design professional or the contractor. This decision needs to be made consciously with an aim towards maximizing the long-term usefulness of the documentation. If the owner has a high confidence level in the ability of the design professionals or contractor to prepare these documents, then they can be assigned the responsibility through the construction documents. If the Commissioning Authority is regarded as providing the best deliverable for the owner's needs, then the contractor can provide the basic information and the Commissioning

Authority's scope of work can include creation of the manual. Either process satisfies the LEED for Commercial Interiors prerequisite.

The Commissioning Authority should review for completeness and applicability all the manuals of commissioned systems and assemblies. The O&M data must be bound in labeled binders liberally divided with tabs, or provided electronically, to provide efficient access. Manuals should include the name, address and telephone number of the manufacturer or vendor and installing contractor; submittal data; and operations and maintenance instructions with the model and features for this site clearly marked. The manual should only include data for equipment that is actually installed.

Data requirements include instructions for installation, maintenance, replacement, start-up, special maintenance and replacement sources, a parts list, a list of special tools, performance data, and warranty information. The manual should also include a documentation package on as-built controls that includes a narrative for normal operation, shutdown, unoccupied operation, seasonal changeover, manual operation, controls setup and programming, troubleshooting, alarms, control drawings and schematics, and final sequences of operation.

Re-commissioning

When the project is pursuing EA Credit 2, in addition to the O&M manuals, a single manual must be prepared containing the information required for re-commissioning of the energy related systems for the tenant space. The commissioning authority, if not responsible for preparing it, will need to review and approve it.

Training

To meet the requirements of EA Credit 2, the Commissioning Authority must assemble written verification that training was conducted for all commissioned features and systems. The training may be performed by the contractor or the Commissioning Authority utilizing qualified individuals for a sufficient duration to ensure that facility staff has all the information needed to optimally operate, maintain and replace the commissioned features and systems. Training must address the issues in **Table 5**.

Commissioning Report

A commissioning report must be presented to the owner within a reasonable time after occupancy. The report must include a list of each commissioned system and assembly, as well as the disposition of the Commissioning Authority regarding their compliance to the owner's project requirements. Required components of the commissioning report are listed in **Table 6**.

Outstanding Issues

The written list of all outstanding commissioning issues and any testing that is scheduled for a later date, justified by seasonal conditions, must be included. A list of any compromises in the environmentally responsive features must be provided. All outstanding environmentally responsive feature deficiencies must be corrected or listed in the commissioning report. All completed functional tests

SS	WE	**EA**	MR	EQ	ID
		Prerequisite 1			

SS	WE	**EA**	MR	EQ	ID
		Credit 2			

Table 5: Training Issues to be Addressed by the Commissioning Authority. Optional for EAp1. Required for EAc2.

Training Issues
General purpose of the system (design intent)
Use of the O&M manuals
Review of control drawings and schematics
Start-up, normal operation, shutdown, unoccupied operation, seasonal changeover, manual operation, control set-up and programming, troubleshooting, and alarms
Interactions with other systems, adjustments and optimizing methods for energy conservation, relevant health and safety issues
Adjustments and optimizing methods for energy conservation
Relevant health and safety issues
Special maintenance and replacement sources
Tenant interaction issues
Discussion of how the feature or system is environmentally responsive

Table 6: Commissioning Report Components

Commissioning Report Components
Description of the owner's project requirements
Description of the project specifications
Verification of installation (construction checklist disposition)
Functional performance testing results and forms
O&M documentation evaluation
Training program evaluation (EAc2)
Value of the commissioning process
Outstanding issues
Contract and plan for resolution , 8 to 10 months after final acceptance (EAc2)

should be listed in an appendix to the commissioning report.

Review 8 to 10 Months After Final Acceptance

For EA Credit 2, the Commissioning Authority must review tenant space operations with O&M staff and occupants to address any outstanding commission-related issues. This occurs between 8 to 10 months following the final acceptance of the systems. For those outstanding issues, a plan for resolution must be prepared.

Submittal Documentation

EA Prerequisite 1

Complete the declaration in the LEED for Commercial Interiors Submittal Template confirming that the commissioning requirements for the project's energy-related systems have been successfully executed. In the case of the verification of the installation performance and commissioning report, if they are not completed, confirm that they are under contract to be executed.

Narrative

For the prerequisite submittal, provide a narrative and diagrams indicating how the HVAC system works, what portions are shared with other tenants in the building, what was included in the project scope of work, and if improvements were made in conjunction with the project by others to any common building systems supplying the tenant area. Understand that this narrative is used to facilitate the review of the submittal not only for the prerequisite but also other EA and EQ credits.

EA Credit 2

Complete the declaration in the LEED for Commercial Interiors Submittal Template confirming that the enhanced commissioning process requirements 1 and 2 have been successfully executed; these requirements are the commissioning

design review and contractor energy-related submittal review. If the remaining items have not been completed at the time of submittal, the declaration must confirm that they will be completed under an existing contract; these two items are the single manuals required for re-commissioning, and verification of training and review 8 to 10 months after final acceptance.

Additional Documentation EA Prerequisite 1

For potential use during submittal review, it is suggested that the project team compile and maintain the commissioning documentation that will demonstrate that the requirements have been met. The information may include, but is not limited to, a narrative outlining the role of the Commissioning Agent, and their relationship to the project team. Have evidence of the basis of design review, a copy of the commissioning plan, prefunctional data, commissioning specs, and excerpts from or a summary of the commissioning report. For those items that may be under contract at the time of submittal, be prepared to supply an excerpt from the contract demonstrating prerequisite achievement.

Additional Documentation EA Credit 2

For potential use during submittal review, it is suggested that the project team compile and maintain additional information beyond that listed for the prerequisite. Be able to demonstrate for those particular functions where it is a credit requirement, that in fact, the Commissioning Agent is an independent third party. Be able to provide a copy of the review completed prior to the end of design development. Have confirming examples that the Commissioning Authority reviewed contractor submittals. Be able to provide an executive summary or excerpts from the re-commissioning manual and evidence of resolution of outstanding commissioning issues. For those items that may be under contract at the time of submittal, be prepared to supply an excerpt from the contract demonstrating credit achievement.

Considerations

Implementation of the commissioning process maintains the focus on high performance building principles from project inception through operation. It typically results in optimized mechanical, electrical and architectural systems—maximizing energy efficiency and thereby minimizing environmental impacts. A properly designed and executed commissioning plan generates substantial operational cost savings. Successful implementation of the commissioning process often increases energy efficiency by 5% to 10%.

In addition to energy performance, occupant wellbeing and productivity are potential benefits when commissioning results in systems functioning as intended. Such benefits include avoiding employee illness, tenant turnover and vacant office space, liability related to indoor air quality and premature equipment replacement.

Owners may find that architects and engineers who have not previously implemented the commissioning process have additional expense associated with incorporating commissioning activities into the project specifications, and documenting the basis of design in a format suitable for the owner. Once learned however, they charge the same or less. Savings during construction and operations from reduced requests for information and change orders, and potentially lower professional liability insurance rates can be byproducts of the commissioning process.

Resources

Please see USGBC Web site at www.usgbc.org/resources for more specific resources on materials sources and other technical information.

Web Sites

American Society of Heating, Refrigeration and Air-Conditioning Engineers (ASHRAE)

www.ashrae.org

(800) 527-4723

Building Commissioning Association

www.bcxa.org

(425) 774-6909

Promotes building commissioning practices that maintain high professional standards and fulfill building owners' expectations. The association offers a five-day intensive course focusing on how to implement the commissioning process, intended for Commissioning Authorities with at least two years' experience.

Building Commissioning Guide

Office of Energy Efficiency and Renewable Energy Federal Energy Management Program

US Department of Energy

www.eere.energy.gov

(800) DIAL-DOE

The Energy Policy Act of 1992 requires each federal agency to adopt procedures necessary to ensure that new federal buildings meet or exceed the federal building energy standards established by the U.S. Department of Energy (DOE). DOE's Federal Energy Management Program, in cooperation with the General Services Administration, developed the Building Commissioning Guide.

Commissioning for Better Buildings in Oregon

Oregon Office of Energy

http://egov.oregon.gov/ENERGY/CONS/BUS/comm/bldgcx.shtml

(503) 378-4040

SS	WE	**EA**	MR	EQ	ID
Prerequisite 1					

SS	WE	**EA**	MR	EQ	ID
Credit 2					

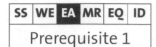

Prerequisite 1

Credit 2

This document (and Web site of the same name) contains a comprehensive introduction to the commissioning process, including research, financial benefits and case studies.

PECI Model Building Commissioning Plan and Guide Specifications

Portland Energy Conservation Inc.

www.peci.org

(503) 248-4636

Details the commissioning process for new equipment during design and construction phases for larger projects. In addition to commissioning guidelines, the document provides boilerplate language, content, format and forms for specifying and executing commissioning. The document builds upon the HVAC Commissioning Process, ASHRAE Guideline 1–1996, with significant additional detail, clarification and interpretation.

University of Wisconsin, Madison, Department of Engineering Professional Development

epdwww.engr.wisc.edu

(800) 462-0876

Offers commissioning process training courses for building owners, architects, engineers, operations and maintenance staff, and other interested parties. The program also offers accreditation of commissioning process providers and managers.

Print Media

ASHRAE Guideline 1–1996: The HVAC Commissioning Process, American Society of Heating, Refrigerating and Air-Conditioning Engineers, 1996.

www.ashrae.org

(800) 527-4723

The purpose of this guideline is to describe the commissioning process to ensure that heating, ventilating and air-conditioning (HVAC) systems perform in conformity with design intent. The procedures, methods and documentation requirements in this guideline cover each phase of the commissioning process for all types and sizes of HVAC systems, from pre-design through final acceptance and post-occupancy, including changes in building and occupancy requirements after initial occupancy.

ASHRAE Guideline 4–1993: Preparation of Operations & Maintenance Documentation for Building Systems,

American Society of Heating, Refrigerating and Air-Conditioning Engineers, 1993.

www.ashrae.org

(800) 527-4723

The purpose of this guideline is to guide individuals responsible for the design, construction and commissioning of HVAC building systems in preparing and delivering O&M documentation.

Sustainable Building Technical Manual, Public Technology, Inc., 1996

www.pti.org

Definitions

Basis of Design includes all information necessary to accomplish the design intent, including weather data, interior environmental criteria, other pertinent design assumptions, cost goals, and references to applicable codes, standards, regulations and guidelines.

Commissioning is the process of ensuring that systems are designed, installed, functionally tested, and capable of being operated and maintained to perform in conformity with the design intent.

Commissioning Plan is a document defining the commissioning process, which is developed in increasing detail as the project progresses through its various phases.

Commissioning Report is the document that records the results of the commissioning process, including the as-built performance of the HVAC system and unresolved issues.

Commissioning Specification is the contract document that details the objective, scope and implementation of the construction and acceptance phases of the commissioning process as developed in the design-phase commissioning plan.

The **Commissioning Team** includes those people responsible for working together to carry out the commissioning process.

Design Intent is a detailed explanation of the ideas, concepts and criteria that are defined by the owner to be important. This typically is an expansion of the information provided in the owner's program.

Functional Performance Testing (FPT) is the process of determining the ability of the HVAC system to deliver heating, ventilating and air-conditioning services in accordance with the final design intent.

Verification includes the full range of checks and tests carried out to determine if all components, subsystems, systems, and interfaces between systems operate in accordance with the contract documents. In this context, "operate" includes all modes and sequences of control operation, interlocks and conditional control responses, and specified responses to abnormal or emergency conditions.

SS	WE	**EA**	MR	EQ	ID
Prerequisite 1					

SS	WE	**EA**	MR	EQ	ID
Credit 2					

SS	WE	EA	MR	EQ	ID
Prerequisite 1					

SS	WE	EA	MR	EQ	ID
Credit 2					

Minimum Energy Performance

Intent

Establish the minimum level of energy efficiency for the tenant space systems.

Requirements

Design portions of the building as covered by the tenant's scope of work to comply with ANSI/ASHRAE/IESNA Standard 90.1-2004 or the local energy code, whichever is more stringent.

Submittals

Provide the LEED for Commercial Interiors Submittal Template, signed by the licensed professional engineer, architect or responsible party, stating that the tenant space complies with Standard 90.1-2004* or local energy codes, whichever is more stringent. If local energy codes were applied, demonstrate that the local energy code is more stringent than Standard 90.1-2004.

California Title 24 2001 has been deemed to be more stringent than Standard 90.1-2004 for LEED purposes. No demonstration of equivalency is required for project teams implementing Title 24 2001.

Potential Technologies & Strategies

Design the systems in the tenant's scope of work to maximize energy performance. Use a computer simulation model to assess the energy performance and identify the most cost effective energy measures. Quantify energy performance as compared to the baseline building.

Summary of Referenced Standard

ANSI/ASHRAE/IESNA 90.1-2004: Energy Standard for Buildings Except Low-Rise Residential Buildings

American Society of Heating, Refrigerating and Air-Conditioning Engineers

www.ashrae.org

Standard 90.1-2004 was formulated by the American Society of Heating, Refrigerating and Air-Conditioning Engineers, Inc. (ASHRAE), under an American National Standards Institute (ANSI) consensus process. The project committee consisted of more than 90 individuals and organizations interested in commercial building energy codes for non-residential projects (commercial, institutional and some portions of industrial buildings) as well as for high-rise residential buildings. The Illuminating Engineering Society of North America (IESNA) is a joint sponsor of the standard.

Standard 90.1-2004 establishes minimum requirements for the energy-efficient design of buildings, except low-rise residential buildings. The provisions of this standard do not apply to single-family houses, multi-family structures of three habitable stories or fewer above grade, manufactured houses (mobile and modular homes), buildings that do not use either electricity or fossil fuel, or equipment and portions of buildings systems that use energy primarily for industrial, manufacturing or commercial processes. Building envelope requirements are provided for semi-heated spaces, such as warehouses.

The standard provides criteria in the following general categories: building envelope (section 5); heating, ventilating and air-conditioning (section 6); service water heating (section 7); power (section 8); lighting (section 9); and other equipment (section 10). Within each section, there are mandatory provisions that must always be complied with, as well as additional prescriptive requirements. Some sections also contain a performance alternate.

The Energy Cost Budget Method (Section 11) allows the user to exceed some of the prescriptive requirements provided energy cost savings are made in other areas. However, in all cases, the mandatory provisions must still be met.

---

*When USGBC membership approved the LEED for Commercial Interiors Rating System in October, 2004, ASHRAE/IESNA 90.1-2001 (with all addenda) was the referenced standard. Because it is considered to set the same requirements as ANSI/ASHRAE/IESNA 90.1-2004, the new version was positioned to supersede the earlier edition. This change and potentially others are noted by Errata, and are available at www.usgbc.org.

In this Reference Guide for LEED for Commercial Interiors v2.0, all references to specific sections come from Standard 90.1-2004.

Credit Interpretation Rulings

In addition to LEED for Commercial Interiors Credit Interpretation Rulings (CIRs), applicable LEED for New Construction CIRs may also apply to LEED for Commercial Interiors projects.

The LEED for New Construction v2 rulings concerning EA Prerequisite 2 may not uniformly apply to LEED for Commercial Interiors projects for two primary reasons. First, the application of the standard to new systems and equipment in existing buildings–which commercial interior projects typically are–does not uniformly follow the same sections of ASHRAE 90.1 that new buildings and new portions of buildings must follow. Second, rulings for projects registered under v2.1 of LEED for New Construction are based on ASHRAE 90.1-1999. v2.0 of LEED for Commercial Interiors is based on the later Standard 90.1-2004, so similar situations may not necessarily result in the same ruling.

Approach and Implementation

Design the building so that it complies with Standard 90.1–2004 or local code, whichever is more stringent. Research the status of individual state energy codes compared with energy standards on the U.S. Department of Energy's Building Energy Codes Web site (see the Resources section for more details).

More Stringent Local Code

Standard 90.1-2004 is the baseline criteria that registered projects must meet to satisfy the prerequisite requirement. When the local code, or any particular provision in it, is more stringent, then its more stringent requirement becomes the prerequisite requirement as well. Where this is the case, provide an explanation with the submittal. California Title 24 is accepted as being more stringent with no further evaluation needed.

Less Stringent Local Code

In LEED for Commercial Interiors, the prerequisite limits the application of the standard to the tenant's scope of work to allow those locating in an existing core and shell building to certify their project without having to force the building owner to make revisions to existing systems. This provision was not added to the LEED for Commercial Interiors prerequisite to provide a means to avoid meeting the intent of the prerequisite, which is to establish the minimum level of energy efficiency for the space systems.

When the local code is less stringent, Standard 90.1-2004 should still be followed. Project teams may not arbitrarily delineate a tenant scope of work to circumvent the application of the standard. Whenever possible, work being done for the benefit of the tenant should meet the more stringent provisions of ASHRAE 90.1-2004.

Applying ASHRAE 90.1-2004

Section 2.1(a) of the standard specifies minimum energy efficiency requirements for the following construction types:

1. new buildings and their systems

2. new portions of buildings and their systems

3. new systems and equipment in existing buildings

The third approach applies to most commercial interior projects and is addressed in this discussion. As stated in Section 4.2.1.3, alterations of existing buildings shall comply with the provisions of Sections 5, 6, 7, 8, 9 and 10, so long that in meeting the provisions there is no increase in the building's energy consumption. See **Table 1**. Each section describes the applicability of the provisions (e.g., definitions and the building elements of interest), lists the mandatory provisions, and gives the applicable prescriptive criteria. The standard has exceptions for certain ap-

Table 1: Scope of Requirements Addressed by ASHRAE 90.1-2004

Mandatory Sections	
Section 5	Building Envelope
Section 6	Heating, Ventilating, and Air Conditioning
Section 7	Service Water Heating
Section 8	Power
Section 9	Lighting
Section 10	Other Equipment

Other Sections Used in LEED-CI	
Section 11	Energy Cost Budget Method
Appendix G	Performance Rating Method

plications, such as historic buildings and 24-hour facilities, that are recognized by this prerequisite.

EA Prerequisite 2 does not preclude the use of the exceptions provided for historic buildings or annual energy consumption comparison when compensating changes are made in more than one applicable requirement section.

Section 5 Building Envelope

To the limited extent it may occur on a commercial interior project, the project must comply with the mandatory provisions of Section 5.4. It must also use one of three compliance paths: Section 5.5 Prescriptive Path, or Section 5.6 Building Envelope Trade-Off Option, or Section 11 Energy Cost Budget Method.

Section 6 Heating, Ventilating and Air Conditioning

Alterations and replacement of these systems in existing buildings follow the requirements of Section 6.1.1.3. Direct replacement of existing HVAC equipment must meet the minimum efficiency requirements set by the standard. Note that projects considering EA Credit 1.3 Option 1 should consult the New Build-

ings Institute, Inc. publication *Advanced Buildings: Energy Benchmark for High Performance Buildings (E-Benchmark)* Prescriptive Criteria E, 2.5 for more stringent minimum efficiency requirements.

Air conditioning added for spaces previously not air conditioned must meet the requirements of Section 6.2. Alterations to existing systems are not to reduce economizer capability unless they meet the criteria set out in Section 6.5.1.

EA Prerequisite 2 does not preclude the use of any of the exceptions provided in 6.1.1.3 that cover equipment modifications and repairs, alterations involving extensive revisions to other systems, refrigerant change, relocation of existing equipment, or access limitations for ducts and pipes.

Section 6 provides three compliance paths, any of which if justified and properly followed meet the requirement of the prerequisite. 6.3 is the Simplified Approach Option for HVAC Systems that is limited to small building sizes where the HVAC design meets prescribed criteria.

All other projects need to meet the mandatory provisions of Section 6.4, and either the prescriptive path in Section 6.5, or the Energy Cost Budget Method in Section 11.

The mandatory provisions of Section 6.4 cover several areas, including minimum equipment efficiencies, controls, and HVAC system construction and insulation, which address ducts, plenums and piping.

When a project is not using the Energy Cost Budget Method, it must follow Section 6.5, Prescriptive Path, which sets the requirements for economizers, simultaneous heating and cooling limitations (significant to energy use reductions), humidification, air system design and control, hydronic system design and control, energy recovery, exhaust hoods and radiant heating systems.

Section 7 Service Water Heating

Section 7 covers heating water for domestic or commercial purposes (restrooms, kitchens, etc.). Alterations within existing buildings follow the same requirements set out for new construction, with the exception provided for insufficient space or access. All projects need to meet the mandatory provisions of Section 7.4, and either the prescriptive path in Section 7.5, or the Energy Cost Budget Method in Section 11. The mandatory provisions of Section 7.5 cover efficiency, controls, pools and heat traps for storage tanks.

Section 8 Power

Section 8 describes mandatory provisions covering voltage drops in the power distribution system.

Section 9 Lighting

Section 9 covers replacement lighting systems and new systems in the same manner. If the scope of the lighting work is replacing less than half of the existing fixtures with new ones using no additional power, all other provisions of the section apply.

The two compliance paths include the same mandatory provisions and the prescriptive requirements of either the Building Area Method or Space-by-Space Method.

Section 9.4 describes the mandatory provisions for automatic lighting shutoff, space controls, exterior lighting controls, additional controls including task lighting, tandem wiring, exit signs, exterior building and grounds lighting. Special attention should be given to Section 9.4.1 Lighting Control. Buildings over 5000 sq.ft. must have an automatic control device to shut off building lighting in all spaces. The shut-off device may be a programmable control to schedule time-of-day control for areas no greater than 25,000 sq.ft. but no less than every floor. The approach may use occupant sensors to turn lights off within 30 minutes of an occupant leaving a space, or a signal from another control

or alarm system that indicates the area is unoccupied. EA Prerequisite 2 does not preclude the use of any of the exceptions provided in Section 9.4.1.1 for 24-hour operations, patient care areas, and where automatic shutoff would endanger the safety or security of occupants.

A space control device must be provided in each space enclosed by ceiling-height partitions, and if the "on" function is manual, the device must be readily accessible and located so the users can see it function. Classrooms, conference and meeting rooms and employee lunch and break rooms must be equipped with a control that turns lights off within 30 minutes of all occupants leaving. In all other spaces, the "on" function may be either manual or an occupancy sensor. There must be at least one control for every 2500 sq.ft. for rooms 10,000 sq.ft. or less, and at least one every 10,000 sq.ft. if larger. If it is capable of overriding the time-of-day scheduled shutoff control, it may not do it for periods longer than four hours.

LEED for Commercial Interiors recognizes additional lighting controls in EA Credit 1.2 for daylight responsive controls and EQ Credit 6.1 for controllability for individual task needs and in all multi-occupant spaces where transient groups must share lighting controls. The function of these additional controls must comply with ASHRAE/IESNA 90.1-2004.

The Building Area Method Compliance Path uses a limited number of building area types. The interior lighting power allowance is determined by multiplying the gross lighted floor area of the building type by the lighting power density provided in the associated table. More than one building area type may be used; trade-offs among building area types are permitted provided that the total installed interior lighting power does not exceed the interior lighting power allowance.

The Space-by-Space Method is more flexible than the Building Area Method and allows each space to be addressed individually. For each area, the lighting power density is multiplied by the space's square footage. The interior lighting power allowance is the sum of the individual spaces. Trade-offs between different spaces are allowed as long as the total proposed lighting power density is less than the sum of the lighting power budget allowances for all individual occupancies. Additional interior lighting power may be added to the allowance for certain applications (Section 9.6.3).

Section 10 Other Equipment

This section establishes mandatory efficiency standards for electric motors.

Section 11 Energy Cost Budget Method (ECB)

The standard provides an alternative to the prescriptive approach where each Section must be satisfied separate from the others. The Energy Cost Budget Method requires the simulation of the proposed design and a budget case that follows the prescriptive requirements of each section. Most generally the calculation requires computer modeling. The modeling must cover at least the segment of the building serviced by the same HVAC system supplying the project space. If ECB is used to demonstrate compliance with EA Prerequisite 2, note that the only permitted trade-offs between regulated systems may be within the project space. Additional discussion of this method and the Performance Rating Method (Appendix G) is included in EA Credit 1.3.

Submittal Documentation

Provide the LEED for Commercial Interiors Submittal Template declaration that the tenant space complies with Standard 90.1-2004. When another code other than California Title 24 is used, demonstrate that it is more stringent than Standard 90.1-2004.

Additional Documentation

For potential use during submittal review, it is suggested that the project team compile and maintain the compliance documentation found in ASHRAE publication *90.1 User's Manual* (2004). When the Energy Cost Budget Method is used, prepare a narrative highlighting energy saving measures incorporated in the design. Include a table listing budget and design quantities similar to that included in the Submittal Templates for EA Credit 1.3. Explain which model variables were constant and changed between the ECB and the Design Energy Cost. Demonstrate how much lower (by a percentage) the design energy cost is as compared to the energy cost budget as defined in Standard 90.1-2004, Section 11. Compare local code requirements to proposed building characteristics if applicable. Provide a completed and signed copy of the Energy Cost Budget (ECB) Compliance Form along with sample output from the energy model summary.

Considerations

Complying with the requirements of Standard 90.1-2004 decreases operating costs by reducing total energy consumption. These reductions in energy consumption mean less combustion of fossil fuels for heating and cooling and electrical use within the building. Less pollution is created.

Resources

Please see USGBC Web site at www.usgbc.org/resources for more specific resources on materials sources and other technical information.

Web Sites

Advanced Buildings

www.advancedbuildings.org

Hosted by a Canadian public/private consortium, this site provides explanations, costs, and information sources for 90 technologies and practices that improve the energy and resource efficiency of commercial and multi-unit residential buildings.

American Council for an Energy Efficient Economy

www.aceee.org

(202) 429-8873

ACEEE is a nonprofit organization dedicated to advancing energy efficiency as a means of promoting both economic prosperity and environmental protection.

Buildings Upgrade Manual

ENERGY STAR®

www.energystar.gov/index.cfm?c=business. bus_upgrade_manual

(888) 782-7937

This document from the EPA is a guide for ENERGY STAR® Buildings Partners to use in planning and implementing profitable energy-efficiency upgrades in their facilities and can be used as a comprehensive framework for an energy strategy.

New Buildings Institute, Inc.

www.newbuildings.org

(509) 493-4468

The New Buildings Institute is a nonprofit, public-benefits corporation dedicated to making buildings better for people and the environment. Its mission is to promote energy efficiency in buildings through technology research, guidelines and codes.

Building Energy Codes Program

U.S. Department of Energy

www.energycodes.gov

(800) DIAL-DOE

The Building Energy Codes program provides comprehensive resources for states and code users, including news, compliance software, code comparisons and the Status of State Energy Codes database. The database includes state energy contacts, code status, code history, DOE grants awarded and construction data.

The program is also updating the ComCheck-EZ compliance tool to include Standard 90.1-2004. This compliance tool includes the prescriptive path and trade-off compliance methods. The software generates appropriate compliance forms as well.

Office of Energy Efficiency and Renewable Energy

U.S. Department of Energy

www.eere.energy.gov

(800) DIAL-DOE

A comprehensive resource for Department of Energy information on energy efficiency and renewable energy, including access to energy links and downloadable documents.

Print Media

ASHRAE *90.1 User's Manual*

The 90.1 User's Manual was developed as a companion document to the Standard Standard 90.1–2004 (Energy Standard for Buildings Except Low-Rise Residential Buildings). The User's Manual explains the new standard and includes sample calculations, useful reference material, and information on the intent and application of the standard. The User's Manual is abundantly illustrated and contains numerous examples and tables of reference data. The manual also includes a complete set of compliance forms and worksheets that can be used to document compliance with the standard.

The User's Manual is helpful to architects and engineers applying the standard to the design of buildings; plan examiners and field inspectors who must enforce the standard in areas where it is adopted as code; and contractors who must construct buildings in compliance with the standard. A compact disc accompanies the User's Manual and contains the EnvStd

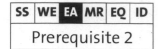

Prerequisite 2

4.0 Computer Program for performing building envelope trade-offs, plus electronic versions of the compliance forms found in the User's Manual.

Commercial Lighting Efficiency Resource Book, EPRI, 1991.

Sustainable Building Technical Manual, Public Technology, Inc., 1996.

CFC Reduction in HVAC&R Equipment

Intent

Reduce ozone depletion.

Requirements

Zero use of CFC-based refrigerants in new tenant HVAC&R systems when within scope of work.

Submittals

Provide the LEED for Commercial Interiors Submittal Template, signed by a professional engineer or other responsible party, declaring that there are no CFCs in HVAC&R systems that have been installed or renovated within the LEED for Commercial Interiors project scope.

Potential Technologies & Strategies

When reusing existing HVAC systems, conduct an inventory to identify equipment which uses CFC refrigerants and replace or retrofit these systems with non-CFC refrigerants. For new installations, specify new HVAC equipment that uses no CFC refrigerants.

Credit Interpretation Rulings

Credit interpretation rulings concerning this prerequisite on LEED for Commercial Interiors and LEED for New Construction project requests are applicable.

Approach and Implementation

Specify only non-CFC-based refrigerants in all base building HVAC&R and fire suppression systems. Consider the characteristics of various CFC substitutes. Refrigerants have varying applications, lifetimes, ozone-depleting potentials (ODPs) and global-warming potentials (GWPs). **Table 1** provides examples of environmental lifetimes, ODP values and GWP values for a variety of refrigerants. Refrigerants should be chosen that have short environmental lifetimes, small ODP values and small GWP values. No "ideal" alternative for CFCs has been developed. See the EPA's List of Substitutes for Ozone-Depleting Substances (www.epa.gov/ozone/snap) for a current listing of alternatives to CFC refrigerants. Note that some alternatives are not suitable for retrofits.

Submittal Documentation

Complete the declaration included in the LEED for Commercial Interiors Submittal Template, confirming that no CFCs in HVAC&R systems have been installed as part of the project's scope of work.

Additional Documentation

For potential use during submittal review, it is suggested that the project team assemble and retain equipment schedules and cut sheets highlighting refrigerant information for all HVAC&R components.

Exemplary Performance

Project teams may earn an Innovation in Design point for attaining a quantifiable positive environmental impact for items not recognized in the LEED for Commercial Interiors Rating System. With the acknowledgement that this prerequisite confirms only statutory requirements, project teams who demonstrate that they have eliminated the use of ozone depleting materials or materials with global warming potential from their project may qualify for an ID point. It is advisable to determine the potential compliance path in advance by reviewing other LEED rating systems, the LEED for Commercial Interiors Credit Interpretation Rulings, and by submitting a Credit Interpretation Request with project details.

Considerations

Older refrigeration equipment uses chlorofluorocarbons (CFCs) in refriger-

Table 1: Refrigerant Environmental Data

Refrigerant	Lifetime [years]	ODP	GWP
CFC-11	45	1	4,000
CFC-12	100	1	8,500
CFC-13	640	1	11,700
CFC-113	85	1	5,000
CFC-114	300	1	9,300
CFC-115	1,700	1	9,500
Halon 1211	11	3	n/a
Halon 1301	65	10	5,600
Halon 2402	n/a	6	n/a
HCFC-22	12	0.06	1,700
HCFC-123	1	0.02	93
HCFC-124	6	0.02	480
HCFC-141b	9	0.11	630
HCFC-142b	19	0.07	2,000
HFC-32	5.6	0	650
HFC-125	32.6	0	2,800
HFC-134a	14.6	0	1,300
HFC-143a	48.3	0	3,800
HFC-152a	1.5	0	140
HFC-236fa	209	0	6,300

ants. CFCs are the root cause of serious environmental and health problems. The reaction between a CFC and an ozone molecule in the earth's stratosphere destroys the ozone and reduces the stratosphere's ability to absorb a portion of the sun's ultraviolet (UV) radiation. Overexposure to UV rays can lead to skin cancer, cataracts and weakened immune systems. Increased UV can also lead to reduced crop yield and disruptions in the marine food chain.

CFCs fall into a larger category of ozone-depleting substances (ODSs). The United States is one of the world's largest emitters of ODSs. As such, actions taken in the United States to limit the release of ODSs have a significant impact on global ODS release. Recognizing the profound human health risks associated with ozone depletion, 160 countries have agreed to follow the Montreal Protocol on Substances that Deplete the Ozone Layer since the late 1980s. This treaty includes a timetable for the phase-out of production and use of ODSs. In compliance with the Montreal Protocol, CFC production in the United States ended in 1995.

As part of the U.S. commitment to implementing the Montreal Protocol, Congress added new provisions to the Clean Air Act designed to help preserve and protect the stratospheric ozone layer. These amendments require the U.S. Environmental Protection Agency (EPA) to develop and implement regulations for the responsible management of ozone-depleting substances in the United States. EPA regulations include programs that ended the domestic production of ODSs, identified safe and effective alternatives to ODSs, and require manufacturers to label products either containing or made with chemicals that have a significant ozone-depleting potential.

Banning the use of CFCs in refrigerants slows the depletion of the ozone layer and reduces the accumulation of green-house gases and the potential for global climate change. Thoughtfully choosing equipment can also result in greater energy efficiency. Specification of non-CFC building equipment is now standard. Existing building renovations will require additional first costs to convert or replace systems currently using CFCs. Most new non-CFC HVAC systems and refrigerants are cost-competitive with CFC equipment. Replacement rather than conversion of HVAC systems may increase equipment efficiencies and enable projects to reap energy savings over the life of the building.

Resources

Please see USGBC Web site at www.usgbc.org/resources for more specific resources on materials sources and other technical information.

Web Sites

Benefits of CFC Phase-out

U.S. Environmental Protection Agency

www.epa.gov/ozone/geninfo/benefits.html

(800) 296-1996

An EPA document on the benefits of CFC phase-out, including brief case studies.

Ozone Depletion

U.S. Environmental Protection Agency

www.epa.gov/ozone

(800) 296-1996

Provides information about the science of ozone depletion, the regulatory approach to protecting the ozone layer (including phase-out schedules) and alternatives to ozone-depleting substances.

Significant New Alternatives Policy (SNAP)

U.S. Environmental Protection Agency

www.epa.gov/ozone/snap

(800) 296-1996

An EPA program to identify alternatives to ozone-depleting substances, the SNAP Program maintains up-to-date lists of more environmentally sound substitutes for refrigeration and air conditioning equipment, solvents, fire suppression systems, adhesives, coatings and other substances.

The Treatment by LEED of the Environmental Impact of HVAC Refrigerants

U.S. Green Building Council

www.usgbc.org/DisplayPage.aspx?CMSPageID=154

(202) 82-USGBC

This report was prepared under the auspices of the U.S. Green Building Council's LEED Technical and Scientific Advisory Committee (TSAC), in response to a charge given to TSAC by the LEED Steering Committee to review the atmospheric environmental impacts arising from the use of halocarbons as refrigerants in building heating, ventilating, and air conditioning (HVAC) equipment.

Print Media

Building Systems Analysis & Retrofit Manual, SMACNA, 1995.

CFCs, HCFC and Halons: Professional and Practical Guidance on Substances that Deplete the Ozone Layer, ASHRAE, 2000.

The Refrigerant Manual: Managing The Phase-Out of CFCs, BOMA International, 1993.

Definitions

Chlorofluorocarbons (CFCs) are hydrocarbons that deplete the stratospheric ozone layer.

Hydrochlorofluorocarbons (HCFCs) are refrigerants that cause significantly less depletion of the stratospheric ozone layer compared to CFCs.

Refrigerants are the working fluids of refrigeration cycles. They absorb heat from a reservoir at low temperatures and reject heat at higher temperatures.

Optimize Energy Performance

Lighting Power

Intent

Achieve increasing levels of energy consumption below the prerequisite standard to reduce environmental impacts associated with excessive energy use.

Requirements

Reduce connected lighting power density below that allowed by ANSI/ASHRAE/IESNA Standard 90.1-2004* using either the Space-by-Space Method or by applying the whole building lighting power allowance to the entire tenant space.

Option A. Reduce lighting power density to 15% below the standard,

OR

Option B. Reduce lighting power density to 25% below the standard,

OR

Option C. Reduce lighting power density to 35% below the standard.

Submittals

Provide the LEED for Commercial Interiors Submittal Template, signed by the professional engineer or responsible party, stating that the lighting power density is reduced below ASHRAE requirements consistent with the level of credit being sought.

Complete the Lighting Compliance Documentation provided in the Standard 90.1-2004 User's Manual. Provide a separate calculation that shows the percentage reduction in lighting power.

Potential Technologies & Strategies

Design the connected lighting power to maximize energy performance. If the project warrants, consider a computer simulation model to assess the performance and identify the most cost effective energy efficiency measures.

---

*When USGBC membership approved the LEED for Commercial Interiors Rating System in October, 2004, ASHRAE/IESNA 90.1-2001 (with all addenda) was the referenced standard. Because it is considered to set the same requirements as Standard 90.1-2004, the new version was positioned to supercede the earlier edition. This change and potentially others are noted by Errata, and available from www.usgbc.org.

In this Reference Guide for LEED for Commercial Interiors v2.0, all references to specific sections come from Standard 90.1-2004.

Credit Interpretation Rulings

In LEED for Commercial Interiors, EA Credit 1.1 addresses only lighting power density. Credit Interpretation Rulings concerning this credit on LEED for Commercial Interiors project requests are applicable.

Even though a lower wattage lamp may be used in a luminaire, the rated wattage of the luminaire must be used in the calculation.

Approach and Implementation

Design the connected lighting power to maximize energy performance. Consider using a computer simulation model to assess the performance.

This credit uses the percentage of the installed interior lighting power that is below the interior lighting power allowance. It uses either of the two methods used in Standard 90.1-2004. The installed interior lighting power, **Equation 1**, is the power in watts of all permanently installed general, task, and furniture lighting systems and luminaires. Section 9.2.2.3 provides a list of lighting equipment that does not need to be included in the calculation for installed interior lighting power.

Building Area Method

In using this approach to determine the interior lighting power allowance, follow the steps in Section 9.5, beginning by selecting the appropriate building area type from the list in Table 9.5.1. For each building area type there is a lighting power density (W/sq.ft.). For example, the office building area type lighting power density is 1.0 W/sq.ft. Next determine the interior lighting power allowance (watts) by multiplying the lighting power density by the gross lighted floor area of the building area type. See **Equation 2**. When there is more than one building area type on a project, add the interior lighting power allowances together to reach the total interior lighting power allowance (watts).

Space-by-Space Method

This approach, found in Section 9.6, is nearly identical to the building area method, but there are considerably more space types, which allows each space to be addressed individually. In the Space-by-Space Method, areas enclosed by partitions 80% or greater than ceiling height may be considered as a separate area. Gross interior floor area is measured from the center of partition walls.

Again, determine the interior lighting power allowance for each space by multiplying the gross floor area by the light power density for the space. Total the individual space allowances. See **Equation 3** and **Table 1**.

In the Space-by-Space Method, Section 9.6.3 provides three situations that permit increases to the interior power allowance described above. They are chandelier-type luminaires, lighting connected with visual display terminals, and lighting in retail spaces. LEED for Commercial Interiors will allow them in determining the total interior lighting power allowance only to the extent they are actually used. See the additional submittal requirements.

Lighting Power Reduction Achieved

Simply subtract the installed interior lighting power from the code interior lighting power allowance. See **Equation 4**. Finally, determine the percentage reduction, **Equation 5**, by dividing the lighting power reduction by the interior lighting power allowance. The credit thresholds for one, two or three points are 15%, 25% or 35%.

California Title 24

Though Title 24 is recognized as being more stringent for EA Prerequisite 2, for consistency, and fairness, projects in California must use Standard 90.1-

2004 in determining performance in EA Credit 1.1.

Submittal Documentation

Complete the declaration in the LEED for Commercial Interiors Submittal Template stating that the installed interior lighting power is reduced below the ASHRAE requirements consistent with the level of credit being sought.

Complete the Lighting Compliance Documentation found in ASHRAE publication *90.1 User's Manual* and the table provided with the LEED for Commercial Interiors Submittal Template. Indicate the compliance method used. If increases provided in Section 9.6.3 were included, provide details to confirm the calculation; at a minimum, provide a plan showing the area involved and cut sheets of the luminaires used.

Additional Documentation

For potential use during submittal review, it is suggested that the project team compile and maintain floor plans showing the lighting layout, the schedule of lighting fixtures and copies of the cut sheets indicating the rated wattage.

Exemplary Performance

Project teams may earn an Innovation in Design point for exemplary performance when the project satisfies the next incremental step. For Optimize Energy Performance, Lighting Power, the credit calculation must be 45% or greater.

Considerations

For commercial interior projects, the reduction of interior lighting power stands to be the greatest energy conservation method available. When high efficiency luminaires are combined with proper control systems and daylighting, the end result is lower operating costs, lower air conditioning loads and improved occupant wellbeing.

Resources

Please see USGBC Web site at www.usgbc.org/resources for more specific resources on materials sources and other technical information.

Equation 1: Installed Interior Lighting Power

Installed Interior Lighting Power = Σ (Quantity by type of Luminaires x Rated Wattage by type Luminaire)
[watts]   [watts]

Equation 2: Interior Lighting Power Allowance Using the Building Area Method

Interior Lighting Power Allowance = Gross Lighted Floor Area x Building Area Type Lighting Power Density
[watts]   [sq. ft.]   [watts / sq. ft.]

Equation 3: Interior Lighting Power Allowance Using the Space-by-Space Method

Interior Lighting Power Allowance = Σ (Space Floor Area x Space Type Lighting Power Density)
[watts]   [sq. ft.]   [watts / sq. ft.]

Equation 4: Lighting Power Reduction Achieved [watts]

Lighting Power Reduction Achieved = Interior Lighting Power Allowance - Installed Interior Lighting Power
[watts]   [watts]   [watts]

Equation 5: Lighting Power Reduction Achieved [%]

$$\text{Lighting Power Reduction Achieved [\%]} = \frac{\text{Lighting Power Reduction Achieved [watts]}}{\text{Interior Lighting Power Allowance [watts]}}$$

Table 1: Interior Lighting Power Allowance and Performance Calculation

Building Area Type or Space Type	Lighting Power Density [watts / sq. ft.]		Gross Area [sq. ft.]		Lighting Power Allowance [watts]
Office-Enclosed	1.1	x	720	=	792
Office-Open Plan	1.1	x	16,180	=	17,798
Conference	1.3	x	850	=	1,105
Training	1.4	x	1,200	=	1,680
Lobby	1.3	x	330	=	429
Corridor	0.5	x	720	=	360
Total Floor Area [sq. ft.]			20,000		
Interior Lighting Power Allowance [watts]					22,164
Installed Interior Lighting Power [watts]					16,440
Lighting Power Reduction Achieved [watts]					5,724
Lighting Power Reduction Achieved [5,724 / 22,164] = **25.8%**					
25.8% > 25%, 2 Points Earned					

Web Sites

Building Energy Codes Program

U.S. Department of Energy

www.energycodes.gov

(800) DIAL-DOE

The Building Energy Codes program is updating the ComCheck-EZ compliance tool to include Standard 90.1-2004. This compliance tool includes the prescriptive path and trade-off compliance methods. The software generates appropriate compliance forms as well.

Print Media

ASHRAE Publication *90.1 User's Manual*

The Standard 90.1–2004 User's Manual was developed as a companion document to the Standard 90.1–2004 (Energy Standard for Buildings Except Low-Rise Residential Buildings). The User's Manual explains the new standard and includes sample calculations, useful reference material, and information on the intent and application of the standard.

IESNA Lighting Handbook (Ninth Edition), IESNA, 2000.

ANSI/IESNA RP-1-04, American National Standard Practice for Office Lighting, ANSI

Definitions

Interior Lighting Power Allowance is the maximum light power in watts allowed for the interior of a building.

Lighting Power Density (LPD) is the maximum lighting power, per unit area, of a building classification of space function.

A **Luminaire** is a complete lighting unit consisting of a lamp or lamps together with the housing designed to distribute the light, position and protect the lamps and connect the lamps to the power supply.

Optimize Energy Performance

Lighting Controls

Intent

Achieve increasing levels of energy conservation beyond the prerequisite standard to reduce environmental impacts associated with excessive energy use.

Requirements

Install daylight responsive controls in all regularly occupied spaces within 15 feet of windows and under skylights.

Submittals

Provide the LEED for Commercial Interiors Submittal Template, signed by the professional engineer or responsible party, stating that lighting controls were installed consistent with the credit requirement.

AND

Provide a narrative describing the lighting controls that have been incorporated in the tenant space design. Include a plan of lighting control zones showing each control device and lighting equipment controlled. Provide a schedule of lighting controls showing model, type, and other characteristics.

Potential Technologies & Strategies

Design the lighting controls to maximize energy performance.

Credit Interpretation Rulings

In LEED for Commercial Interiors, EA Credit 1.2 addresses only daylight responsive controls. Credit Interpretation Rulings concerning this credit are applicable.

Approach and Implementation

The primary objective of daylight-responsive controls is to reduce energy consumption. However, other than proximity requirements to windows and skylights, the credit is subjective as to how the project team accomplishes it, and as to the amount of energy reduction that should be achieved.

Ideally, the use of daylight responsive controls is one element in an overall lighting strategy. The strategy optimizes natural daylighting while minimizing artificial illumination, and provides appropriate task/ambient working conditions while offering occupant control. There is no requirement that a project simultaneously earn LEED for Commercial Interiors EQ Credits 6.1, 8.1 and 8.2, but the association should not be overlooked. Consider developing a comprehensive program during schematic design; if available, include pertinent excerpts in the submittal narrative.

Design Approach for Daylight – Responsive Controls

Implement the daylighting control portion of the overall lighting strategy by establishing the zones that are to be controlled. For the submittal prepare a plan and a narrative. The plan should illustrate the zones and the narrative should explain how they were determined.

At a minimum, perimeter areas within a radius of at least 15 feet from windows must be controlled. Areas beneath skylights are also to be controlled. For both situations, provide a plan showing the individual zones and their relationship to the fenestration. If areas are being excluded, document them as well. Anticipate shading from neighboring buildings and landscape; indicate their impact on the zoning.

Daylighting controls typically include a photosensor in the circuit with the luminaires. Good designs go much further, anticipating occupant activities and comfort, avoiding drastic changes in lighting levels and minimizing glare. Refined approaches go beyond on/off controls, employing bi-level switching, step-dimming ballasts, and better yet, continuous dimming. All major commercial lamps can now be dimmed, including incandescent, fluorescent and HID.

When describing the design, indicate the functionality provided in each zone, the relationship to individual controls, and the combined logic of the mandatory occupancy sensors, shut-off and daylighting-responsive controls.

Provide a schedule, similar to the sample in **Table 1**, listing all the lighting controls, complete with model designation, function and characteristics. The schedule must relate to the plan and narrative.

Finally, when possible, indicate the anticipated annual reduction in electrical consumption the design should produce; the comparison may use the criteria for interior lighting power density provided in Section 9 of Standard 90.1-2004.

Submittal Documentation

Provide the LEED for Commercial Interiors Submittal Template, stating that daylight-responsive lighting controls were installed on the project. In addition provide a narrative, plan and schedule. Include the level of detail indicated above.

Additional Documentation

If the initial submittal is comprehensive, no additional information should be needed.

Exemplary Performance

No established criteria have been set for exemplary performance for EA Credit 1.2.

Considerations

Daylighting improves the indoor environment. Having it supplement or even eliminate the need for artificial lighting is generally satisfying to the occupants and reduces lighting power consumption. When planned in conjunction with heating and air conditioning requirements, the net cost of utilities can be reduced as well.

Resources

Please see USGBC Web site at www. usgbc.org/resources for more specific resources on materials sources and other technical information.

Print Media

Design Brief – Lighting Controls

Energy Design Resources

www.energydesignresources.com

Developed by Southern California Edison.

Daylight in Buildings: A Source Book on Daylighting Systems and Components, Chapter 5 – Daylight-Responsive Controls

International Energy Agency Solar Heating and Cooling Programme

www.iea-shc.org

A report of the International Energy Agency (IEA) Solar Heating and Cooling Programme, Energy Conservation in Buildings and Community Systems (IEA SHC Task 21 / ECBCS Annex 29, July 2000). Published by the Lawrence Berkeley National Laboratory with support from the Energy Design Resources. LBNL Report Number: LBNL-47493.

Advanced Lighting Guidelines: 2001 Edition, Chapter 8 – Lighting Controls

New Buildings Institute, Inc.

www.newbuildings.org/lighting.htm

Published by New Buildings Inc. Available as a free download or purchased as a printed manual of 390 pages.

Definitions

Daylighting is the controlled admission of natural light into a space through glazing with the intent of reducing or eliminating electric lighting. By utilizing solar light, daylighting creates a stimulating and productive environment for building occupants.

Daylight-Responsive Lighting Controls are photosensors used in conjunction with other switching and dimming devices that control the amount of artificial lighting in relationship to the amount and quality of natural daylight.

SS	WE	EA	MR	EQ	ID

Credit 1.2

Credit 1.2

Table 1: Sample Daylight Responsive Lighting Control Schedule Template

Zone	Occupancy	Control Method Step-dimming switching/ Step-dimming ballast/ Continuous dimming	Control Type Sensor/ Programmable Timer	Control Device Make/Model

Optimize Energy Performance

HVAC

Intent

Achieve increasing levels of energy conservation beyond the prerequisite standard to reduce environmental impacts associated with excessive energy use.

Requirements

OPTION A

Implement one or both of the following strategies:

- Equipment Efficiency: (1 point)

  Install HVAC systems which comply with the efficiency requirements outlined in the New Buildings Institute, Inc.'s publication "Advanced Buildings: Energy Benchmark for High Performance Buildings (E-Benchmark)" prescriptive criteria for mechanical equipment efficiency requirements, sections 2.4 (less ASHRAE Standard 55), 2.5 and 2.6.

- Appropriate Zoning and Controls: (1 point)

  Zone tenant fit-out of spaces to meet the following requirements:

  - Every Solar Exposure must have a separate control zone

  - Interior spaces must be separately zoned

  - Private offices and specialty occupancies (conference rooms, kitchens, etc.) must have active controls capable of sensing space use and modulating HVAC system in response to space demand

OPTION B

Reduce design energy cost compared to the energy cost budget for regulated energy components described in the requirements of ANSI/ASHRAE/IESNA Standard 90.1- 2004*.

- Demonstrate that HVAC system component performance criteria used for tenant space are 15% better than a system that is in minimum compliance with ANSI/ASHRAE/IESNA Standard 90.1-2004*. (1 point)

OR

- Demonstrate that HVAC system component performance criteria used for tenant space are 30% better than a system that is in minimum compliance with ANSI/ASHRAE/IESNA Standard 90.1-2004*. (2 points)

Submittals

Option A:

Provide the LEED for Commercial Interiors Submittal Template, signed by a licensed professional engineer or architect, stating that the strategy employed meets the credit requirements.

Provide a narrative description of the HVAC system serving the tenant space as well as a description of the building level system. Plans and specifications should

have an HVAC equipment schedule and plans showing the equipment within the space. Demonstrate in the narrative and plans submitted that the installed HVAC systems comply with the requirements of the credit.

Or

Option B

Provide the LEED for Commercial Interiors Submittal Template, signed by the licensed professional engineer or architect, stating that the HVAC system energy consumption is 15% or 30% (depending on credit taken) lower than a budget or baseline case system defined in Standard 90.1-2004*, Section 11 or Appendix G.

Provide a completed copy of the Energy Cost Budget (ECB) Compliance Form. Provide a narrative description of the HVAC system serving the Tenant space as well as a description of the building level system. Plans and specifications should have an HVAC equipment schedule and plans showing the equipment within the space.

Potential Technologies & Strategies

Design the HVAC system components to maximize energy performance. Review compliance options for EA Credit 1.3 and determine the most appropriate approach. Option A provides a more prescriptive approach to recognizing energy-efficient HVAC design, while Option B is performance based.

Summary of Referenced Standards

Advanced Buildings: Energy Benchmark for High Performance Buildings (E-Benchmark)

New Buildings Institute, Inc.

www.newbuildings.org

(509) 493-4468

The New Buildings Institute, Inc. is a not-for-profit public benefits corporation dedicated to making buildings better for people and the environment. Their mission is to promote energy efficiency in buildings through policy development, research, guidelines and codes.

"Advanced Buildings: Energy Benchmark for High Performance Buildings (E-Benchmark)" establishes criteria to attain energy efficient buildings. In many ways it is analogous to LEED. The sections from the publication used in EA Credit 1.3 are only a portion of its criteria.

ANSI/ASHRAE/IESNA 90.1-2004: Energy Standard for Buildings Except Low-Rise Residential Buildings

www.ashrae.org

American Society of Heating, Refrigerating and Air-Conditioning Engineers

Standard 90.1-2004 was formulated by the American Society of Heating, Refrigerating and Air-Conditioning Engineers, Inc. (ASHRAE), under an American National Standards Institute (ANSI) consensus process. The project committee consisted of more than 90 individuals and organizations interested in commercial building energy codes for non-residential projects (commercial, institutional, and some portions of industrial buildings) as well as for high-rise residential buildings. The Illuminating Engineering Society of North America (IESNA) is a joint sponsor of the standard.

Standard 90.1 establishes minimum requirements for the energy-efficient design of buildings, except low-rise residential buildings. The provisions of this standard do not apply to single-family houses, multi-family structures of three habitable stories or fewer above grade, manufactured houses (mobile and modular homes), buildings that do not use either electricity or fossil fuel, or equipment and portions of buildings systems that use energy primarily for industrial, manufacturing or commercial processes. Building envelope requirements are provided for semi-heated spaces, such as warehouses.

---

*When USGBC membership approved the LEED for Commercial Interiors Rating System in October, 2004, ASHRAE/IESNA 90.1-2001 (with all addenda) was the referenced standard. Because it is considered to set the same requirements as Standard 90.1-2004, the new version was positioned to supercede the earlier edition. This change and potentially others are noted by Errata, available at www.usgbc.org.

In this Reference Guide for LEED for Commercial Interiors v2.0, all references to specific sections come from 90.1-2004.

Credit Interpretation Rulings

In LEED for Commercial Interiors, EA Credit 1.3 addresses only HVAC energy performance. Dissimilar approaches of demonstrating energy performance are used in other LEED rating systems. Option A is unique to LEED for Commercial Interiors. Option B relies to a certain extent on the energy modeling approach used in LEED for New Construction v2.1; where applicable, those LEED for New Construction CIRs may have some bearing on LEED for Commercial Interiors projects.

Option A. Equipment Efficiency

Approach and Implementation

The equipment efficiency approach draws on three criteria from Advanced Buildings: Energy Benchmark for High Performance Buildings (E-Benchmark) shown in **Table 1**. It is offered as a prescriptive approach, whereas the ASHRAE/IESNA Section 11 is performance based. A major difference between Option A and Option B is that the minimum equipment efficiency requirements in Option A are more stringent than the minimum requirements in Standard 90.1-2004. The minimum horsepower requirement for variable speed controls are also lower than in Standard 90.1-2004.

The E-Benchmark approach, which could encompass a new building HVAC system, may be used for smaller projects, so long as the project scope is adequate to apply the criteria. Criteria 2.4, which covers mechanical system design, has been abridged, dropping the requirement to meet ASHRAE Standard 55, covered in LEED for Commercial Interiors EQ Credit 7.1. The referenced Tables in Criteria 2.5 may be found on the New Buildings Institute, Inc. Web site at www.newbuildings.org.

Submittal Documentation

Complete the LEED for Commercial Interiors Submittal Template indicating that the Equipment Efficiency strategy has been employed and the requirements have been met. Provide a narrative description of the HVAC system serving the tenant space as well as a description of the building-level system, which may be the same one provided with EA Prerequisite 1. Include detail to confirm the extent that the design process outlined in Criteria 2.4 was followed. Include plans and specification to confirm the balance of the requirements.

Additional Documentation

For potential use during submittal review, it is suggested that the project team develop and maintain a schedule of the mechanical equipment used on its project with both the actual and E-Benchmark efficiency requirements. Assemble the manufacturer's information confirming the performance. Identify on the plan the location of the pumps and fans covered by the Criteria in 2.6. Assemble the manufacturer's information confirming the performance.

Exemplary Performance

There is no opportunity for Innovation in Design credit when using Option A of EA Credit 1.3.

Option A. Appropriate Zoning and Controls

Approach and Implementation

The second part of Option A is a prescriptive approach to the zoning and controls for commercial interior projects. For limited sized projects, it should still be readily attainable. The requirements need only apply to the extent of the project scope.

Advanced Buildings: Energy Benchmark for High Performance Buildings (E-Benchmark)

2.4 Mechanical System Design

The design engineer shall document the following actions in the design process:

1. When sizing the heating and cooling equipment, perform load calculations using interior load assumptions that are consistent with the *E-Benchmark*. This includes using the design interior lighting, accounting for the actual glazing characteristics, providing credit for displaced loads if displacement or underfloor systems are used, and base miscellaneous loads on field-verified measurements or field-based research rather than typical owner programming assumptions. Where not feasible, document the non-standard load assumptions for owner concurrence.

2. When sizing the fan and air distribution systems, document fan sizing calculations with zone-by-zone load calculations. Perform calculations to determine critical path supply duct pressure loss. Compare fitting selections for the critical branch to minimize fan horsepower requirements. Utilize round or oval duct wherever feasible to lower leakage and reduce pressure loss. Separate all fittings in medium and high-pressure duct work by several duct diameters to reduce system effects wherever feasible. Use relief fans in lieu of return fans where possible and provide automatic dampers on exhaust in lieu of barometric dampers to reduce fan power and increase barometric relief.

3. Perform a second set of calculations using part-load conditions (maximum likely load and/or standard operating conditions). This includes using benchmark data, average daytime temperatures and non-peak solar gain, and other assumptions to define part load conditions for the heating and cooling system. Include diversity factors for interior loads and other factors that will allow proper assessment of part-load operation.

4. Describe the system operation at these conditions and describe features of the design that will facilitate efficient operation at these part-load conditions.

2.5 Mechanical Equipment Efficiency Requirements

Mechanical equipment shall meet the following:

1. Package unitary equipment shall meet the minimum efficiency requirements in Tables 2.5.1 and 2.5.2 and be Energy Star labeled (where applicable).
2. Gas Unit Heaters shall include an intermittent ignition device and have either power venting or a flue damper.
3. Package Terminal Air Conditioners and Heat Pumps shall meet the minimum efficiency requirements in Table 2.5.3.
4. Boilers over 300,000 Btu/hr shall meet the minimum efficiency requirements in Table 2.5.4.
5. Electric chillers shall meet the energy efficiency requirements in Table 2.5.5.
6. Absorption chillers shall meet the minimum efficiency requirements in Table 2.5.6.
7. Equipment not listed shall meet Energy Star criteria where applicable.

2.6 Variable Speed Control

Individual pumps serving variable flow systems and VAV fans having a motor horsepower of 10 hp or larger shall have controls and/or devices (such as variable speed control) that will result in pump or fan motor demand of no more than 30% of design wattage at 50% of design flow.

The requirements above have Copyright protection and are reprinted here by permission from the New Buildings Institute, Inc. The above requirements are abridged. The full version of the publication, which includes the referenced tables, is available by following links found on the New Buildings Institute's web site, www.newbuildings.org, in a read only format.

Every solar exposure must have a separate control zone. The impetus for this requirement is to have the mechanical systems be an integral part of the architectural design. The primary energy conservation opportunity is to capture desired solar heat gain. However, it should not be done at the sacrifice of thermal comfort.

Each side of a rectangular building with fenestration should be zoned separately. Interior skylights are another source of solar exposure and may warrant a separate zone as well. Interior spaces must also be separately zoned. These requirements have avoided establishing design guidelines as to when an area must be zoned separately; no minimum window-to-floor area ratio, and no unit amount of solar gain or thermal loss are given. The project design team will need to evaluate the project particulars and provide reasonable justification for its zones and controls.

Interior spaces must be separately zoned. Again the criteria has not been made explicit, but because all sections of the requirement need to be satisfied, the project design team, as a point of practice, will need to evaluate the project particulars and provide as part of the submittal reasonable justification for its zones and controls.

Finally, private offices and specialty occupancies (conference rooms, kitchens, etc.) must have active controls capable of sensing space use and modulating HVAC systems in response to space demand. Occupancy sensors are a means to reducing energy consumption by modulating the supply of outdoor air. If the space temperature can be maintained in an unoccupied zone using less air volume than needed to meet the occupied minimum outdoor air rate, energy consumption is reduced. In smaller spaces this control approach can often be accomplished with occupancy sensors, potentially integral to those controlling lighting.

In larger spaces, demand control ventilation (DCV) is worth considering to avoid the conditioning of excess outdoor air.

In zones where occupancy density fluctuates from high to low, such as in a lecture hall or gymnasium, the need for outdoor air will also fluctuate. To avoid the conditioning of excess outdoor air, DCV systems sense the human occupancy and activity levels in a space and modulate the supply of outside air. This approach conserves energy. CO_2 levels rise with human occupancy and activity levels and CO_2 sensors have been found to be a reliable means of controlling DCV systems.

Submittal Documentation

Complete the LEED for Commercial Interiors Submittal Template indicating that the Equipment Efficiency strategy has been employed and the requirements have been met. Provide a narrative description of the HVAC system serving the tenant space as well as a description of the building-level system, which may be the same one to be provided with EA Prerequisite 1. In the narrative explain how the zones were determined, the control logic and the potential energy savings. A floor plan showing where the zones are located should accompany the narrative, along with a list of the type and function of the controls.

Additional Documentation

If the initial submittal is complete, no additional materials should be needed.

Exemplary Performance

There is no opportunity for Innovation in Design credit based on this portion of Option A of EA Credit 1.3.

Option B. Energy Reduction— Energy Cost Budget

Approach and Implementation

In this option to EA Credit 1.3, a comparison is made between the calculated annual energy bill to heat, ventilate and air condition the project area as designed, and the annual cost to do the same meeting the minimum ASHRAE 90.1-2004 standards. Only energy costs for space heating, space cooling and associated fans and pumps are considered; however, the performance of these systems is influenced by the performance of other building systems.

To determine the reduction in annual costs for the project area, the evaluation needs to consider the entire building area that is served by the HVAC plant serving the project area since the building design and the operations beyond the project space influence the design and operation of the HVAC plant.

The Energy Efficient Building

Project teams should make every effort to locate in an energy efficient building. In selecting a location, review the utility bills for energy and water use, ideally evaluating a three-year history. Clarify how utilities will be prorated in a multi-tenant building.

Landscaping protects the building from wind and provides shade, reducing the heat island effects of paving. Characteristically, buildings oriented along east-west axis obtain the most effective exterior shading.

Confirm that the building the project team selects is weather tight and meets code-minimum insulation levels.

Lighting comprises a major portion of a commercial building's energy budget. Efficient lighting in common areas, inside and out, reduces costs. Check to see that the owner has established lighting density standards for all tenant spaces.

Availability of natural light for daylighting and opportunities for natural ventilation are promising. Windows high on walls, clerestories and light shelves will maximize daylight penetration into a space. Light pipes or fiber-optic devices can be used to introduce daylight in less accessible spaces.

The existing HVAC system should be inspected. Discuss opportunities for specifying high efficiency HVAC equipment. When part of the project scope, specify high-performance chillers and boilers, with optimal part-load operation. Variable-speed chillers and boilers with modulating burners are such options. Specify high-efficiency motors for all applications and variable speed drives for fans, chillers and pumps.

Confirm that a building energy management system exists and is functional. If the project space is to be part of a larger building, determine when it is appropriate to have the building controls interface with the functions within the project area. A good energy management system will facilitate smooth building start-ups and shutdowns as well as optimize efficiency and occupant comfort.

Calculation

Overview

Option B of EA Credit 1.3 rewards the reduction of the annual cost for electricity and fuel to drive the HVAC system. A comparison is made of the results from two simulation models, one based on the actual design and a second, similar model based on meeting all applicable mandatory and prescriptive provisions of Standard 90.1–2004.

The standard has two energy comparison methods, both of which are appropriate for demonstrating energy cost savings to earn this credit. The Energy Cost Budget (ECB) Method, found in Section 11 of the standard, was developed to allow projects to trade-off energy performance between building systems so long as the calculated annual energy cost is no greater than that for the budget case. The second, the Performance Rating Method (PRM), found in Appendix G, is a modification of ECB that was developed to rate the energy efficiency of buildings relative to a baseline that represents more "typical" construction practices. The primary difference in the methods is identification of the budget or baseline HVAC system. Another important difference is that the ECB Method does not recognize energy-efficient design of air distribution systems; however, PRM does.

Both methods include all end-use load components, including exhaust fans, parking garage ventilation, snow-melt and freeze-protection equipment, façade lighting, swimming pool heaters and pumps, elevators and escalators, refrigeration and cooking. If an end-use does not affect trade-offs between systems, they can be excluded in the ECB. For the typical commercial interior projects, where the project space is only one of several tenants being served by a common HVAC system, the ECB method is adequate and more direct. PRM is recognized as being more rigorous and comprehensive, and is more appropriate for projects using unconventional HVAC systems.

In using the ASHRAE 90.1 method for Option B of EA Credit 1.3, modifications need to be made to the modeling requirements. This procedure is outlined in **Table 2**. The relationship of the energy end usage to the calculations is shown in **Table 3**, with the modifications to the ASHRAE/IESNA 90.1 modeling requirements listed in **Table 4**. The referenced sections and terminology in the tables and the following narrative is for the ECB method found in Section 11.

Select Modeler

The calculation will, in all likelihood, require computer simulation modeling. Section 11.2 and G2.2 detail the require-

ments and mention possible software. Project teams may find that their logical first step is to identify an individual or firm experienced with the energy modeling programs.

Determine Building Segment

The simulation generally will need to be done on more than just the project space. The building segment that is served by the common HVAC system serving the project area will need to be modeled. For example, if the project area takes up the third floor of a five story building, and the building has a single central plant, then the entire building will need to be modeled.

Select Modeling Method

Decide which of the two Standard 90.1-2004 modeling methods to use. When cost is a consideration, Section 11 Energy Cost Budget is less demanding. However, some host buildings may already have been modeled using Appendix G Performance Rating Method. You may have the good fortune to find the building owner has already completed much of the work; this probability goes up when locating in a LEED certified building.

Building Information

Short of having access to the earlier computer modeling run and report, the modeler, possibly with the assistance of the project mechanical engineer or architect, will need to review the as-built drawings of the building and scout the premises to determine the existing conditions for at least that segment of the building with which the project area shares a common central HVAC system. The existing building envelope is used for the entire building segment being modeled, including the project area. The existing conditions for operational schedules, lighting, HVAC systems and zones, and possibly service hot water systems will be needed for the balance of the building segment beyond the project area. Though not intended to be a com-

Table 2: Option B Procedure

| SS | WE | **EA** | MR | EQ | ID |

Credit 1.3

Activities

1 **Select Modeler.** Select qualified individual or firm to perform simulation model.

2 **Determine Building Segment.** When the HVAC system serves more than just the project area, the simulation model will need to cover at least that portion of the building being serviced by the common HVAC system.

3 **Select Modeling Method.** Either ECB (Section 11) or PRM (Appendix G) may be used; confirm that software program will satisfy needs.

4 **Building Information.** When the project area shares the central HVAC system with other portions of the building, the following information will be needed for that entire building segment served by the central HVAC system;
determine the HVAC zones for use in the thermal blocks calculations;
determine the plug loads of occupied area;
determine the occupancy types for occupied spaces;
follow unoccupied spaces follow Section 9.5.1 or 9.6.1.

5 **Model Design Case.** Using proposed Project Area HVAC and Lighting and existing conditions for balance of the building segment included in the simulation modeling, determine the Design Energy Cost (DEC); additional detail shown in Table 3.

6 **Model Baseline Case.** Use the requirements of ASHRAE/IESNA 90.1-2004, Section 11 or Appendix G, using the mandatory and prescriptive requirements for the project area; use the existing conditions for the balance of the building segment being modeled. See Table 4 for additional detail.

6a **Alternative Baseline Case.** This alternative is provided as a means to recognize those projects locating in a highly energy efficient building. Use the requirements of ASHRAE/IESNA 90.1-2004, Section 11 or Appendix G, using the mandatory and prescriptive requirements for both the project area and the balance of the building segment being modeled. See Table 4 for additional detail.

8 **Energy Reduction Calculation.** Use Equations Z to A to complete the credit calculations.

plete list, information should include the quantity of fenestration and its exposure, the thermal conductivity of all exterior walls, windows and doors, plus the type of HVAC system, and the size and efficiency of the components. For the occupied areas other than the project space, document the type of occupancy and operation schedule. Project the existing lighting and plug loads for these areas as well.

Model Design Case

For the project area, use the existing building envelope. However, use the project design for heating, cooling, fans and pump, lighting and plug loads and,

if needed, service water heating. Any modifications to the HVAC central plant being made in conjunction with the project should be included in the design case. These changes do not have to be physically within the demise of the project area. Also, the changes do not have to be part of the project's contractual scope of work if they are being done for the project occupants' benefit. Including these changes should improve the performance being measured under this credit.

If the project has attained SS Credit 1 Option J and/or WE Credit 1, the design case may reflect the reduced volumes of

Table 3: Energy End Uses and how they are used in EA Credit 1.3 Option B Modeling Calculation when ASHRAE/IESNA 90.1-2004 Section 11 is used.

Energy End Uses	Design Case Design Energy Cost DEC	Baseline Case Energy Cost Budget ECB
Heating	Needed to model DEC Used in Option 2 calculation	Needed to model ECB Used in Option 2 calculation
Cooling	Needed to model DEC Used in Option 2 calculation	Needed to model ECB Used in Option 2 calculation
Fans / Pumps	Needed to model DEC Used in Option 2 calculation	Needed to model ECB Used in Option 2 calculation
Lighting	Needed to model DEC But Costs are Not Included	Needed to model ECB But Costs are Not Included
Plug and Process Loads	Needed to model DEC But Costs are Not Included	Needed to model ECB But Costs are Not Included
Service Water Heating	May be used to model DEC But Costs are Not Included	May be used to model ECB But Costs are Not Included
Miscellaneous Loads	Not required	Not required

water for service hot water systems. The HVAC energy costs should not include the energy costs associated with service hot water systems.

For the balance of the building segment being modeled, use the existing conditions. Together, these will generate the Design Energy Cost, or DEC. Follow Section 11 or Appendix G and the additional information in **Table 4**.

Model Baseline Case

The objective of the baseline case is to provide a means to determine the reduction in the annual energy consumption resulting from the design of the project. This objective is accomplished by replacing the design conditions of the project area with the standard's mandatory and prescriptive requirements.

For lighting, either the Building Area Method in Section 9.5 or the Space-by-Space Method in Section 9.6 may be used.

For the baseline HVAC model, where no revisions were made in the central plant,

change only those items within the project area to the mandatory and prescriptive requirements of the standard. Follow the requirements outlined in Table 11.3.1 of section 11 or Table G.3.1 in Appendix G of the standard, and the additional notes in **Table 4**. For the balance of the building segment, model it using the same existing building conditions used in the design case.

When there have been modifications to the central plant that are included in the design case modeling, replace them in the baseline case with the mandatory and prescriptive equivalent. For example, if pumps were replaced with efficiencies higher than required, use the required equivalent in the baseline model. When extensive HVAC revisions have been made, follow the procedure outlined in Section 11 or Appendix G, using Figure 11.3.2 or Table G3.1.1 to determine the budget building design criteria. If using Section 11, the baseline budget building condenser cooling source may be defined as air regardless of the proposed design, if the changed cooling equipment has

Table 4: Option B Procedure

SS | WE | **EA** | MR | EQ | ID

Credit 1.3

ASHRAE/IENSA 90.1 Section	Design Energy Cost Model DEC	Energy Cost Budget Model ECB
1. Design Model	Follow Table 11.3.1, using the proposed design of the project space, and the existing conditions for the balance of the modeled building segment, as field verified (step 4 in the procedure) for the design case.	Baseline Case: Follow Table 11.3.1, using the mandatory and prescriptive requirements for the project space, but use the existing conditions for the balance of the modeled building segment. Alternative Baseline Case: Follow Table 11.3.1, using the mandatory and prescriptive requirements for both the project space and the balance of the modeled building segment.
2. Additions and Alterations	Follow Table 11.3.1. See (b) concerning the exclusion of HVAC systems not part of the modeled building segment.	Follow Table 11.3.1.
3. Space Use Classification	Follow Table 11.3.1.	Follow Table 11.3.1
4. Schedules	Follow Table 11.3.1 when field verification can not be attained.	Use the same schedule for DEC, ECB and A-ECB.
5. Building Envelope	Follow Table 11.3.1, using the proposed design of the project space, and the existing envelope conditions for the balance of the modeled building segment, as field verified (step 4 in the procedure) for the design case.	Baseline Case: Follow Table 11.3.1, using the proposed design of the project space, and the existing envelope conditions for the balance of the modeled building segment. Alternative Baseline Case: Follow Table 11.3.1, using the mandatory and prescriptive requirements, as described, for the baseline case.
6. Lighting	Follow Table 11.3.1, using the proposed design of the project space, and the field verified lighting for the balance of the modeled building segment.	Baseline Case: For the project space, use either 9.5 or 9.6; for the balance of the modeled building segment, use the same values used in the DEC model. Alternative Baseline Case: For both the project space and the balance of the modeled building segment, use either 9.5 or 9.6.
7, 8, 9. Thermal Blocks	Follow Table 11.3.1.	Same as DEC model.
10. HVAC Systems	Follow Table 11.3.1, using the proposed design of the project space, and the field verified HVAC system information of the central plant when existing.	Follow Table 11.3.1, which references Figure 11.3.2, Table 11.3.2A.
11. Service Hot Water Systems	Follow Table 11.3.1. If the project space has attained WE Credit 1, the model may reflect the reduced volumes. If the building has attained SS Credit 1 Option J, the model may reflect the reduced volumes.	Follow Table 11.3.1.
12. Miscellaneous Loads	Follow Table 11.3.1. If the project space anticipates attaining EA Credit 1.4, the DEC may use a lower value reflecting the actual plug load planned for the project area. In the balance of the modeled building segment, use the field verified plug load (step 4 in the procedure). End-uses excluded in Section 13 and 14 of Table 11.3.1 may be exclude; these include exhaust fans, parking garage ventilation fans, exterior building lighting, swimming pool heaters and pumps, elevators and escalators, refrigeration equipment and cooking equipment.	Project Space: Follow Table 11.3.1. If the project space anticipates attaining EA Credit 1.4, the ECB shall use a higher plug load value reflecting the occupancy type. If EA Credit 1.4 is not being pursued, use the same plug value in both the DEC and ECB. Balance of the modeled building segment: ECB: Use existing plug load values; A-ECB: Use a higher plug load value reflecting the occupancy type. Both ECB and A-ECB: End-uses excluded in Section 13 and 14 of Table 11.3.1 may be exclude.

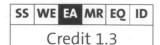
less than 150 tons of cooling capacity. This exception is made to encourage the specification of more efficient water-based cooling systems over air-based cooling systems in smaller equipment sizes. Document the choices made in the narrative included with the submittal.

Alternative Baseline Case

In the above method, the differential between the DEC and ECB increases as the energy efficiency of the existing building decreases. It could be easier to reach the credit thresholds in a less-efficient building. So as not to penalize those project teams that have wisely located in a highly energy efficient building—maybe one already LEED certified—an alternative baseline method is provided.

If the existing conditions are more energy efficient than the prescriptive requirements of Standard 90.1-2004, replace the existing conditions in the baseline model with the Standard 90.1-2004 requirements. Project teams can base their credit calculations on either baseline. Document the choice made in the narrative included with the submittal; if results for both baselines were generated, consider sharing them.

Energy Reduction Calculation

Because of the two Baseline Cases, there are two Energy Reduction Calculations. The reduction using the Model Baseline Case uses Standard 90.1-2004 mandatory and prescriptive requirements in the project area and existing conditions in the balance of the modeled building segment as shown in **Equation 1**. It corrects for the area relationship between the project space and the modeled building segment.

The reduction using the Alternative Baseline, potentially more generous in cases where the building is highly efficient, is shown in **Equation 2** No adjustment is made for the project-to-building segment area because the calculation is evaluating the overall performance of the HVAC system. **Table 5** shows the component HVAC annual energy use and costs.

Submittal Documentation

Complete the LEED for Commercial Interiors Submittal Template stating that the component performance criteria used for the tenant space is either 15% or 30% better than a system that is in minimum compliance with Standard 90.1-2004,

Equation 1: Percent Annual HVAC Energy Cost Reduction
Baseline: Project Area - AHRAE/IESNA 90.1 mandatory and prescriptive requirements
Balance of Modeled Building Segment - Existing Conditions

Percent Annual HVAC Energy Cost Reduction
Baseline: Project Area - AHRAE/IENSA 90.1 mandatory and prescriptive requirements
Balance of Modeled Building Segment - Existing Conditions

$$Reduction = \frac{(ECB_{HVAC} - DEC_{HVAC})}{(ECB_{HVAC}) \times (Project\ Area\ /\ Total\ Segment\ Area)}$$

Equation 2: Percent Annual HVAC Energy Cost Reduction
Baseline: Both Project Area and Balance of Modeled Building Segment - AHRAE/IESNA 90.1 mandatory and prescriptive requirements

Percent Annual HVAC Energy Cost Reduction
Alternate Baseline: Both Project Area and Balance of Modeled Building Segment - AHRAE/IENSA 90.1 mandatory and prescriptive requirements

$$Reduction = \frac{(A\text{-}ECB_{HVAC} - DEC_{HVAC})}{A\text{-}ECB_{HVAC}}$$

Section 11 or Appendix G. Indicate when the Alternative Baseline was used and whether Section 11 or Appendix G was followed. Complete the simplified summary table similar to **Table 4** included with the Submittal Templates, and submit a completed copy of the Energy Cost Budget Compliance Form. The ECB form can be used for the Performance Rating Method as well. Complete the form making the final calculation in dollars.

Include a narrative describing the HVAC system serving the project area as well as a description of the building-level system. Include a plan and specifications of the equipment.

Additional Documentation

If the initial submittal is complete, no additional materials should be needed.

Exemplary Performance

Project teams may earn an Innovation in Design point for exemplary performance when the requirements reach the next incremental step. For EA Credit 1.3 Option B, the credit calculation must be 45% or greater.

Considerations

Energy efficiency reduces the harmful environmental side effects of energy

Table 5: EA 1.3 Option B HVAC Energy Cost Reduction—Energy Cost Model

HVAC Energy Uses Design Case	Energy Type	Electric [kWh]	Gas [CCF]	Energy Use [10^3 Btu]	Annual Cost [$]
Space Heating	Natural Gas		4,550	455,000	$3,223
Space Cooling	Electric	240,300		819,904	$16,800
Fans/Pumps	Electric	120,150		409,952	$8,400
			Design Energy Cost HVAC [DEC$_{HVAC}$]		$28,421
Baseline Case Project Area - Code Balance - Existing Conditions					
Space Heating	Natural Gas		4,575	457,500	$3,239
Space Cooling	Electric	270,000		921,240	$18,876
Fans/Pumps	Electric	122,000		416,264	$8,529
			Baseline Energy Cost Budget HVAC [ECB$_{HVAC}$]		$30,645

Reduction = (ECB$_{HVAC}$ — DEC$_{HVAC}$) / ((ECB$_{HVAC}$) x (Project Area / Total Segment Area))
Reduction = [$30,645— $28,421] / [$30,645 x [20,000 ft^2 / 100,000 ft^2]]
Reduction = 36.3%
36.3% > 30% 2 Points Earned

Alternate Baseline Project Area - Code Balance - Code					
Space Heating	Natural Gas		5,200	520,000	$3,682
Space Cooling	Electric	295,000		1,006,540	$20,624
Fans/Pumps	Electric	135,000		460,620	$9438
			Alternate Baseline Energy Cost Budget HVAC [A-ECB$_{HVAC}$]		$33,744

Reduction = (A-ECB$_{HVAC}$ — DEC$_{HVAC}$) / A-ECB$_{HVAC}$
Reduction = [$33,744 — $28,421] / $33,744
Reduction = 15.8%
15.8% > 15% 1 Point Earned

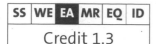
production and use. Institution of energy-efficiency measures can be done at no cost to occupant comfort or building services. Many energy-efficiency measures result in a more comfortable indoor environment while reducing operating and first costs. Even small energy savings have incremental effects on the environment and cost savings.

Environmental Issues

Conventional forms of energy production have devastating environmental effects. Production of electricity from fossil fuels creates air and water pollution; hydroelectric generation plants can make waterways uninhabitable for indigenous fish; and nuclear power has safety concerns as well as problems with disposal of spent fuel. Refer to the Introduction of the Energy & Atmosphere section for more information.

Economic Issues

Many energy-efficiency measures do not require additional first costs. Those measures that do result in higher first costs often create savings realized from lower energy use over the building lifetime, downsized equipment, reduced mechanical space needs and utility rebates. These savings can dwarf the increased first costs. Payback periods for many off-the-shelf energy efficiency measures are generally short.

The importance of even small energy-efficiency measures is significant. For instance, by replacing one incandescent lamp with a fluorescent lamp, production of three-quarters of a ton of carbon dioxide and 15 pounds of sulfur dioxide are avoided over the lifetime of the lamp. This substitution also saves $30-$50 in energy costs over the operating lifetime of the lamp.

Community Issues

Energy-efficiency measures result in a more pleasant indoor environment and can increase worker productivity. For-

ward-thinking businesses are now actively leveraging their facilities as a strategic tool to attract and retain employees. Energy-efficiency measures result in lower and more stable energy prices. Reduced energy use also results in less global-warming potential, limits the impact of natural resource extraction activitie, and prevents water pollution, benefiting everyone.

Resources

Please see USGBC Web site at www.usgbc.org/resources for more specific resources on materials sources and other technical information.

Web Sites

DOE2

www.doe2.com

A comprehensive energy analysis program used to predict hourly performance of a building's energy use and utility costs.

ENERGY STAR®

www.energystar.gov

(888) 782-7937

ENERGY STAR® is a government/industry partnership managed by the U.S. Environmental Protection Agency and the U.S. Department of Energy. The program's Web site offers energy management strategies, benchmarking software tools for buildings, product procurement guidelines and lists of ENERGY STAR®-labeled products and buildings.

National Renewable Energy Program (NREL) Energy-10

www.nrel.gov/buildings/energy10

(303) 275-3000

ENERGY-10 is an award-winning software tool for designing low-energy buildings. ENERGY-10 integrates daylighting, passive solar heating, and low-energy cooling strategies with energy-efficient shell design and mechanical equipment. The program is applicable to commercial and residential buildings of 10,000 square feet or less.

Building Energy Codes Program

U.S. Department of Energy

www.energycodes.gov

(800) DIAL-DOE

The Building Energy Codes program provides comprehensive resources for states and code users, including code comparisons, compliance software, news and the Status of State Energy Codes database. The database includes state energy contacts, code status, code history, DOE grants awarded and construction data.

Office of Energy Efficiency and Renewable Energy

U.S. Department of Energy

www.eere.energy.gov/EE/buildings.html

(877) 337-3463

This extensive Web site for energy efficiency is linked to a number of DOE-funded sites that address buildings and energy. Of particular interest is the tools directory that includes the Commercial Buildings Energy Consumption Tool for estimating end-use consumption in commercial buildings. The tool allows the user to define a set of buildings by principal activity, size, vintage, region, climate zone and fuels (main heat, secondary heat, cooling and water heating), and to view the resulting energy consumption and expenditure estimates in tabular format.

Print Media

ASHRAE Standard 90.1–1999 User's Manual, ASHRAE, 1999.

The new 90.1–1999 User's Manual was developed as a companion document to the ASHRAE/IESNA Standard 90.1–1999 (Energy Standard for Buildings Except Low-Rise Residential Buildings). The User's Manual explains the new standard and includes sample calculations, useful reference material, and information on the intent and application of the standard.

Similar to the 1989 User's Manual, this updated manual is abundantly illustrated and contains numerous examples and tables of reference data. The manual also includes a complete set of compliance forms and worksheets that can be used to document compliance with the standard. The User's Manual is helpful to architects and engineers who must apply the standard to the design of the buildings, plan examiners and field inspectors who must enforce the standard in areas where it is adopted as code, and contractors who must construct buildings in compliance with the standard. A compact disc accompanies the User's Manual and contains the EnvStd 4.0 Computer Program for performing building envelope trade-offs plus electronic versions of the compliance forms found in the User's Manual.

IESNA Lighting Handbook (Ninth Edition), IESNA, 2000.

Mechanical and Electrical Systems for Buildings, 4th Edition, by Benjamin Stein and John S. Reynolds, John Wiley & Sons, 1992.

Sustainable Building Technical Manual, Public Technology, Inc., 1996 (www. pti.org).

Advanced Buildings: Energy Benchmark for High Performance Buildings (E-Benchmark)

2.4 Mechanical System Design

The design engineer shall document the following actions in the design process:

When sizing the heating and cooling equipment, perform load calculations using interior load assumptions that are consistent with the E-Benchmark. This includes using the design interior lighting, accounting for the actual glazing characteristics, providing credit for displaced loads if displacement or underfloor systems are used, and base miscellaneous loads on field-verified measurements or field-based research rather than typical owner programming assumptions. Where not feasible, document the non-standard load assumptions for owner concurrence.

When sizing the fan and air distribution systems, document fan sizing calculations with zone-by-zone load calculations. Perform calculations to determine critical path supply duct pressure loss. Compare fitting selections for the critical branch to minimize fan horsepower requirements. Utilize round or oval duct wherever feasible to lower leakage and reduce pressure loss. Separate all fittings in medium and high-pressure duct work by several duct diameters to reduce system effects wherever feasible. Use relief fans in lieu of return fans where possible and provide automatic dampers on exhaust in lieu of barometric dampers to reduce fan power and increase barometric relief.

Perform a second set of calculations using part-load conditions (maximum likely load and/or standard operating conditions). This includes using benchmark data, average day-time temperatures and non-peak solar gain, and other assumptions to define part load conditions for the heating and cooling system. Include diversity factors for interior loads and other factors that will allow proper assessment of part-load operation.

Describe the system operation at these conditions and describe features of the design that will facilitate efficient operation at these part-load conditions.

2.5 Mechanical Equipment Efficiency Requirements

Mechanical equipment shall meet the following:

Package unitary equipment shall meet the minimum efficiency requirements in Tables 2.5.1 and 2.5.2 and be ENERGY STAR® labeled (where applicable).

Gas Unit Heaters shall include an intermittent ignition device and have either power venting or a flue damper.

Package Terminal Air Conditioners and Heat Pumps shall meet the minimum efficiency requirements in Table 2.5.3.

Boilers over 300,000 Btu/hr shall meet the minimum efficiency requirements in Table 2.5.4.

Electric chillers shall meet the energy efficiency requirements in Table 2.5.5.

Absorption chillers shall meet the minimum efficiency requirements in Table 2.5.6.

Equipment not listed shall meet ENERGY STAR® criteria where applicable.

2.6 Variable Speed Control

Individual pumps serving variable flow systems and VAV fans having a motor horsepower of 10 hp or larger shall have controls and/or devices (such as variable speed control) that will result in pump or fan motor demand of no more than 30% of design wattage at 50% of design flow.

Optimize Energy Performance
Equipment & Appliances

Intent

Achieve increasing levels of energy conservation beyond the prerequisite standard to reduce environmental impacts associated with excessive energy use.

Requirements

For all ENERGY STAR® eligible equipment and appliances installed in the project, including appliances, office equipment, electronics and commercial food service equipment (but excluding HVAC, lighting and building envelope products)

- 70%, by rated-power, of ENERGY STAR® eligible equipment and appliances shall be ENERGY STAR® rated (1 point);

OR

- 90%, by rated-power, of ENERGY STAR® eligible equipment and appliances shall be ENERGY STAR® rated (2 points).

Submittals

Provide the LEED for Commercial Interiors Submittal Template, signed by the responsible party, declaring that ENERGY STAR® eligible equipment and appliances are ENERGY STAR® rated and yield the indicated percentage of the total, determined by rated power.

Provide a narrative describing the equipment and appliances that will be installed in the project. Complete the schedule of equipment listing the types and quantity of equipment and appliances to be installed in the project along with the rated power (or rated fuel input for commercial cooking equipment) of each type of ENERGY STAR® eligible equipment and appliance. Indicate which equipment and appliances are ENERGY STAR® rated. Indicate the overall percentage of equipment and appliances, based on rated electrical power (as well as rated fuel input for commercial cooking equipment), that is ENERGY STAR® rated.

Potential Technologies & Strategies

Select energy efficient equipment and appliances, as qualified by the EPA's ENERGY STAR® Program (www.energystar.gov).

Credit Interpretation Rulings

In LEED for Commercial Interiors, EA Credit 1.4 addresses only the energy performance of ENERGY STAR® listed appliances and equipment. Dissimilar approaches of demonstrating energy performance are used in other LEED rating systems. Therefore, only LEED for Commercial Interiors CIRs apply to this credit.

Approach and Implementation

The credit applies to all installed equipment and appliances listed in the ENERGY STAR® program. **Table 1**, which is similar to the calculator included in the LEED for Commercial Interiors Submittal Templates, lists those categories recognized at the time of this publication. Future additional categories added to the ENERGY STAR® program may be included in your calculation. Review the ENERGY STAR® Web site for the categories. Consult the LEED for Commercial Interiors CIRs for this credit to obtain the rated power to be used in the calculation.

All appliances and equipment installed at the time of occupancy must be included in the submittal.

Table 1: EA Credit 1.4 Calculator

Energy Star Equipment	Rated Power [watts]	Total Number in Project	Number of Energy Star	Total Power in Project [watts]	Power that is Energy Star [watts]
Desktop Computer	120	10	8	1200	960
Notebook Computer	45	20	16	900	720
Display (CRT) 15"	100			0	0
Display (CRT) 17"	200	2	1	400	200
Display (CRT) 21"	300			0	0
Display (LCD) 15"	45	2	2	90	90
Display (LCD) 17"	75	6	4	450	300
Display (LCD) 21"	120			0	0
				0	0
Desktop Laser Printer	120	1	0	120	0
Office Laser Printer	250	2	1	500	250
Desktop copier	225			0	0
Office copier	750	1	1	750	750
				0	0
Fax Machine	45	1	1	45	45
Scanner	45			0	0
				0	0
Refrigerator	750	1	1	750	750
Dishwasher	1200	1	1	1200	1200
Televisions	100			0	0
				0	0
Commercial Refrigerator/Freezer	1000			0	0
Commercial Fryer	10000			0	0
Commercial Hot Food Holding Cabinet	1500			0	0
Commercial Steam Cooker	8000			0	0
				0	0
Clothes washer	350			0	0
Clothes dryer	2000			0	0
TOTALS				6405	5265

Percent Energy Star	82.2%

Sources:
Energy Star Website (www.energystar.gov)
DOE Energy Information Portal (http://www.eere.energy.gov/)
Lawrence Berkeley National Laboratory Website and Reports (http://enduse.lbl.gov/ESTAR.html)

Note: The values in this table represent average rated power figures for equipment based on a variety of government information sources. The values are applicable only for weighting the LEED calculation based on relative power draws of different equipment and are not meant to be accurate estimates of actual power in use.

Upgraded Replacements

As an incentive to upgrade to more efficient equipment, items replaced with new ENERGY STAR® equipment in a different category and a lower rated power, may use the higher rated power value corresponding to the category of the replaced item in the credit calculation. For example, if a desktop computer is replaced with a new ENERGY STAR® notebook computer, 120 watts for the desktop computer may be used as the rated power in place of 45 watts for the notebook computer. Similarly, when a CRT display unit is replaced with a new, more efficient ENERGY STAR® LCD display unit, the higher rated power value of the CRT display may be used in the credit calculation. To qualify, the replacement must occur between the time of project registration and the submittal of certification documentation.

Calculations

This credit is achieved by using ENERGY STAR® equipment and appliances in the project such that 70% (1 point) or 90% (2 points) of the power demand of all eligible equipment is attributable to ENERGY STAR® equipment. The calculation is based on power demand, instead of the number of appliances/equipment, to normalize the anticipated energy savings to the consumption of each item.

Table 1 replicates the calculator that is used on the LEED for Commercial Interiors Submittal Template for this credit. Use the following calculations to determine percentage achievements:

1. For each piece of equipment or appliance in **Table 1** above, count the number present in the project and enter it in column 3 ("Total Number in Project"). Indicate how many of each equipment type are ENERGY STAR® products, and enter that number in column 4 ("Number of ENERGY STAR®").

Note that an upgraded replacement will need to be shown in the row of the item it has replaced to benefit from the higher rated power value of the category of the replaced item.

2. Multiply the total numbers and the ENERGY STAR® numbers by the default power values in column 2 to calculate the total rated power installed and the total rated power that is attributable to ENERGY STAR® equipment.

3. Divide the "Power that is ENERGY STAR®" by the "Total Power" to determine the percent achievement for this credit. 70% or greater achieves 1 point and 90% or greater achieves 2 points.

Please note that the rated power of a piece of equipment is the maximum power it can draw under any conditions. The actual power used by office equipment and appliances is often less than half the rated power (See **Table 4** below). The actual power varies significantly based on factors such as –

- Frequency of use
- Number of simultaneous function
- Screen resolution (for monitors)
- Sleep mode

The default power values used in this credit are not intended to be accurate estimates of the actual power draw of the equipment. Rather, the values are intended to weight the calculation based on the contribution of each piece of equipment or appliance to the overall plug load of the building. For example, if a small office has 20 computers and one refrigerator and purchases ENERGY STAR® models for all computers but a non-rated refrigerator, the office is using ENERGY STAR® equipment for over 90% of the products but only approximately 75% of the power use.

Submittal Documentation

Complete the LEED for Commercial Interiors Submittal Template, confirming that the installed equipment meets the requirements of the credit. Complete the calculation demonstrating compliance.

When new ENERGY STAR® equipment with a lower rated power has been purchased as part of the project to replace existing equipment, provide a narrative documenting the calculation and timing of the replacement.

Additional Documentation

For potential use during submittal review, it is suggested that the project team retain confirming information on the appliances and equipment installed. The documentation will need to confirm that the manufacturer and model are ENERGY STAR® listed; the information may be obtained from the ENERGY STAR® Web site or the manufacturer.

Exemplary Performance

No established threshold is recognized for exemplary performance for EA Credit 1.4.

Considerations

According to the 1999 Energy Information Agency's (EIA) Commercial Building Energy Consumption Survey (CBECS), plug loads account for 21 percent of total commercial building energy consumption, and 29 percent of total electrical consumption. The percentages vary depending on building type, ranging between eight and 60 percent of the total building energy consumption. Due to the magnitude of plug loads in certain building types, encouraging their reduction is very important.

On the other hand, plug loads are hard to regulate. Very little comprehensive data is available for specific types of occupancy, and the data that is available generally shows that end-use consumption is quite variable – both across building types and within building types. ANSI/ASHRAE/IESNA 90.1-2004, addresses it in a limited degree through the Performance Rating Method of Appendix G.

Establishing a concrete metric—such as watts per square foot—or comparing plug loads is problematic. The range of values will vary by occupancy type and within

Table 2: Annual Process Energy Consumption per Square Foot by End Use

Sector	Sector's Percent of Total Building Stock	Total Energy Consumption Regulated + Process [kBtu/SF-yr]	Process Energy Consumption [kBtu/SF-yr]	Office Equipment Portion of Process Consumption [kBtu/SF-yr]	Office Equipment Energy Consumption as Percent of Total
Office	25.9	81.76	17.48	12.65	15.5%
Education	8.5	72.92	4.66	1.21	1.7%
Food Sales[1]	4.6	195.8	114.11	1.05	0.5%
Food Services[2]	6.4	187.76	91.27	1.1	0.6%
Health Care	8.1	261.33	62.04	14.85	5.7%
Laboratory		186.85	55.91	25.21	13.5%

Source: EIA, CBECS 1995. (Note: percentages will not sum to 100 because not all building types are included in table)
[1] Values for facilities over 30,000 SF.
[2] Values are average for "Sit-down" and "Fast-food" establishments; process load per square-foot is greater the smaller the seating area.

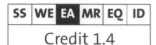
that type. Differing occupant densities and work schedules cause wide variations. A few people in a big space with the least efficient computers will show to use fewer watts per square foot than another office where power management is implemented on laptops and LCD displays. Similarly, fast food restaurants where there is little or no sit-down dining do not favor well when area is included in an evaluation. Here, Btu per meal may be a more reliable metric. In retail stores, sales volume or the number of clients served potentially has a better correlation to process load. The differences from one manufacturing setting to another, from one laboratory to another, points up the challenge.

Using ENERGY STAR® listed products is the most straightforward means of addressing most of the inconsistencies.

While **Table 2** shows how the values vary by occupancy type, it also gives justification to address the plug load of office equipment within offices. **Table 3** provides a comparison of the regulated loads within offices to the unregulated process loads. **Table 4** shows that the rated power of equipment is considerably higher than the actual power draw.

Resources

Please see USGBC Web site at www.usgbc.org/resources for more specific resources on materials sources and other technical information.

Print Media

Electricity Used by Office Equipment and Network Equipment in the U.S.: Detailed Report and Appendices, Kawamoto, et al, February 2001, Ernest Orlando Lawrence Berkeley National Laboratory, University of California, Berkeley, CA 94720; download at http://enduse.lbl.gov/Projects/InfoTech.html and http://eetd.lbl.gov/BEA/SF/GuideR.pdf

Energy Information Agency's (EIA) Commercial Building Energy Consumption Survey (CBECS); www.eia.doe.gov

Table 3: Office Loads

Load	kBtu SF-yr	Watts SF
Heating	11.40	0.38
Cooling	7.46	0.25
Ventilation	3.63	0.12
Water heating	1.87	0.06
Lighting	22.15	0.74
Regulated Subtotal	46.51	1.56
Cooking	1.01	0.03
Refrigeration	0.37	0.01
Office Equipment	12.65	0.42
Misc.	3.45	0.12
Process Subtotal	17.48	0.59

Source: EIA, CBECS 1995.

Table 4: Comparison of Actual to Rated Power Draw

Equipment Type	Actual power draw (as a % of rated power draw)	Source
PCs	25 – 50%	Norford et al., 1989
Impact and Inkjet Printers	20 – 25%	
Computer network equipment	30%	Kunz, 1997
Computers	14 – 33%	Komor, 1997
Monitors	~28 – 85%	
Printers	~9 - 32%	
PCs	5 – 35%	Hosni, Jones, and Xu, 1999
Facsimile Machine	20 – 45%	
Network Server	50%	
Monitor	15 – 36%	

U.S. Green Building Council

Definitions

Plug Load refers to all equipment that is plugged into the electrical system, from office equipment to refrigerators.

Rated Power is the nameplate power on a piece of equipment. It represents the capacity of the unit and is the maximum a unit will draw.

SS | WE | **EA** | MR | EQ | ID
Credit 1.4

Enhanced Commissioning

Intent

Verify and ensure that the tenant space is designed, constructed and calibrated to operate as intended.

Requirements

In addition to the Fundamental Commissioning prerequisite, implement or have a contract in place to implement the following additional commissioning process activities:

1. Designate an individual as the Commissioning Authority, independent of the firms represented on the design and construction team, to lead the commissioning design review activities prior to the end of Design Development.

2. Conduct a review of the tenant space's energy related systems contractor submittals.

3. Develop a single manual that contains the information required for re-commissioning the tenant space's energy related systems.

4. Verify that the requirements for training operating personnel and tenant space occupants are completed. Have a contract in place to review tenant space operation with O&M staff and occupants including a plan for resolution of outstanding commissioning-related issues eight to 10 months after final acceptance.

Submittals

Provide the LEED for Commercial Interiors Submittal Template, signed by the owner and independent Commissioning Authority, confirming that the required enhanced commissioning process requirements 1 and 2 have been successfully executed and that a contract for completing requirements 3 and 4 is in place.

Potential Technologies & Strategies

Engage a Commissioning Authority that is an independent third party. In addition to the strategies discussed in EA Prerequisite 1, Fundamental Commissioning, the Commissioning Authority must review the design of all energy-related systems prior to the completion of design development. The Commissioning Authority is also responsible for a review of contractor submittals for all energy-related systems and for the development or review of a re-commissioning plan for the energy-related systems.

SS	WE	**EA**	MR	EQ	ID

Credit 2

Enhanced Commissioning

Please find the information concerning this credit under EA Prerequisite 1, Fundamental Commissioning. Presentation of the two sections together provides a clearer understanding of how the requirements of the prerequisite and this credit relate over the scope of a commercial interior project.

Energy Use
Measurement & Payment Accountability

Intent

Provide for the ongoing accountability and optimization of tenant energy and water consumption performance over time.

Requirements

CASE A: For those projects with an area that constitute less than 75% of the total building area:

- Install sub-metering equipment to measure and record energy uses within the tenant space. (1 point)

- Negotiate a lease where energy costs are paid by the tenant and not included in the base rent. (1 point)

OR

CASE B: For those projects with an area that constitutes 75% or more of the total building area (2 points):

- Install continuous metering equipment for the following end-uses:
  - Lighting systems and controls
  - Constant and variable motor loads
  - Variable frequency drive (VFD) operation
  - Chiller efficiency at variable loads (kW/ton)
  - Cooling load
  - Air and water economizer and heat recovery cycles
  - Air distribution static pressures and ventilation air volumes
  - Boiler efficiencies
  - Building-related process energy systems and equipment
  - Indoor water riser and outdoor irrigation systems

- Develop a Measurement and Verification plan that incorporates the monitoring information from the above end-uses and is consistent with Option B, C or D of the 2001 *International Performance Measurement & Verification Protocol (IPMVP) Volume I: Concepts and Options for Determining Energy and Water Savings*.

Submittals

For projects with an area that constitutes less than 75% of the total building area, provide the LEED for Commercial Interiors Submittal Template, signed by a licensed engineer or other responsible party, describing the metering equipment installed for each end use, and/or indicating that energy costs are paid by the tenant and not included in the base rent, which must be confirmed by providing a copy of the applicable portion of the lease.

OR

For projects with an area that constitutes 75% or more of the total building area, provide the LEED for Commercial Interiors Submittal Template, signed by a licensed engineer or other responsible party, indicating that metering equipment has been installed for each end-use and declaring the option to be followed under IPMVP, 2001 version, plus provide a copy of the M&V plan following IPMVP, 2001 version, including an executive summary.

Potential Technologies & Strategies

For projects with an area that constitutes less than 75% of the total building area, tenant space is sub-metered and has a direct pay clause in their lease for energy actually used instead of on a square foot basis. For projects with an area that constitutes 75% or more of the total building area, model the energy and water systems to predict savings. Design the project with equipment to measure energy and water performance. Draft a Measurement & Verification Plan to apply during building operation that compares predicted savings to those actually achieved in the field.

Summary of Referenced Standard

International Performance Measurement and Verification Protocol Volume 1, 2001 Version

www.ipmvp.org

The IPMVP presents best practice techniques available for verifying savings produced by energy- and water-efficiency projects. While the emphasis is on a methodology geared toward performance contracting for retrofits, the protocol identifies the required steps for new building design in Section 6.0. Section 3.0 provides a general approach, procedures and issues, while Section 4.0 provides guidance on retrofit projects.

Credit Interpretation Rulings

In LEED for Commercial Interiors, EA Credit 3 provides two compliance paths, one for project areas that constitute less than 75% of the building area, and a second for those 75% or more. In reviewing Credit Interpretation Rulings, confirm that the ruling applies to your project situation. The second compliance path, which involves the installation of continuous metering equipment and the development of a measurement and verification plan, should review LEED for New Construction v2.1 EA Credit 5 CIRs.

Credit Interpretation Rulings concerning this credit are applicable to LEED for Commercial Interiors projects.

Approach and Implementation

The two compliance paths differ in terms of the relative proportion of the project area to the total building area. While the split at 75% may seem arbitrary, during the LEED for Commercial Interiors pilot it was found that only one of the first 57 projects fell in a band between 60% and 80%. With this history in hand, it was decided that those 75% or above will need to do more than merely get their utilities connected to satisfy the intent.

Projects Less Than 75% of the Total Building Area

The objective of the requirements is to encourage efficient operation of leased spaces through measurement and the accountability associated with paying for what is used.

Sub-metering

Sub-metering is simply metering a utility for a designated portion of a building. In a commercial office building that has a master electric meter, sub-meters on individual tenants permit them to know their actual consumption. For electrical service, the equipment and installation of sub-meters is not a major expense. In tests of commercial and residential situations, paying based on sub-metered use has resulted in conservation.

To satisfy the credit requirement, the sub-metering need only be by energy source, or utility. The electricity used for lighting, plug loads and to run HVAC equipment may be measured on one meter and reported together. The same follows for natural gas, which may be used for both space heating and service water heating. The following forms of energy, fuels and other utilities are to be considered –

- Electricity
- Natural gas
- Fuel oil
- District or Distributed Energy Sources
- Steam
- Chilled water
- Other fuels
- Process Water

Payment

The credit requires that tenants negotiate a lease where energy costs are paid by the tenant and not included in the base rent. The lease must not be a "gross" lease, the commercial real estate industry term for leases where one payment covers everything. The most direct means to satisfy both requirements for the credit would be separate metering and payments to the utility.

When the individual tenant is not paying for the utility directly, the tenant's payments must be based on actual consumption. The typical approach, where the landlord prorates the utilities based on the tenant's portion of the total leasable area, meets the credit requirement. Flat rates set by the landlord at the time of lease negotiation do not satisfy the requirement. The tenant's payments must be a proration of the true quantities used, and the landlord needs to present the tenant this information and keep a written record. The practice of periodically adjusting tenant payments and rates is acceptable as long as the adjustments reflect true consumption.

Service Water

Water used for the convenience of the occupants does not need to be sub-metered. This usage includes restrooms and changing facilities, water fountains, break rooms and janitorial uses. The payment must be based on actual consumption, even if costs have been prorated by the size of the tenant space or occupancy count. See **Table 1**.

Process Uses

All energy and utilities consumed in connection with the manufacture of a product or delivering service, such as in the brewing of beer or operation of a restaurant, must be sub-metered. The payment must be based on actual use and may not be prorated. Not only the water used for dishwashing, but also the natural gas used to heat the water must be metered with payment based on actual consumption.

Owner-Occupied Spaces

When a project occupies less than 75% of a total building, complex or campus, it is still eligible to demonstrate credit compliance. The sub-metering requirements remain unchanged. The applicant will need

Table 1: Sub-metering and Payment Requirements for Projects Less Than 75% of the Total Building Area

Function	Typical Energy Sources	Sub-metering Requirements	Payment Requirements
Lighting	Electric	Required	Required
Plug Loads	Electric	Required	Required
Heating	Fuels Electric Steam	Sub-metering is required unless included in pro-rated building payment for a central plant serving multiple tenants.	
Cooling	Electric Fuels Chilled Water		
Service Water	Water	Not Required	Required
Process Uses	Water Electric Fuels	Sub-metering is required; payment must be based on actual use and may not be prorated.	

to make the case that the accountability for payment meets the requirements of the credit.

Submittal Documentation

For projects with an area that constitutes less than 75% of the total building area, make the declaration for one or both of the requirements. Indicate how the utilities are measured and paid. Describe the metering equipment installed for each utility. When utility payments are not direct, provide a copy of the applicable portion of the lease confirming the procedure being followed.

Additional Documentation

For potential use during submittal review, it is suggested that the project team retain copies of the utility invoices or landlord statements confirming that payment is based on actual consumption. Have available a means to demonstrate the relationship of the tenant area to total building area.

Exemplary Performance

No means have been previously recognized for exemplary performance for these credit requirements.

Projects with Areas 75% or Greater to the Total Building Area

The LEED Commissioning prerequisite and credit provide quality assurance that a project meets the design intent, ensuring that it is functioning as intended at the beginning of occupancy. The LEED Measurement & Verification (M&V) credit provides an extension of this quality assurance effort by ensuring that the predicted performance of the functioning building is actually producing savings to the owner.

The referenced standard describes a methodology to ensure that the design team consistently addresses the three basic aspects of energy and water conservation performance:

1. Accurate cataloging of baseline conditions

2. Verification of the complete installation and proper operation of new equipment and systems specified in the contract documents

3. Confirmation of the quantity of energy and water savings, as well as energy and water cost savings, that occur during the period of analysis

The three applicable M&V options are listed in **Table 2**. Each method provides a greater level of rigor than those previous. The appropriate level for a particular project is dependent on project specifics such as scope, level of owner interest in M&V, and contractual relationships of the design team.

The first technique, Option A, is not listed and does not satisfy the requirements of the LEED M&V credit. The remaining options (B, C and D) satisfy the LEED requirements when implemented correctly. Compliance with the credit requirements can be demonstrated through engineering calculations, operational estimates, and utility meter-billing analysis, or through more rigorous statistical sampling, metering and monitoring, and computer simulations.

All of the options in the referenced standard require the design team to specify equipment for installation in the building systems to allow for comparison, management and optimization of actual versus estimated energy and water performance. The mechanical engineer in particular should take advantage of the building automation systems to perform M&V functions where applicable. Elements of the M&V Plan that are required to comply with the requirements of this credit are listed in **Table 3**.

Table 2: Measurement and Verification Options for New and Renovation Construction Projects

M&V Option	Option Description	Savings Calculations	Cost
B	Savings are determined after project completion by short-term or continuous measurements taken throughout the term of the contract at the device or system level. Both performance and operations factors are monitored.	Engineering calculations using metered data.	Typically 3-10% of project construction cost, dependent on number and type of systems measured and the term of analysis/metering.
C	After project completion, savings are determined at the "whole- building" or facility level using current year and historical utility meter (gas or electricity) or sub-meter data.	Analysis of utility meter (or submeter) data using techniques from simple comparison to multivariate (hourly or monthy) regression analysis.	Typically 1-10% of project construction cost, dependent on number and complexity of parameters in analysis.
D	Savings are determined through simulation of facility components and/or the whole facility.	Calibrated energy simulation and modeling; calibrated with hourly or monthly utility billing data and/or end-use metering.	Typically 3-10% of project construction cost, dependent on number and complexity of systems evaluated.

Retrofits

Use of Option B in retrofits is appropriate when the end use capacity, demand or power level of the baseline, can be measured *and* the energy/water consumption of the equipment or subsystem is to be measured post-installation over time. This option can involve continuous measurement of energy/water both before and after the retrofit for the specific equipment, or it can be measurements for a limited period of time necessary to determine the retrofit savings. Portable monitoring equipment may be installed for a period of time or continuously to measure in-situ, baseline and post-installation periods. Periodic inspection of the equipment is recommended. Energy/water consumption is then calculated by developing statistical models of the end use capacity.

Creating the M&V Plan

The steps to create a Measurement & Verification Plan are as follows:

List all measures to be monitored and verified

Create a summary of any whole-building or system-specific energy or water conservation measures that will be implemented in the project. In most cases, these will be presented in other LEED credit documentation and should be referenced here.

Define the Baseline

Defining a building baseline is a two-part process. First, develop and define a baseline case. This baseline can range from the stipulation of specific baseline equipment to specifying whole-building compliance with energy codes or standards.

Once the baseline case has been established, use computer-aided analytical tools to estimate the associated performance of the baseline. It is sometimes appropriate to develop a baseline by deleting specific ECMs or features from the energy-efficient building. This approach can be particularly useful for whole building M&V by using Option C with computer simulation methods.

Requirements

1. IPMVP standard language and terminology should be employed.

2. State which option and method from the document will be used.

3. Indicate who will conduct the M&V.

4. State key assumptions about significant variables or unknowns.

5. Create an accurate baseline using techniques appropriate to the project.

6. Describe the method of ensuring accurate energy savings determination.

7. Define a post installation inspection plan.

8. Specify criteria for equipment metering, calibration, measurement period.

9. Define the level of accuracy to be achieved for all key components.

10. Indicate quality assurance measures.

11. Describe the contents of reports to be prepared, along with a schedule.

For retrofits, the baseline is the existing systems in place.

Besides defining the expected resource usage quantity for the baseline case, include additional assumptions relating to energy and water unit costs, weather, utility distribution, system schedule, occupancy or other factors and their anticipated adjustment to the baseline.

Projected Savings

Computer-aided tools are used to estimate performance of the final design, which is subtracted from the baseline performance to generate projected savings. Present the resource quantity and associated cost reductions to be achieved on a monthly measure-specific basis. The estimation process should also include the identification and, if possible, quantification of factors that could affect the performance of both the baseline and green design.

Define the General M&V Approach

LEED requires Option B as a minimum level of precision for the process. Option B is directed at end-use measures, and Option C addresses whole-building M&V methods. The relative suitability of each approach is a function of –

- M&V objectives and requirements of any related performance contracts
- Number of ECMs and the degree of interaction with each other and with other systems
- Practicality issues associated with M&V of particular ECMs or whole-building ECMs
- Trends towards holistic building design, which are guiding M&V requirements towards Option C

Prepare a Project-Specific M&V Plan

Development of an effective and efficient M&V plan for new buildings tends to be more involved than retrofit projects since performance strategies are usually more complex and the technical issues to address are more challenging.

Technical analyses that are performed in support of design decisions during the building design process provide a starting point in defining the M&V objectives and approach. The key elements of energy analyses are also usually key factors in M&V. Therefore, the energy analyses and projections should be well documented and organized with this in mind. M&V considerations should influence certain design decisions such as instrumentation and building systems organization. Identify any applicable data sources (e.g., utility bills, control system points and trending periods, and portable metering), the method of data collection (including equipment calibration requirements and other quality assurance practices), and the identity of monitoring personnel.

Verify Installation and Commissioning of ECMs or Energy-Efficient Strategies

Installation and proper operation is verified through site inspections as necessary, and combined with a review of reports such as commissioning reports and fluid/air test and balance reports. Any deviations should be noted and addressed through adjustment of the affected performance projections.

Determine Savings Under Actual Post-Installation Conditions

Virtually all performance projections are predicated upon certain assumptions regarding operational conditions (e.g., occupancy and weather). These assumptions affect the baseline and design estimations. Deviations from the operational assumptions must be tracked by an appropriate mechanism (e.g., site survey or short and/or long term metering) and the baseline and design projections modified accordingly to determine actual savings.

Describe any engineering calculations and/or software tools that will be used to process the data to demonstrate the savings achieved. This will include identification of any stipulated variables or values to be used in the calculations, as well as baseline adjustment factors, regression analysis (or other) tools to determine significance and weighting of such factors.

Reevaluate at Appropriate Intervals

Ongoing performance of ECMs or green building strategies and the associated savings must be reevaluated and verified at intervals and over a timeframe appropriate to M&V and related performance contract requirements. This also allows ongoing management and correction of significant deviations from projected performance.

It is important to link contractor final payments to documented M&V system performance. Require that the contractor provides all documentation in the final report. The contractor must also provide an ongoing M&V system maintenance and operating plan in the building operations and maintenance manuals.

Submittal Documentation

For projects with an area that constitutes 75% or more of the total building area, complete the LEED for Commercial Interiors Submittal Template indicating that metering equipment has been installed for each end-use, and declaring the option to be followed under IPMVP, 2001 version. Provide a copy of the M&V plan following IPMVP 2001 version, including an executive summary.

Additional Documentation

No additional information should be needed if the initial submittal is complete.

Considerations

The benefits of optimal building operation, especially in terms of energy and water performance, are substantial. The lifetime of many buildings is greater than 50 years. Even minor energy and water savings are significant when considered in aggregate. These long-term benefits often go unrealized due to maintenance personnel changes, aging of building equipment, and changing utility rate structures. Therefore, it is important to institute Measurement & Verification (M&V)

procedures to achieve and maintain optimal performance over the lifetime of the building through continuous monitoring. The goal of M&V activities is to provide building owners with the tools and data necessary to identify systems that are not functioning as expected, and to optimize building system performance.

Environmental Issues

Measurement & Verification of a building's ongoing energy and water consumption allows for optimization of related systems over the lifetime of the building. As a result, the cost and environmental impacts associated with energy and water use can be minimized.

Economic Issues

Building retrofits that institute effective M&V practices, such as Options B and C outlined in the referenced standard, experience energy savings that are on average 10% to 20% greater than buildings retrofitted with little or no M&V practices. It should be noted that M&V practices will predict performance improvements achieved through Energy Conservation Measures (ECMs) and commissioning, and contribute to savings.

The added cost to institute a rigorous M&V program for retrofitting buildings with energy and water equipment is typically 1% to 5% of the total retrofit cost. These additional first costs are generally repaid within a few months of operation due to energy and water utility savings as well as reduced operations and maintenance costs. It is important to remember that the goal of this credit is to allow building owners the ability to identify problems and achieve improved system performance. A significant amount of money can be spent on M&V systems that do not accomplish this goal. Careful planning and implementation are always necessary for a truly effective M&V system.

Community Issues

The collateral benefits of energy and water efficiency to the community are often diffuse and difficult to quantify over time. However, a healthy workforce and a healthy ecosystem are both indicators of a long-term pattern of sustainable development. Continuous measurement of resource use at individual projects will facilitate documentation and aggregation of emissions reductions benefits and contribute to providing benefits to the community over several generations; extending the resource base they enjoy and depend upon.

Resources

Please see USGBC Web site at www.usgbc.org/resources for more specific resources on materials sources and other technical information.

Web Sites

ENERGY STAR®

www.energystar.gov

(888) STAR-YES

ENERGY STAR® was introduced by the Environmental Protection Agency in 1992 as a voluntary labeling program designed to identify and promote energy-efficient products and buildings, in order to reduce carbon dioxide emissions. EPA partnered with the Department of Energy in 1996 to promote the ENERGY STAR® label, with each agency taking responsibility for particular product categories. ENERGY STAR® has expanded to cover most of the buildings sector.

International Performance Measurement and Verification Protocol

www.ipmvp.org

The IPMVP presents internationally developed best practice techniques for verifying results of energy efficiency, water efficiency and renewable energy projects in commercial and industrial facilities.

SS | WE | **EA** | MR | EQ | ID

Credit 3

Measurement & Verification Documents

ateam.lbl.gov/mv

(510) 486-5001

A list of M&V resources provided by Lawrence Berkeley National Laboratory, ranging from implementation guidelines to hands-on checklists.

Definition

Energy Conservation Measures (ECMs) are installations of equipment or systems, or modifications of equipment or systems, for the purpose of reducing energy use and/or costs.

Green Power

Intent

Encourage the development and use of grid-source, renewable energy technologies on a net zero pollution basis.

Requirements

Provide at least 50% of tenant's electricity from renewable sources by engaging in at least a two-year renewable energy contract. Renewable sources are as defined by the Center for Resource Solutions (CRS) Green-e products certification requirements. Green power may be procured from a Green-e certified power marketer, a Green-e accredited utility program, through Green-e Tradable Renewable Certificates, or from a supply that meets the Green-e Renewable Power definition.

Submittals

Provide the LEED for Commercial Interiors Submittal Template, signed by the owner or other responsible party, documenting that the supplied power is equal to 50% of the project's energy consumption and the sources meet the Green-e definition of renewable energy. Provide a copy of the two-year electric utility purchase contract for power generated from renewable sources.

Potential Technologies & Strategies

Estimate the energy needs of the tenant space and investigate opportunities to engage in a green power contract with the local utility. Green power is derived from solar, wind geothermal, biomass, or low-impact hydro sources. Green power may be procured from a Green-e certified power marketer, a Green-e accredited utility program, through Green-e certified Tradable Renewable Certificates, or from a supply that meets the Green-e renewable power definition. Visit www.grccn-c.org for details about the Green-e program.

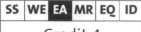
Summary of Referenced Standard

Center for Resource Solutions

Green-e Renewable Electricity Certification Program

www.green-e.org

(888) 634-7336

The Green-e Program is a voluntary certification and verification program for green electricity products. Those products exhibiting the Green-e logo are greener and cleaner than the average retail electricity product sold in that particular region. To be eligible for the Green-e logo, companies must meet certain threshold criteria for their products. Criteria include qualified sources of renewable energy content such as solar electric, wind, geothermal, biomass and small or certified low-impact hydro facilities; "new" renewable energy content (to support new generation capacity); emissions criteria for the non-renewable portion of the energy product; absence of nuclear power; and other criteria regarding renewable portfolio standards and block products. Criteria are often specific per state or region of the United States. Refer to the standard for more details.

Credit Interpretation Rulings

Credit Interpretation Rulings concerning this credit on LEED for Commercial Interiors and LEED for New Construction project requests are applicable. Review LEED for New Construction v2.1 EA Credit 6 CIRs.

Approach and Implementation

The credit recognizes three approaches of contracting for Green-e generated electrical power as defined by Center for Resource Solutions (CRS):

1. In an open-market state, the source may be a Green-e certified power marketer. In this arrangement, the purchaser (i.e.; tenant) secures a two-year contract for 50% of their estimated power consumption. See detail below on estimating electrical power consumptions.

2. If the existing utility has a Green-e accredited utility program, the purchaser may agree to purchase the electrical power through the program. In most cases, there is a premium added to the monthly billing.

3. When the tenant purchases Green-e Tradable Renewable Certificates in a quantity equal to their estimated 50% electrical power consumption for two years, they satisfy the credit requirements. These "tags" compensate Green-e generators for the premium of production over the market rate they sell to the grid. This approach is very useful when neither of the first two options are available, or where the electrical power comes through a building owner not willing to participate in a Green-e program. The cost of the certificates are over and above the cost of the electricity purchased from the utility.

When the tenant purchases electricity from the building owner

If the building owner is the contracting entity for any of the three approaches, the building owner will need to provide documentation confirming that it has entered into the purchase agreement that meets the credit requirements for the project. It should indicate that either no other tenant is receiving credit for the same contract, or provide details of the proration.

Calculations

Applicants have three ways to calculate the amount to be contracted. The unit of measure is in kilowatt-hours (kWh).

DEC

The first calculation is based on the Design Energy Cost calculation that the project team may have done in Option B of EA Credit 1.3. The modeling is based on ANSI/ASHRAE/IESNA 90.1-2004 Section 11 Energy Cost Budget Method or Appendix G Performance Rating Method. From the simulation model for the building segment that shares the same HVAC system with the project area, the needed values for this credit may be obtained. They include the "regulated electrical end uses." These include the electrical consumption projected for lighting within the project area, the prorated share of the electrical consumption for space cooling and HVAC fans and pumps that serve the project area, and other "regulated" electrical components. Refer to Tables 11.3.1 or G.3.1 in ASHRAE 90.1-2004 for a detailed discussion of regulated loads.

Complete the approach using **Equation 1**. Note that the calculation adjusts for the relationship of the project area to the modeled building segment (20,000 sq.ft./100,000 sq.ft.).

Actual Electricity Consumption

Project teams who have a record of a full year's consumption may use 50% the actual kilowatt-hour amount totaled from the electricity utility bills. This amount, if it includes the electrical plug loads and other process loads (i.e., dishwashers in a kitchen), may exclude the space cooling, fans and pumps and the list of other "regulated" electricity components. If the separation of regulated and non-regulated electricity loads is impractical or impossible, the team may use the Default Electricity Consumption calculation methodology described below.

Default Electricity Consumption

The Green-e annual electrical contract amount may be based on the product of 8 kilowatt-hours per square foot times the area of the project. A total of 16 kWh/sq.ft. would have to be purchased over two years for exemplary performance for this credit. Default energy usage is based

on Department of Energy (DOE) Commercial Buildings Energy Consumption Survey (CBECS) data. As shown in **Equation 2**, the product is not cut in half.

Example

Let's assume the project area is 20,000 sq.ft., the third floor of a 100,000 sq.ft. commercial office building. The tenant space is served by a single, common HVAC system supplying the entire building, certified LEED for Core & Shell Gold, where the design team modeled the energy usage using a DOE2 simulation. The owner also has installed an on-site renewable energy source that will reduce the minimum amount of Green-e power that must be purchased. The values in **Table 1** are from the modeling. They are used in the calculation shown in **Equation 1**. The Office Occupancy Default calculation for the same 20,000 sq.ft. space is shown in **Equation 2**.

Submittal Documentation

Complete the LEED for Commercial Interiors Submittal Template documenting that the amount under contract is equal to

Table 1: Regulated Electrical Use in 100,000 SF Modeled Building Segment

Regulated Electrical End Uses	Design Energy Costs [kWh]
Lighting	160,200
Space Cooling	240,300
Fans/Pumps	120,150
Other "regulated" electrical components	20,000
(DEC') =	540,650
Renewable Energy Equivalent	- 65,641
Net Regulated Electrical Usage (DEC")	475,009

Equation 1: Determination of Annual Green Power Contract Amount Using Design Energy Cost

Determination of Annual Green Power Contract Amount Using Design Energy Cost

Annual Green Power Contract = 50 % x [(Tenant Area)/(Building Area)] x DEC"
= 50 % x [(20,000 ft²)/(100,000 ft²)] x 475,009 kWh
Annual Green Power Contract = 47,501 kWh

Equation 2: Determination of Annual Green Power Contract Amount Using Office Occupancy Default

Determination of Annual Green Power Contract Amount using Office Occupancy Default

Annual Green Power Contract = (Tenant Area) x (8 k Wh /yr-ft²)
= 20,000 ft² x 8 k Wh /yr-ft²
Annual Green Power Contract = 160,000 kWh

50% of the project's energy consumption, or 8 kWh/sq.ft./yr; and that the source meets the Green-e definition of renewable energy. Indicate which of the three Green-e agreements was entered into, and which of the three calculation methods was used to determine the annual green power contract amount. Provide a copy of the two-year agreement, or certificates.

Additional Documentation

For potential use during submittal review, it is suggested that the project team have available information supporting the determination of the annual green power contract amount. When the Design Energy Cost amount was used, have available a summary of the simulation. When annual utility costs were used, have copies of the electric utility bills available. Be able to confirm the building components—lighting, plug loads, process uses—were covered by that service.

When the project occupant is not the holder of the Green-e contract, (i.e. as in the case when the building owner holds the contract), be able to provide the details on any proration.

Exemplary Performance

Project teams may earn an Innovation in Design point for exemplary performance when the requirements reach the next incremental step. For green power, the annual green power contract amount must be for 100% of the calculated annual usage. To earn the innovation credit, the annual electricity usage either has to have been measured or would have had to been calculated using the Energy Cost Budget Method or Performance Rating Method in ANSI/ASHRAE/IESNA 90.1-2004. A default of 16 kWh/sq.ft./yr is needed to achieve an Innovation in Design point.

Considerations

Energy production is a significant contributor to air pollution in the United States. Air pollutants released from energy production include sulfur dioxide, nitrogen oxide and carbon dioxide. These pollutants are primary contributors to acid rain, smog and global warming. With other associated pollutants, they have widespread and adverse effects on human health in general, especially on human respiratory systems. The Green-e Program was established by the Center for Resource Solutions to promote green electricity products and provide consumers with a rigorous and nationally recognized method to identify green electricity products. These products reduce the air pollution impacts of electricity generation by relying on renewable energy sources such as solar, water, wind, biomass and geothermal sources. In addition, the use

of ecologically responsive energy sources avoids reliance on nuclear power and large-scale hydropower. Nuclear power continues to be controversial due to security and environmental issues related to waste reprocessing, transportation and storage. Deregulated energy markets have enabled hydroelectric generation activities to market their electricity in regions unaffected by the regional impacts that dams can have on endangered aquatic species. While green electricity is not entirely environmentally benign, it greatly lessens the environmental impacts of power generation.

Costs for green power products may be somewhat greater than conventional energy products. However, green power products are derived, in part, from renewable energy sources with stable energy costs. As the green power market matures and impacts on the environment and human health are factored into power costs, green power products are expected to be less expensive than conventional power products.

Resources

Please see USGBC Web site at www.usgbc.org/resources for more specific resources on materials sources and other technical information.

Web Sites

The Green Power Network

U.S. Department of Energy

www.eere.energy.gov/greenpower

Provides news on green power markets and utility pricing programs—both domestic and international. It contains up-to-date information on green power providers, product offerings, consumer issues and in-depth analyses of issues and policies affecting green power markets. The Web site is maintained by the National Renewable Energy Laboratory for the Department of Energy.

Green-e Program

www.green-e.org

(888) 634-7336

See the Summary of Referenced Standard for more information.

Clean Energy

Union of Concerned Scientists

www.ucsusa.org/clean_energy

(617) 547-5552

UCS is an independent nonprofit that analyzes and advocates energy solutions that are sustainable both environmentally and economically. The site provides news and information on research and public policy.

Green Power Partnership

U.S. Environmental Protection Agency (EPA)

www.epa.gov/greenpower

EPA's Green Power Partnership is a new voluntary program designed to reduce the environmental impact of electricity generation by promoting renewable energy. The Partnership will demonstrate the advantages of choosing renewable energy, provide objective and current information about the green power market, and reduce the transaction costs of acquiring green power.

Materials and Resources

Overview

Building materials choices are important in sustainable design because of the extensive network of extraction, processing and transportation steps required to process them. Activities to create building materials may pollute the air and water, destroy natural habitats and deplete natural resources. Construction and demolition wastes constitute about 40% of the total solid waste stream in the United States.

Reuse of existing buildings, versus building new structures, is one of the most effective strategies for minimizing environmental impacts. When rehabilitation of existing buildings components is included in the strategy, waste volumes can be reduced or diverted from landfills. An effective way to use salvaged interior components is to specify them in the construction documents. Maintaining occupancy rates in existing buildings reduces redundant development and the associated environmental impact of producing and delivering all new materials. Reuse results in less habitat disturbance and typically less infrastructure.

The actions of an increasing number of public and private waste management operations have reduced construction debris volumes by recycling these materials. Recovery activities typically begin with job-site separation into multiple bins or disposal areas. Additional off-site sorting facilitates reuse.

When materials are selected for a project, it is important to evaluate new and different sources. Salvaged materials can be substituted for new materials, save costs and add character. Recycled-content materials reuse waste products that would otherwise be deposited in landfills. Use of local materials supports the local economy and reduces transportation. Use of rapidly renewable materials minimize natural resource consumption. Use of third-party certified wood improves the stewardship of those materials. Because material content is such a major portion of the overall budget on commercial interior projects, particularly because furniture and furnishings are included, there is considerable opportunity to make a positive impact.

Credit Timing

As **Table 1** shows, most of the decision making needed to successfully earn these credits occurs among the design team members. Contractor and supplier participation is very important in determining the actual values and ensuring compliance.

Only in LEED for Commercial Interiors MR Credit 1.1, Tenant Space, Long-Term Commitment, is the decision over and done before the start of design. The configuration of the space selected has a major influence on earning LEED for Commercial Interiors MR Credit 1.2 and 1.3, Building Reuse, Maintain 40% or 60% of Interior Non-Structural Components. To improve the odds, select a space that closely matches the design intent with minimal construction.

No Default Value

Because of the variability of project scopes, the LEED for Commercial Interiors Rating System does not have an automatic default relationship between material costs and the total construction cost. Unlike LEED for New Construction, the LEED for Commercial Interiors Submittal Templates do not automatically provide a 45% calculation.

Division 12, Furniture

Regardless of the parties specifying and providing the furniture and furnishings,

Overview of LEED® Prerequisites and Credits

MR Prerequisite 1
Storage and Collection of Recyclables

MR Credit 1.1
Tenant Space, Long-Term Commitment

MR Credit 1.2
Building Reuse, Maintain 40% of Interior Non-Structural Components

MR Credit 1.3
Building Reuse, Maintain 60% of Interior Non-Structural Components

MR Credit 2.1
Construction Waste Management, Divert 50% from Landfill

MR Credit 2.2
Construction Waste Management, Divert 75% from Landfill

MR Credit 3.1
Resource Reuse, 5%

MR Credit 3.2
Resource Reuse, 10%

MR Credit 3.3
Resource Reuse, 30% Furniture and Furnishings

MR Credit 4.1
Recycled Content, 10% (post-consumer + 1/2 pre-consumer)

MR Credit 4.2
Recycled Content, 20% (post-consumer + 1/2 pre-consumer)

MR Credit 5.1
Regional Materials, 20% Manufactured Regionally

MR Credit 5.2
Regional Materials, 10% Extracted and Manufactured Regionally

MR Credit 6.1
Rapidly Renewable Materials

MR Credit 7
Certified Wood

every furnishing in the project should be included in calculations for LEED for Commercial Interiors. Unlike in other LEED rating systems, project teams do not have the option to exclude certain materials. Within the Materials & Resources credits, furniture and furnishings are defined as those materials included in CSI MasterFormat™ Division 12. See **Table 2** for more information on the specific credits where they are included. Because the value of these materials can be very significant, the design and construction team will want to work closely with the facility manager, interior designer, furniture dealership and installers from the outset.

Table 1: Timing on Prerequisite and Credit Decisions and Actions

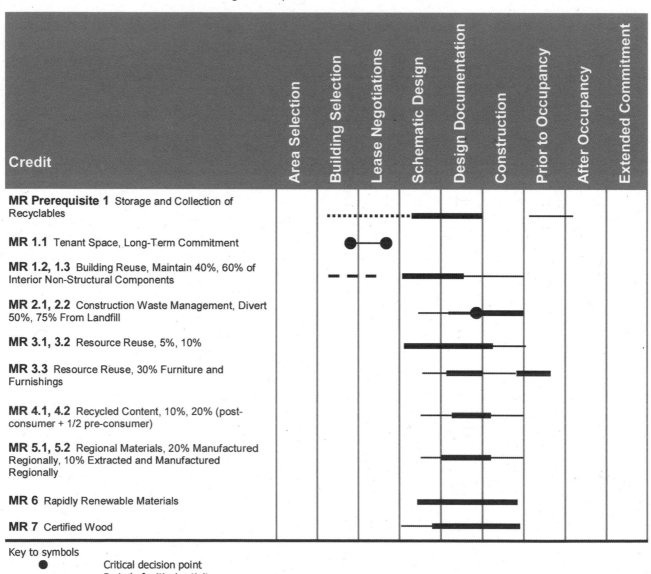

Credit	Area Selection	Building Selection	Lease Negotiations	Schematic Design	Design Documentation	Construction	Prior to Occupancy	After Occupancy	Extended Commitment
MR Prerequisite 1 Storage and Collection of Recyclables									
MR 1.1 Tenant Space, Long-Term Commitment									
MR 1.2, 1.3 Building Reuse, Maintain 40%, 60% of Interior Non-Structural Components									
MR 2.1, 2.2 Construction Waste Management, Divert 50%, 75% From Landfill									
MR 3.1, 3.2 Resource Reuse, 5%, 10%									
MR 3.3 Resource Reuse, 30% Furniture and Furnishings									
MR 4.1, 4.2 Recycled Content, 10%, 20% (post-consumer + 1/2 pre-consumer)									
MR 5.1, 5.2 Regional Materials, 20% Manufactured Regionally, 10% Extracted and Manufactured Regionally									
MR 6 Rapidly Renewable Materials									
MR 7 Certified Wood									

Key to symbols
● Critical decision point
▬▬▬ Period of critical activity
──── Period of activity
- - - - Period of possible activity

Table 2: Units of Measure for Materials & Resources Credits

Material	MR 1.2, 1.3 Building Reuse	MR 2.1, 2.2 Construction Waste Management[1]	MR 3.1, 3.2 Resource Reuse	MR 3.3 Resource Reuse, Furniture, Furnishings	MR 4.1, 4.2 Recycled Content	MR 5.1 Manufactured Regionally	MR 5.2 Extracted and Manufactured Regionally	MR 6 Rapidly Renewable	MR 7 Certified Wood
Mechanical	X	Either Pounds or Cubic Feet but Consistent Throughout	X	X	X[2]	X[2]	X[2]	X	Identify all wood-based materials, then exclude salvaged and refurbished materials and post-consumer recycled wood fiber portion of any products. Cost New [$]
Electrical	X		X	X	X	X	X	X	
Ceiling	SF		Replacement Value [$]	X	Exclude salvaged and refurbished materials counted in MR 3 Cost New [$]	Cost New [$]	Cost New [$]	Cost New [$]	
Floors	SF			X					
Walls	SF			X					
Doors	SF			X					
Case Goods	ST			X					
Windows	- SF			X					
All Other Construction Materials	X			X					
Furniture and Furnishings (CSI Division 12)	X	X	X	Replacement Value [$]					

[1] Do not include hazardous waste and excavated soil in MR 2.1, 2.2 calculations.
[2] Plumbing products may be included in calculations; if included for one credit, items must be in all applicable credits.

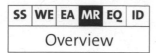

Storage and Collection of Recyclables

Intent

Facilitate the reduction of waste generated by building occupants that is hauled to and disposed of in landfills.

Requirements

Provide an easily accessible dedicated area that serves the tenant space for the collection and storage of materials for recycling including (at a minimum) paper, corrugated cardboard, glass, plastics and metals.

Submittals

Provide the LEED for Commercial Interiors Submittal Template, signed by the architect, interior designer, tenant or landlord, declaring that the area dedicated to recycling is easily accessible and accommodates the tenant's recycling needs. Provide a plan showing the area(s) dedicated to recycled material collection and storage, or provide a letter from landlord outlining the building's recycling program.

Potential Technologies & Strategies

Designate a space for the collection and storage of recycled materials that is appropriately sized and located in a convenient area. Identify local waste handlers and buyers for glass, plastic, metals, office paper, newspaper, cardboard and organic waste. Instruct occupants on building recycling procedures. Consider employing cardboard balers, aluminum can crushers, recycling chutes and other waste management technologies to further enhance the recycling program.

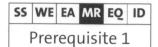
Credit Interpretation Rulings

In addition to LEED for Commercial Interiors Credit Interpretation Rulings (CIRs), applicable LEED for New Construction CIRs may also apply to LEED for Commercial Interiors projects.

LEED for Commercial Interiors projects that occupy less than a full building do not necessarily need to provide an outdoor collection area if one is provided to all building occupants or when the materials hauler or landlord makes pick ups within the tenant space.

Approach and Implementation

Strategies

As part of the building selection process, determine the extent of services available in the region. When the project will be in a leased facility, determine what services are offered by the building owner. If there is a building-wide recycling program, confirm that it meets the requirements of the prerequisite. Delineate mutually acceptable space that is adequate and convenient for collection and storage of recycling. If a common collection area exists, it must be either sized to adequately handle the full building occupancy, or the tenant will need to have their own dedicated and secure space per requirements.

Identify local waste handlers to determine the extent of their services; often they will assist in setting up your program. When a project's waste generation warrants, identify buyers for glass, plastic, metals, office paper, newspaper, cardboard and organic wastes.

Technologies

Consider employing cardboard balers, aluminum can crushers, recycling chutes and other waste management technologies to further enhance the recycling program.

Synergies and Trade-Offs

Dense urban areas typically have a recycling infrastructure in place, but additional space for collection and storage may be costly. It is possible that recyclable collection and storage space could increase the project footprint in some instances. It is important to address possible indoor environmental quality (IEQ) impacts on occupants due to recycling activities. Those activities that create odors, noise and air contaminants should be isolated or performed during non-occupant hours to maintain optimal IEQ.

Design Phase

In the design phase, designate well-marked collection and storage areas for recyclables including office paper, cardboard, glass, plastic and metals. Locate a central collection and storage area in the basement or on the ground level with easy access for collection vehicles. Within the tenant spaces, locate a collection area convenient to a freight elevator for custodial pick-up. Size the collection and storage space to accommodate recyclables storage. Research local recycling efforts to find the best method of diverting recyclable materials from the waste stream.

Provide instruction to occupants and maintenance personnel on recycling procedures. Encourage activities to reduce and reuse materials before recycling in order to reduce the amount of recyclable volumes handled. For instance, building occupants can reduce the solid waste stream by using reusable bottles, bags and other containers.

Table 1: Recycling Area Guidelines

Commercial Building Square Footage [SF]	Minimum Recycling Area [SF]
0 to 5,000	82
5,001 to 15,000	125
15,001 to 50,000	175
50,001 to 100,000	225
100,001 to 200,000	275
200,001 or more	500

Area Approach

The city of Seattle passed an ordinance to require minimum areas for recycling and storage of recyclables in commercial buildings. The ordinance is based on the total square footage of the building. Minimum areas for residential buildings were also specified. **Table 1**, which is based on this initiative, may be used as a guideline to size your recycling area. Note that LEED for Commercial Interiors does not require adherence to these guidelines.

Occupancy Approach

An alternative, also voluntary in LEED for Commercial Interiors, was developed using research by the California Integrated Waste Management Board's (CIWMB) 1999 Statewide Waste Characterization Study in which the waste disposal rates of 1,200 businesses were measured. This approach calculated the estimated weekly quantity of paper, cardboard, glass, plastic and metal based on the business type and employee count.

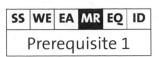
Table 2: Occupancy Approach, Business Types

Recyclable Generation Group 1 — Light Waste Generation

General Office and Financial Institutions

- Legal services
- Insurance agencies
- Real estate agencies
- Banks
- Investment offices
- Security and commodity brokers
- Personal services
- Public administrative offices
- Social services

Wholesale trade, durable and non-durable goods

- Fabricated metal products
- Paper and allied products
- Industrial and commercial machinery and computer equipment
- Transportation Equipment
- Electronic and other electrical equipment and components (except computer equipment)

Parking

Automotive repairs and services

General merchandise stores

Amusement and recreation services

Museums, galleries, botanical and zoological gardens

Recyclable Generation Group 2 — Medium Waste Generation

Engineering, accounting, research, management and related services

Manufacturing

- Lumber and wood products
- Food products
- Furniture
- Scientific and medical instruments

Printing, publishing and allied industries

Hotels, rooming houses, camps, lodges

Health services facilities

Educational facilities

Motor freight transportation and warehousing

Recyclable Generation Group 3 — Heavy Waste Generation

Retail

- Building materials, hardware, garden supplies
- Food stores
- Apparel and accessory stores
- Home furniture, furniture and equipment stores

Eating and drinking establishment

Heavy Manufacturing

Petroleum refining and related industries

Table Note: For more complete classifications, see www.ciwmb.ca.gov/WasteChar/WasteGenRates/defautlt.htm which include the Standard Industrial Classification; www.osha.gov/oshstats/sicser.html provides details for each SIC classification.

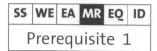
The calculation uses two worksheets. **Worksheet 1** is used to determine the weekly volume generated and the number of containers required for each type of recyclable material. **Worksheet 2** is used to determine the floor area needed for collection and storage between pick ups. If this approach is elected, begin by using **Table 2** to select the business group your project most nearly matches. Based on the group, obtain the average volume per employee for each type of recyclable materials from **Table 3**. When on-site compaction is done, obtain the compaction factor from **Table 4**.

In completing the calculations, use total employment, not full-time equivalents used in other LEED calculations. For seasonal businesses, use the maximum number of employees working during the busiest season.

The compaction adjustment ratios in **Table 4** require at least manual compaction during the consolidation at the collection and storage area. For example, the value of 0.05 for cardboard assumes that boxes originally placed in the trash containers at an individual's workstation are broken or flattened down, but are not compressed

any further. On the other hand, avoid overestimating the amount of compaction. For example, the plastics compaction ratio of 0.4 and the glass compaction ratio of 0.15 cannot be attained without crushing. When mechanical compactors are being used, follow the equipment manufacturer's recommendations. When unsure, assume no compaction by using 1.0 in **Worksheet 1**.

The worksheet also provides an adjustment for the frequency of pick-ups. For weekly pick-ups use 1, for twice-weekly use 2, and use 0.5 for every other week.

To complete the calculation, use **Worksheet 2**. Select the containers to be used for each type of recyclable material. Many recycling haulers will help develop your strategy and they often provide the containers.

Submittal Documentation

The LEED for Commercial Interiors Submittal Template declaration asks for confirmation that at a minimum paper, corrugated cardboard, glass, plastics and metals are collected separately. Include with the submittal a floor plan that shows the location and size of the collection

Table 3: Occupancy Approach. Recyclables Generated by Business Type—Volume per Employee per Week

Recyclable Material Volumes—Non-compacted [cubic feet per employee per week]			
Recyclable Material	Group 1	Group 2	Group 3
Paper	2	4	4
Cardboard	6	20	30
Glass	0.2	0.4	2
Plastic	8	20	20
Metal	0.2	0.2	0.3

Table 4: Occupancy Approach. Volume Adjustment for On-Site Compaction

Recyclable Material	All Groups
Paper	0.5
Cardboard	0.05
Glass	0.15
Plastic	0.4
Metal	1.0

area or provide a letter from the landlord outlining the building's recycling program and how it meets the prerequisite requirements.

Additional Documentation

In the case of an audit, additional documentation may be requested including the calculations used in determining the area required for storage, and any correspondence with the building owner concerning the availability and adequacy of building-wide collection and storage.

Considerations

Environmental Issues

By creating convenient recycling opportunities for building occupants, a significant portion of the solid waste stream can be diverted from landfills. Recycling of paper, metals, cardboard and plastics reduces the need to extract virgin natural resources. For example, recycling one ton of paper prevents the processing of 17 trees and saves three cubic yards of landfill space. Recycled aluminum requires only 5% of the energy required to produce virgin aluminum from

Worksheet 1: Occupancy Approach. Recyclable Container Volume Calculation Table

Overall Recyclable Material Volume										
Recyclable Material	Number of Employees		Volume Per Employee [ft^3 / week]		Compaction Ratio		Pick-ups Per Week		Overall Volume [ft^3]	
Paper		x		x		÷		=		
Cardboard		x		x		÷		=		
Glass		x		x		÷		=		
Plastic		x		x		÷		=		
Metal		x		x		÷		=		

Worksheet 2: Occupancy Approach. Recycle Area Calculation

Storage Area Determination										
Recyclable Material	Overall Volume [ft^3]		Container Volume [ft^3]		Container Count		Container Footprint [ft^2]		Total Area [ft^2]	
Paper		÷		=		x	.		=	
Cardboard		÷		=		x			=	
Glass		÷		=		x			=	
Plastic		÷		=		x			=	
Metal		÷		=		x			=	
							Circulation			
							Total Floor Area			

bauxite, its raw material. Recycling also reduces environmental impacts of waste in landfills. Land, water and air pollution impacts can all be reduced by minimizing the volume of waste sent to landfills.

Economic Issues

Recycling requires minimal initial cost and offers significant savings in reduced landfill disposal costs or tipping fees. However, recycling activities use floor space that could be used otherwise. In larger projects, processing equipment such as can crushers and cardboard balers are effective at minimizing the space required for recycling activities. Some recyclables can generate revenue which can help to offset the cost of their collection and processing.

Community Issues

Many communities sponsor recycling programs and encourage participation to reduce the amount of waste landfilled. These efforts return valuable resources to the production process and may increase employment. Additionally, the reduced dependence on virgin resources helps maintain existing habitat areas. Community-wide participation results in higher recycling rates, and in turn more stable markets for the recycled materials.

Resources

Please see the USGBC Web site at www. usgbc.org/resources for more specific resources on materials sources and other technical information.

Web Sites

Solid Waste Characterization Database, Estimated Solid Waste Generation Rates

California Integrated Waste Management Board

www.ciwmb.ca.gov/WasteChar/

Earth 911

www.earth911.org/master.asp

(480) 889-2650 or 877-EARTH911

Information and education programs on recycling as well as regional links to recyclers.

Recycling at Work

U.S. Conference of Mayors

www.usmayors.org/USCM/recycle

(202) 293-7330

A program of the U.S. Conference of Mayors that provides information on workplace recycling efforts.

Waste at Work

Inform: Strategies for a Better Environment

www.informinc.org/wasteatwork

(212) 788-7900

An online document from Inform, Inc., and the Council on the Environment of New York City on strategies and case studies to reduce workplace waste generation.

Print Media

Composting and Recycling Municipal Solid Waste by Luis Diaz et al., CRC Press, 1993.

McGraw-Hill Recycling Handbook by Herbert F. Lund, McGraw-Hill, 2000.

Definitions

Recycling is the collection, reprocessing, marketing and use of materials that were diverted or recovered from the solid waste stream.

A **Landfill** is a waste disposal site for the deposit of solid waste from human activities.

Tenant Space
Long-Term Commitment

1 point

Intent

Encourage choices that will conserve resources, reduce waste and reduce the environmental impacts of tenancy as they relate to materials, manufacturing and transport.

Requirements

Occupant commits to remain in the same location for not less than 10 years.

Submittals

Provide the LEED for Commercial Interiors Submittal Template, signed by the building owner or other responsible party, declaring that the occupant either owns its space or has signed a lease for not less than 10 years.

Potential Technologies & Strategies

Suggest negotiations resulting in longer leases or ownership.

Credit Interpretation Rulings

Credit interpretation rulings concerning MR Credit 1.1 made to LEED for Commercial Interiors project requests apply to LEED for Commercial Interiors projects. The requirements of this credit are not currently found in other LEED rating systems.

Approach and Implementation

The credit requirements are satisfied when the project area is either owned by the occupant or is currently included in a lease with a term of not less than 10 years.

Condominium ownerships satisfy the credit requirement.

The requirement does not stipulate a relationship between the start of the lease period and the project construction activities.

Though it may be necessary to displace occupants during the construction, there are no stipulations concerning temporary relocations.

Submittal Documentation

The LEED for Commercial Interiors Submittal Template requires a declaration that the occupant either owns the space or currently has a lease with a term of not less than 10 years in length. Indicate the type of commitment, either ownership or leaseholder.

Additional Documentation

For the submittal review process, where the project is in a leased space, the project team should maintain documentation demonstrating the lease commitment.

Considerations

Environmental Issues

Ownership and long-term leases reduce the frequency of relocation and the associated construction activities. With longer-term commitments there is a greater return on energy efficiency and improvements that benefit the occupants' wellbeing.

Community Issues

There are numerous associated location decisions that follow the selection of the project location, often including where employees reside and shop and the length of their commutes. Community improvements, from mass transit to cultural amenities, take time to develop. Longer and more stable tenancy improves the entire community.

Resources

Please see the USGBC Web site at www. usgbc.org/resources for more specific resources on materials sources and other technical information.

Web Sites

CoreNet Global Corporate Real Estate Network

www.corenetglobal.org

(404) 589-3200

An organization of corporate real estate executives.

Congress for the New Urbanism

www.cnu.org

(312) 551-7300

An organization of planners and designers who have identified and apply principles that foster community.

Print Media

How Buildings Learn: What Happens After They're Built, by Stewart Brand.

Definitions

Tenant is one who pays to occupy land or space that is owned by someone else.

Owner is an entity that owns land, a space or a building that is used either by themselves or by another.

Occupant is the entity that uses the project space either by leasing or owning.

Building Reuse

Maintain 40% of Interior Non-Structural Components

Intent

Extend the life cycle of existing building stock, conserve resources, retain cultural resources, reduce waste and reduce environmental impacts of new buildings as they relate to materials manufacturing and transport.

Requirements

Maintain at least 40% by area of the existing non-shell, non-structure components (walls, flooring and ceilings).

Submittals

Provide the LEED for Commercial Interiors Submittal Template, signed by the architect, interior designer, owner or other responsible party, listing the retained elements and declaring that the credit requirements have been met.

Potential Technologies & Strategies

Identify during the selection and design of the tenant space the potential to maintain as many of the existing interior elements as possible. Remove elements that pose contamination risk to occupants and update outdated components. Quantify the extent of reuse.

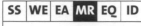
1 point
in addition to
MR 1.2

Building Reuse
Maintain 60% of Interior Non-Structural Components

Intent

Extend the life cycle of existing building stock, conserve resources, retain cultural resources, reduce waste, and reduce environmental impacts of new buildings as they relate to materials manufacturing and transport.

Requirements

Maintain at least 60% by area of the existing non-shell, non-structure components (walls, flooring, and ceiling systems).

Submittals

Provide the LEED for Commercial Interiors Submittal Template, signed by the architect, interior designer, owner or other responsible party, listing the retained elements and declaring that the credit requirements have been met.

Potential Technologies & Strategies

Identify during the selection and design of the tenant space the potential to maintain as many of the existing interior elements as possible. Remove elements that pose contamination risk to occupants and update outdated components. Quantify the extent of reuse.

Credit Interpretation Rulings

In LEED for Commercial Interiors, MR Credits 1.2 and 1.3 address only interior non-structural components. The means of determining the percentage of area retained is particular to the LEED for Commercial Interiors version of the credits and may vary from that used in other LEED rating systems. Credit interpretation rulings concerning MR Credits 1.2 and 1.3 made to LEED for Commercial Interiors project requests apply to LEED for Commercial Interiors projects.

Fixed items, such as walls and doors, that are found on site are included in this credit and count toward the percentage of reuse when they perform the same function (i.e., doors reused as doors). If they are used for another purpose (i.e., doors made into tables), they contribute to earning MR credits 3.1 and 3.2. Note that the area of these items, even when not reused, must be included in the prior condition area calculation of MR Credits 1.2 and 1.3.

Full-height wall systems are to be included in MR credits 1.2 and 1.3; Division 12 items, including furniture and furnishings, are addressed in MR Credit 3.3.

Approach and Implementation

These credits recognize the importance of selecting a space where the existing interior aligns with the anticipated use. They also recognize when the design and construction successfully maintain the existing interior construction. These two objectives are accomplished by basing the percentage on the larger of the following two areas: either the area of components

in the prior condition, or the area of the components in the completed design. See **Equation 1** and the sample calculation shown in **Table 1**.

Strategies

To the extent possible, develop the architectural program prior to selecting the project space. Use the program to match the anticipated needs for enclosed spaces with those in potential buildings under consideration.

Planning

Once the final space is selected and prior to any demolition, the project team should inventory the prior condition. Develop a floor plan showing the location of finished ceilings, finished flooring, interior wall partitions, doors within the interior walls, exterior and party walls, and exterior windows and doors. If there are built-in case goods that will be reused, they should be documented as well. The drawings should provide the detail needed to determine the surface area of all these elements.

Construction Phase

Confirm that the items designated for reuse can be reused. Take the needed steps to retain them in the finished work.

Submittal Documentation

The LEED for Commercial Interiors Submittal Template provides a table that matches **Table 1** used in the example below. No other materials are required with the certification submittal.

Additional Documentation

Documentation that may be requested to demonstrate credit achievement may include two distinct plans: one that

SS	WE	EA	MR	EQ	ID
Credit 1.2					

SS	WE	EA	MR	EQ	ID
Credit 1.3					

Equation 1: Determination of Maintained Area

$$\text{Interior Non-Structural Component Reuse [\%]} = \frac{\text{Total Retained Components Area [ft}^2\text{]}}{\text{Larger of Prior Condition OR Completed Design Area [ft}^2\text{]}}$$

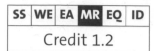

Table 1: Sample Finished Surface Area Calculation

Finished Surface Areas			
Element	Prior Condition Area [ft²]	Completed Design Area [ft²]	Retained Components Area [ft²]
Finished Ceiling	20,000	20,000	12,610
Finished Flooring	10,200	20,000	1,800
Interior Wall Partitions	8,640	8,380	5,520
Doors within Interior Walls	1,400	800	500
Built-in case goods	500	800	400
Exterior and Party Walls	13,820	13,820	13,820
Less Exterior Windows and Doors	-2,280	-2,280	-2,280
Totals	52,280	61,520	32,370

Determine the Larger
Completed Design Area > Prior Condition Area   61,520 > 52,280

Interior Non-Structural Component Reuse
[32,370 / 61,520]   53%

40% < 53% < 60% earns MR 1.2 but not MR 1.3

documents the prior condition, the other a final plan showing where the retained components are located. These documents may be the same ones used to convey to the contractors what is to be reused. In addition, the project team should maintain its take off of the areas used in the calculation. Periodic progress photos starting prior to demolition and taken through occupancy are ideal means for confirming performance on this credit.

Exemplary Performance

Project teams may earn an Innovation in Design point for exemplary performance when the requirements reach the next incremental step. For Building Reuse, Maintain Interior Non-Structural Components, the credit calculation must be 80% or greater.

Calculations

Quantity of Finished Area

This credit is based on surface areas. The components included in the calculation are finished ceilings, walls, doors, flooring and built-in case goods. The measurements are made in the same way as would be completed by a contractor preparing a bid for flooring, ceiling or painting. Finished ceilings and flooring areas are straightforward. For walls, determine the finished area between floor and ceiling. For interior wall partitions and doors, count the area of both sides. For exterior and party walls, count only one side. Subtract the area of exterior windows and exterior doors from both the prior condition and completed design tallies. For built-in case goods, determine the finished area, as would a painter.

Figure 1: Sample Comparison of Floor

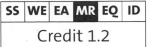

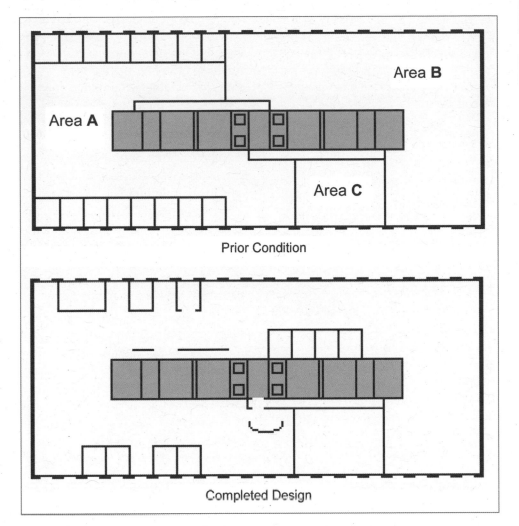

Prior Condition

Determine the total finished areas that existed prior to the start of the project and any demolition. If the ceiling is exposed both prior to construction and in the final design, include this area in both. If there was a lay-in ceiling prior to construction but none after, include the ceiling area in both the prior condition and completed design area, but not in the retained components area.

Completed Design

Determine the total finished area in the completed design including all new and retained elements.

Retained Components Area

In determining the retained components area, include only the surface area of ceilings, walls, interior doors, floors and built-in case goods that were in the space both prior to construction and in the completed design.

Remember to include in this tabulation items that have been saved but may have been relocated, such as full-height demountable walls and doors that were re-hung in a new section of wall. Items counted in this credit are not to be included in LEED for Commercial Interiors MR Credits 3.1 and 3.2.

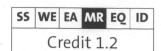

Percent Maintained

Complete **Table 1**. In determining the Interior Non-structural Component Reuse, divide the Total Retained Components Area into the larger of either the total Prior Condition Area or total Completed Design Area.

By using the larger of the two values as the denominator, both projects that have optimized component reuse from the prior condition, and projects that have minimized material use in the completed design are on equal footing.

Example

Prior Condition

The tenant has taken the entire 20,000 sq.ft. floor in an existing commercial office building that has 6-foot wide floor-to-ceiling windows at 12-foot centers on the long elevations of the building. Area A was previously built out with a 2'x 2' lay-in ceiling at 10 feet above the carpeted floor. Drywall partitions enclosed 16 private offices. Area B had never been occupied, but the building owner had completed the ceiling system, plus the exterior and common area walls. Area C was built as a training facility with floating acoustic panels and a mix of reclaimed wood and recycled rubber flooring. The corridors to the stairs had the same ceiling system as Area A, plus carpet tiles.

Completed Design

The design team had the opportunity to open up the space by eliminating one of the hallways and a party wall. They saved several of the existing private offices from Area A. In Area B, the new occupants kept the ceiling and added four enclosed areas to serve as a copy area, recycling storage and conferencing. They found the training facility, Area C, needed only a fresh coat of paint.

The quantities shown in **Table 1** are from this example.

Considerations

Many opportunities exist to rehabilitate existing buildings. Commercial real estate companies often rehabilitate old industrial buildings to take advantage of prime location, lower building costs and desirable building characteristics.

Environmental Issues

Commercial interior projects reusing the interior non-structural components of an existing building significantly reduce construction waste volumes. Reuse strategies also reduce environmental impacts associated with raw material extraction, manufacture and transportation.

Economic Issues

Reuse of existing components can reduce the cost of construction substantially. For instance, the new headquarters for WorkingBuildings, LLC of Atlanta maintained over 75% of the interior non-structural components on its project, contributing to earning a LEED Silver certification during the LEED for Commercial Interiors pilot.

Community Issues

The character of a neighborhood is often defined by existing historic buildings. Building reuse maintains the vital link between neighborhoods of the past and present. Commercial interior projects that reuse a high percentage of the non-structural components serve as an example for future tenants in their building or others in the community.

Resources

Please see the USGBC Web site at www.usgbc.org/resources for more specific resources on materials sources and other technical information.

Print Media

How Buildings Learn: What Happens After They're Built, by Stewart Brand.

Definitions

Prior Condition is the state the project space was in at the time it was selected. Moving the demolition out of the project scope by making it the building owner's responsibility defeats the objective of this credit.

Prior Condition Area is the total finished areas of finished ceilings, finished floors, full height walls and demountable partitions, interior doors and built-in case goods that existed when the project area was selected: exterior windows and exterior doors are not considered.

Completed Design Area is the total finished area of finished ceilings, finished floors, full height walls and demountable partitions, interior doors and built-in case goods in the space when the project is completed: exterior windows and exterior doors are not considered.

Retained Components are those portions of the finished ceilings, finished floors, full height walls and demountable partitions, interior doors and built-in case goods that existed in the prior condition and remained in the completed design.

Interior Non-Structural Components Reuse is determined by dividing the area of retained components by the larger of the area of the prior condition or the area of the completed design.

SS	WE	EA	MR	EQ	ID
Credit 1.2					

SS	WE	EA	MR	EQ	ID
Credit 1.3					

SS	WE	EA	**MR**	EQ	ID
Credit 1.2					

SS	WE	EA	**MR**	EQ	ID
Credit 1.3					

Construction Waste Management

Divert 50% From Landfill

Intent

Divert construction, demolition and land clearing debris from landfill disposal. Redirect recyclable recovered resources back to the manufacturing process. Redirect reusable materials to appropriate sites.

Requirements

Develop and implement a construction waste management plan, quantifying material diversion goals. Recycle and/or salvage at least 50% of construction, demolition and packaging debris. Calculations may be done by weight or volume, but must be consistent throughout.

Submittals

Provide the LEED for Commercial Interiors Submittal Template, signed by the architect, interior designer, tenant, or other responsible party, tabulating the total waste material, quantities diverted and the means by which diverted, and declaring that the above requirements have been met.

Potential Technologies and Strategies

Establish goals for diversion from disposal in landfills and incinerators and adopt a construction waste management plan to achieve these goals. Consider recycling cardboard, metal, brick, concrete, plastic, clean wood, glass, gypsum wallboard, carpet and insulation. Designate a specific area(s) on the construction site for segregated or commingled collection of recyclable materials, and track recycling efforts throughout the construction process. Identify construction haulers and recyclers to handle the designated materials, and seek verification that the diverted materials are recycled or salvaged, as intended. Note that diversion may include donation of materials to charitable organizations such as Habitat for Humanity®.

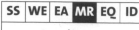
Construction Waste Management
Divert 75% From Landfill

Intent

Divert construction, demolition and land clearing debris from landfill disposal. Redirect recyclable recovered resources back to the manufacturing process. Redirect reusable materials to appropriate sites.

Requirements

Develop and implement a construction waste management plan, quantifying material diversion goals. Recycle and/or salvage at least 75% of construction, demolition and packaging debris. Calculations may be done by weight or volume, but must be consistent throughout.

Submittals

Provide the LEED for Commercial Interiors Submittal Template, signed by the architect, interior designer, tenant, or other responsible party, tabulating the total waste material, quantities diverted and the means by which diverted, and declaring that the above requirements have been met.

Potential Technologies and Strategies

Establish goals for diversion from disposal in landfills and incinerators and adopt a construction waste management plan to achieve these goals. Consider recycling cardboard, metal, brick, concrete, plastic, clean wood, glass, gypsum wallboard, carpet and insulation. Designate a specific area(s) on the construction site for segregated or commingled collection of recyclable materials, and track recycling efforts throughout the construction process. Identify construction haulers and recyclers to handle the designated materials, and seek verification that the diverted materials are recycled or salvaged, as intended. Note that diversion may include donation of materials to charitable organizations such as Habitat for Humanity®.

Credit Interpretation Rulings

In addition to LEED for Commercial Interiors Credit Interpretation Rulings (CIRs), applicable LEED for New Construction CIRs may also apply to LEED for Commercial Interiors projects.

Hazardous materials that are required to be removed, such as asbestos and lead, may be excluded from the calculation based on the understanding that these materials are unsuitable for any further use.

Materials included in MR Credit 3 cannot be applied to this credit.

Approach and Implementation

LEED for Commercial Interiors MR Credits 2.1 and 2.2 apply to materials that leave the site and recognize the efforts made both during design and construction to divert as much material as possible from the landfill. The percentage is simply the amount diverted through recycling and salvage divided by the total of that diverted plus that landfilled. See **Equation 1**.

Strategies

Establish goals for diversion from disposal in landfills and incinerators and adopt a construction waste management plan to achieve these goals. Identify construction haulers and recyclers to handle the designated materials; they often serve as valuable partners in this effort. Consider recycling cardboard, metal, brick, concrete, plastic, clean wood, glass, gypsum wallboard, carpet, cabling, ceiling tiles, doors and frames and insulation. Reduce the amount of packing material delivered to the site by specifying alternative packaging (for

example, blankets in lieu of bubble wrap). Designate specific areas on the construction site for the collection of recyclable and non-recycleable materials. Make sure jobsite personnel understand and participate in the program, with updates throughout the construction process. Obtain and retain verification records (waste haul reciepts, spreadsheets, etc.) that the diverted materials have been recycled or salvaged as intended. Note that diversion may include donations to charitable organizations such as Habitat for Humanity®.

Synergies and Trade-Offs

The waste management plan should address construction area housekeeping to avoid the contamination of the building and subsequent impacts on indoor air quality.

Project sites within an existing building may have little available space for waste separation activities. Recycling areas should be chosen carefully to avoid contaminating stormwater runoff and to protect stockpiled recyclable materials from theft and the elements.

Submittal Documentation

The LEED for Commercial Interiors Submittal Template provides the declaration that the credit requirements have been met, and a table that matches the example that appears in **Table 1**. No other materials are required with the initial certification submittal.

Additional Documentation

Documentation that may be requested to demonstrate credit achievement may include a copy of the project's construction waste management plan and the demoli-

SS	WE	EA	**MR**	EQ	ID
Credit 2.1					

SS	WE	EA	**MR**	EQ	ID
Credit 2.2					

Equation 1: Diversion Rate

$$\text{Recycling Rate [\%]} = \frac{\text{Recycled Waste}}{\text{Recycled Waste + Garbage}}$$

Table 1: Sample Construction Waste Management Diversion Summary

Material Diverted	Method of Diversion	Diverted Material, in: • tons • cubic yards
Carpet tiles	Donation to Salvation Army	25
Cardboard packaging	Recycler	10
Ceiling tiles	Returned to manufacturer	32
Steel studs	Recycler	8
Drywall	Recycler	12
	Total quantity of diverted waste	87
	Material sent to landfill	63
	Total quantity of waste	150
	Percentage of waste diverted [87 / 150]	58%

MR 2.1 (50%) earned, but MR 2.2 (75%) was not earned

Table 2: Solid Waste Conversion Factors

Materials	Density (lbs/CY)
Cardboard	100
Gypsum Wallboard	500
Mixed Waste	350
Rubble	1,400
Steel	1,000
Wood	300

tion plan. It is important to be able to verify the total quantities; so haul tickets and receipts provided by the recipients of salvaged and recycled materials should also be maintained and made available.

Exemplary Performance

Project teams may earn an Innovation in Design point for exemplary performance in Construction Waste Management when the percent diverted is 95% of total waste or greater.

Calculations

Because space is limited in the table included with the LEED for Commercial Interiors Submittal Templates, it is recommended that the project team develop a separate spreadsheet to track the full extent of activities covered by this credit. This spreadsheet, in conjunction with the densities shown in **Table 2**, can be used to convert all quantities to either weights or volumes.

Considerations

Construction and demolition activities generate enormous quantities of solid waste. The U.S. EPA estimates that 136 million tons of C&D debris (versus 209.7 million tons of municipal solid waste) was generated in 1996—57% of it from non-residential construction, renovation and demolition activities. This equates to 2.8 pounds per capita per day. Commercial construction generates between 2 and 2.5 pounds of solid waste per square foot, and the majority of this waste can potentially be recycled. The city of Portland, Oregon, has instituted programs to reduce solid waste generation and promote recyclable material markets. In 1993, the city was successful in diverting 47% of all construction and demolition waste from landfills. In one project, 76% of the waste from the construction of a

5,000 sq.ft. restaurant was diverted from landfilling (61% was recyclable or reusable wood, 11% was cardboard, and 4% was gypsum wallboard).

Recycling opportunities are expanding rapidly in many communities. Metal, vegetation, concrete and asphalt recycling opportunities have long been available and economical in most communities. Paper, corrugated cardboard, plastics and clean wood markets vary by regional and local recycling infrastructure, but are recycled in most communities. Some materials, such as gypsum wallboard, have recycling opportunities only in communities where reprocessing plants exist or where soil can handle the material as a stabilizing agent. The recyclability of a demolished material is often dependant on the amount of contamination attached to it. Demolished wood, for instance, is often not reusable or recyclable unless it is deconstructed and de-nailed.

Environmental Issues

Recycling of construction and demolition debris reduces demand for virgin resources, and, in turn, reduces the environmental impacts associated with resource extraction, processing and, in many cases, transportation. Landfills contaminate groundwater and encroach upon valuable green space. Through effective construction waste management, it is possible to extend the lifetime of existing landfills, avoiding the need for expansion or new landfill sites.

Economic Issues

In the past, when landfill capacity was readily available and disposal fees were low, recycling or reuse of construction waste was not economically feasible. Construction materials were inexpensive compared to the cost of labor and, thus, construction jobsite managers focused on worker productivity rather than materials conservation. In addition, recycling infrastructure and materials marketplaces to

process and resell construction debris did not exist. In recent years, particularly with the advent of international competition for both raw and recycled materials, the economics of recycling have improved. During this same period disposal costs have increased. Recognition for and enactment of more stringent waste disposal regulations coupled with ever decreasing landfill capacity have changed the waste management equation.

Waste management plans require time and money to draft and implement but they can guide a project to achieve substantial savings throughout the construction process.

Recyclable materials have differing market values depending on the presence of local recycling facilities, reprocessing costs and the availability of virgin materials on the market. In general, it is economically beneficial to recycle metals, concrete, asphalt and cardboard. In most cases it is possible to receive revenue as well as to avoid paying a landfill tipping fee. Market values normally fluctuate from month to month. When no revenue is received for materials, often the case for scrap wood and gypsum wallboard, it is still possible to benefit from potentially shorter hauling distances and by avoiding landfill tipping fees. The conventional approach to removing all waste and starting over with a "clean slate" is giving over to strategies that begin with planning and incorporate waste management in the project construction schedule.

Community Issues

Recycling supports local processing facilities, creates jobs and reduces the need for additional landfill capacity. Seek out charitable organizations such as Habitat for Humanity® to take salvageable materials; donate or sell existing furniture.

Resources

Please see the USGBC Web site at www. usgbc.org/resources for more specific

SS	WE	EA	**MR**	EQ	ID
Credit 2.1					

SS	WE	EA	**MR**	EQ	ID
Credit 2.2					

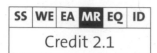

Credit 2.1

Credit 2.2

resources on materials sources and other technical information.

Web Sites

Construction and Demolition Debris Recycling Information

California Integrated Waste Management Board

www.ciwmb.ca.gov/ConDemo

(916) 341-6499

A program by the California Integrated Waste Management Board including case studies, fact sheets and links.

Construction Materials Recycling Association

www.cdrecycling.org

(630)-585-7530

A nonprofit dedicated to information exchange within the North American construction waste and demolition debris processing and recycling industry.

Construction Waste Management Handbook

Smart Growth Online

www.smartgrowth.org/library/articles.asp?art=15

(202) 962-3623

A report by the NAHB Research Center on residential construction waste management for a housing development in Homestead, Florida.

Contractors' Guide to Preventing Waste and Recycling

Resource Venture

www.resourceventure.org/rv/issues/building/publications/index.php

(206) 389-7304

A guidebook on waste prevention in construction from the Business and Industry Resource Venture.

Government Resources

Check with the solid waste and natural resources departments in your city or county. Many local governments provide information about regional recycling opportunities.

Recycling and Waste Management During Construction

King County, OR

www.metrokc.gov/procure/green/wastemgt.htm

Specification language from city of Seattle and Portland Metro projects on construction waste management.

A Sourcebook for Green and Sustainable Building

www.greenbuilder.com/sourcebook/ConstructionWaste.html

A guide to construction waste management from the Sourcebook for Green and Sustainable Building.

Environmental Specifications for Research Triangle Park

U.S. Environmental Protection Agency

www.epa.gov/rtp/new-bldg/environmental/specs.htm

Waste management and other specifications.

Waste Spec: Model Specifications for Construction Waste Reduction, Reuse and Recycling

Triangle J: Council of Governments

www.tjcog.dst.nc.us/cdwaste.htm

(919) 558-9343

Model specifications developed by Triangle J Council of Governments in North Carolina. Ten case studies show results of using the specifications (downloadable pdf document).

Definitions

Construction and demolition debris includes waste and recyclables generated from construction, renovation, and demolition or deconstruction of pre-existing structures.

Recycling is the collection, reprocessing, marketing and use of materials that were diverted or recovered from the solid waste stream.

Reuse is a strategy to return materials to active use in the same or a related capacity.

Tipping Fees are fees charged by a landfill for disposal of waste volumes. The fee is typically quoted for one ton of waste.

SS	WE	EA	MR	EQ	ID
		Credit 2.1			

SS	WE	EA	MR	EQ	ID
		Credit 2.2			

SS	WE	EA	**MR**	EQ	ID
Credit 2.1					

SS	WE	EA	**MR**	EQ	ID
Credit 2.2					

Resource Reuse

5%

Intent

Reuse building materials and products in order to reduce demand for virgin materials and to reduce waste, thereby reducing impacts associated with the extraction and processing of virgin resources.

Requirements

Use salvaged, refurbished, or reused materials for at least 5% of building (construction) materials, excluding furniture and furnishings.

Submittals

Provide the LEED for Commercial Interiors Submittal Template, signed by the architect, interior designer, owner, or other responsible party, declaring that the credit requirements have been met and listing each material or product used to meet the credit. Include details demonstrating that the project incorporates the required percentage of reused materials and products, showing their costs and the total cost of all materials for the project.

Potential Technologies and Strategies

Identify opportunities to incorporate salvaged materials into project design and research potential material suppliers. Consider salvaged materials such as beams and posts, flooring, paneling, doors and frames, cabinetry, brick and decorative items.

**1 point
in addition to
MR 3.1**

Resource Reuse

10%

Intent

Reuse building materials and products in order to reduce demand for virgin materials and to reduce waste, thereby reducing impacts associated with the extraction and processing of virgin resources.

Requirements

Use salvaged, refurbished or reused materials for at least 10% of building (construction) materials, excluding furniture and furnishings.

Submittals

Provide the LEED for Commercial Interiors Submittal Template, signed by the architect, interior designer, owner, or other responsible party, declaring that the credit requirements have been met and listing each material or product used to meet the credit. Include details demonstrating that the project incorporates the required percentage of reused materials and products showing their costs and the total cost of materials for the project.

Potential Technologies and Strategies

Identify opportunities to incorporate salvaged materials into project design and research potential material suppliers. Consider salvaged materials such as beams and posts, flooring, paneling, doors and frames, cabinetry, brick and decorative items.

Summary of Referenced Standard

There is no standard referenced for this credit.

Credit Interpretation Rulings

In addition to LEED for Commercial Interiors Credit Interpretation Rulings (CIRs), applicable LEED for New Construction CIRs may also apply to LEED for Commercial Interiors projects.

In LEED for Commercial Interiors, MR Credits 3.1 and 3.2 exclude materials included in the Construction Specifications Institute Division 12, in particular, furniture and furnishings. See the further explanation under MR Credit 3.3.

Approach and Implementation

The objective of these credits is to recognize project teams that are able to identify and reuse existing materials found both on- and off-site. Furniture and furnishings (CSI Division 12 components) are excluded from the calculations for this credit, but covered by MR Credit 3.3. **Table 1** clarifies materials covered by this credit.

Materials Found On-Site

For reused materials found on-site, there are two major groups. First are those items that were "fixed" components on-site before the project started. To qualify as reused, these fixed items must have been found to no longer be able to serve their original function, and must then have been reprocessed and installed for a different use. An example would be a fire door removed and modified to serve as the counter top for the receptionist station. The remaining fixed items, such as walls, ceilings and flooring are excluded from this credit, but are covered by MR Credit 1.2 and 1.3.

The second type of reused materials found on-site are "finish" items that were kept and refurbished. These reused components may continue to serve their original function, but underwent refurbishement to become functional. An example would be refurbished door hardware.

Materials Found Off-Site

For reused materials from off-site, the primary stipulation for qualifying as reused is that they must have been previously used. These materials may be purchased as salvaged, similar to any other project material, or they may be relocated from another of the occupant's facilities.

SS	WE	EA	MR	EQ	ID
Credit 3.1					

SS	WE	EA	MR	EQ	ID
Credit 3.2					

Table 1: Materials Covered by MR Credits 3.1 and 3.2

Used Materials Found On Site		Used Materials Found Off Site
Fixed Items	**Modified + New Use**	**Purchased from Others** **Same or New Use**
Example: Door converted to table Excluded: Items included in MR 1.2, 1.3 and 3.3, including demountable full-height walls; mechanical, electrical and plumbing fixtures; reused appliances and equipment.		Example: Demountable full-height walls Exclude: Items covered in MRc3.3; mechanical, electrical and plumbing fixtures; appliances and equipment.
Finish Items	**Refurbished + Reused** **Same or New Use**	**Owned** **Same or New Use**
Examples: Door hardware refinished and re-used. Excluded: Items covered in MRc1.2, 1.3 and 3.3, including demountable full-height walls.		Example: Portable signage Excluded: Items covered in MRc3.3; mechanical, electrical and plumbing fixtures; appliances and equipment.

SS	WE	EA	**MR**	EQ	ID
Credit 3.1					

SS	WE	EA	**MR**	EQ	ID
Credit 3.2					

Strategies

Identify opportunities to incorporate salvaged materials into project design and research potential reused material suppliers. Consider salvaged materials such as beams and posts, flooring, paneling, doors and frames, cabinetry, brick and decorative items.

Synergies and Trade-Offs

The salvaged materials from both on-site and off-site can be applied to MR Credit 5, Regional Materials, if they comply with the requirements of that credit. Materials qualifying as reused for MR Credit 3.1 and 3.2 cannot be applied to MR Credits 1.2, 1.3, 2.1, 2.2, 3.3, 4.1, 4.2, 6 or 7.

Submittal Documentation

Use the LEED for Commercial Interiors Submittal Template, declaring compliance and completing the table that matches **Table 2**. Use this table to list reused resources. For reused fixed items that were on-site, indicate how they were modified. For reused finish items that were on-site, indicate how they have been refurbished. For reused items from off-site, indicate the source.

Additional Documentation

Documentation that may be requested to demonstrate credit achievement may include information that confirms the source of materials, the means of modification or refurbishment, and documentation demonstrating how replacement values were determined.

Exemplary Performance

Project teams may earn an Innovation in Design point for exemplary performance when the next incremental percentage threshold is achieved. For resource reuse, the credit calculation must be 15% or greater.

Calculations

To calculate the percentage of reused materials used on a project, use the LEED for Commercial Interiors Submittal Template that includes a table similar to **Table 2**. In the first column list the salvaged materials.

Table 2: Sample Spreadsheet Example for Salvaged Construction Materials

Salvaged Material	On or Off Site	Modification made to On Site Materials Or Source of Off Site Salvaged Materials	Replacement Value
Wall paneling from wood flooring	On	Salvaged, re-milled	$ 4,000
Stone flooring	Off	Alpha Architectural Reuse	3,640
Ceiling tiles	Off	Project owner's inventory	2,000
Door hardware	On	Finish item refurbished	1,750
Used demountable full-height walls	Off	Xi Walls, salvaged	2,200
Used demountable full-height walls	Off	Project owner's inventory	1,100
		Total Salvaged Material Value	$ 14,490
		Total Construction Material Cost	$ 341,214
		Less MEP Material Value	-158,180
		Net Construction Material Value	$ 183,034
		% Salvaged [14,490 / 183,034]	**7.9%**

MR 3.1 (5.0%) earned, but MR 3.2 (10.0%) was not earned

For items that were formerly fixed items found on-site, indicate both the modified and former uses (i.e., wall paneling from wood flooring). In the second column indicate if the salvaged material came from on or off-site.

The third column follows the logic shown in **Table 1**. If the item is from on-site, indicate either that it is a fixed item that was salvaged and how it was modified, or that it is a finish item that has been refurbished. If the item is from off-site, indicate where it was acquired: the project owner is an acceptable source of off-site reusable materials.

Enter Replacement Value in the right hand column

When the cost of the reused or salvaged material is below the cost of an equivalent new item, use the higher cost as its Replacement Value. When the cost to reclaim an item found on-site is less than the cost of an equivalent new item, use the cost of the new item as the Replacement Value.

Mechanical, Electrical and Plumbing

Mechanical, electrical and plumbing (MEP) components, along with appliances and equipment may not be included in this credit.

Net Construction Material Value

In determining the Net Construction Material Value there is a line for subtracting the MEP Material Cost of all mechanical, plumbing and electrical materials. The Net Construction Material Value is divided into the Total Salvaged Material Value to determine the Percent Salvaged.

Considerations

Use of salvaged and refurbished materials in new building projects extends the life of materials and can reduce overall first costs of construction materials. Use of salvaged materials can also add character

to the building and can be used effectively as architectural details. Some areas of the United States, such as New England, the Pacific Northwest and California, have well-developed markets for salvaged materials while other regions are just beginning to develop these markets.

Environmental Issues

Reuse strategies divert material from the construction waste stream, reducing the need for landfill space and environmental impacts pertaining to associated water and air contamination issues. Use of salvaged materials reduces the environmental impacts of producing new construction products and materials. These impacts are significant since buildings account for a large portion of our natural resources consumption, including 40% of raw stone, gravel and sand, and 25% of virgin wood.

Economic Issues

Some salvaged materials are more costly than new materials due to the high cost of labor involved in recovering and refurbishing processes. However, salvaged materials are often of higher quality and more durable than available new materials. Local demolition companies may be willing to sell materials recovered from existing buildings to avoid landfill tipping fees and to generate income. In some areas, municipalities and waste management companies have established facilities to sell salvaged building materials at landfill sites.

Sometimes salvaged materials are offered at prices that appear to be cost-effective but may include hidden costs such as the need for reprocessing, exorbitant transportation costs or liabilities associated with toxic contamination. Conversely, certain salvaged materials may be impossible to duplicate (such as turn-of-the-century lumber and casework) and may well be worth the higher cost compared to new but inferior materials.

SS	WE	EA	MR	EQ	ID
		Credit 3.1			

SS	WE	EA	MR	EQ	ID
		Credit 3.2			

SS	WE	EA	**MR**	EQ	ID
		Credit 3.1			

SS	WE	EA	**MR**	EQ	ID
		Credit 3.2			

Community Issues

By reusing locally obtained salvaged materials, local salvage businesses are supported. Also, saving landfill capacity benefits the community through lower tipping fees and fewer landfill sites overall.

Resources

Please see the USGBC Web site at www.usgbc.org/resources for more specific resources on materials sources and other technical information.

Web Sites

California Materials Exchange

California Integrated Waste Management Board

www.ciwmb.ca.gov/CalMAX

(877) 520- 9703

A program of the California Integrated Waste Management Board, this site allows users to exchange non-hazardous discarded materials online.

Government Resources

Check with the solid waste authority and natural resources departments in your city or county. Many local governments provide information about regional materials exchanges and other sources.

Guide to Resource-Efficient Building Elements

www.crbt.org/index.html

The Center for Resourceful Building Technology Directory of environmentally responsible building products. This resource provides introductory discussions per topic and contact information for specific products, including salvaged materials. (The CRBT project is no longer active, and the CRBT Web site is no longer updated. The National Center for Appropriate Technology is providing this Web site for archival purposes only).

Materials Exchanges on the Web

Industrial Materials Exchange (IMEX)

Local Hazardous Waste Management Program in King County, OR

www.metrokc.gov/hazwaste/imex/exchanges.html

(206) 296-4899

A listing of materials exchanges on the Web.

Reuse Development Organization (ReDO)

www.redo.org

(410) 669-7245

A national nonprofit located in Indianapolis, Indiana, that promotes reuse as an environmentally sound, socially beneficial and economical means of managing surplus and discarded materials. See the List of ReDO Subscribers for contacts around the United States.

Salvaged Building Materials Exchange

Green Building Resource Guide

www. greenguide.com/exchange/search.html

A searchable database of salvaged building materials.

Building Materials Reuse Association (used to be Used Building Materials Association)

www.ubma.org

(877) 221-UBMA

BMRA is a nonprofit, membership-based organization that represents companies and organizations involved in the acquisition and/or redistribution of used building materials.

Used Building Materials Exchange

www.build.recycle.net

(519) 767-2913

A free marketplace for buying and selling recyclables and salvaged materials.

Old to New: Design Guide, Salvaged Building Materials in New Construction

The Greater Vancouver Regional District (GVRD)

www.gvrd.bc.ca/buildsmart/PDFS/
oldtonewdesignguidesalvbuildmatinnewc.
pdf

A useful and detailed guide book, produced by the Greater Vancouver Regional District, to the use of salvaged materials, with real-life case studies.

SS	WE	EA	**MR**	EQ	ID
Credit 3.1					

SS	WE	EA	**MR**	EQ	ID
Credit 3.2					

Definitions

Reused or Salvaged Materials include recovered construction materials reused in the project. Common salvaged materials include structural beams and posts, flooring, doors, cabinetry, brick and decorative items. Items that were never placed into service, but are being re-sold, are not salvaged materials. The Synergies and Trade-Offs section above provides detail on how the materials in this credit relate to other LEED for Commercial Interiors credits.

Refurbished Materials include those materials that have been restored to serve in place of a new item. The refurbishing typically includes replacement of worn and non-functioning parts, and possibly refinishing.

1 point

Resource Reuse

30% Furniture and Furnishings

Intent

Reuse building products and materials in order to reduce demand for virgin materials and reduce waste, thereby reducing impacts associated with the extraction and processing of virgin resources.

Requirements

Use salvaged, refurbished or used furniture and furnishings for 30% of the total furniture and furnishings budget.

Submittals

Provide the LEED for Commercial Interiors Submittal Template, signed by the architect, interior designer, owner or other responsible party, declaring that the credit requirements have been met. In addition, provide a listing of the reused furniture and furnishings with their replacement value and documentation for the value of the balance of new furniture and furnishings.

Potential Technologies and Strategies

Identify opportunities to salvage and reuse furniture into project design and research potential material suppliers. Consider salvaging and reusing systems furniture and furnishings such as case pieces, seating, filing systems, decorative lighting and accessories.

Credit Interpretation Rulings

Credit interpretation rulings concerning MR Credit 3.3 made to LEED for Commercial Interiors project requests apply to LEED for Commercial Interiors projects registering after their issue. The requirements of this credit are not currently found in other LEED rating systems.

Approach and Implementation

The objective of this credit is to recognize the environmental benefits of reusing furniture and furnishings, plus other reused materials itemized in the Construction Specification Institute MasterFormat™ Division 12. The percentage is based upon calculations that include only the materials in Division 12, using replacement values. See **Equation 1**.

Design Strategy

Identify opportunities to reuse furniture from the occupant's existing inventory or research and purchase used furniture from material suppliers.

Submittal Documentation

Use the LEED for Commercial Interiors Submittal Template, declaring compliance and completing the table that matches **Table 1**.

Additional Documentation

Documentation that may be requested to demonstrate credit achievement may include an inventory of all furniture and furnishings, those that qualify as reused, their source, and documentation demonstrating how replacement values were determined.

Exemplary Performance

Project teams may earn an Innovation in Design point for exemplary performance when the next incremental percentage threshold is achieved. For resource reuse of furniture and furnishings, the credit calculation must be 60% or greater.

Calculations

To calculate the percentage of reused furniture and furnishings used on a project, use the LEED for Commercial Interiors Submittal Template that includes a table

Table 1: Spreadsheet Example for Salvaged Furniture and Furnishings Materials

Product name	Source	Replacement Value
Reused Workstation	Owner's former site	$ 103,300
Reused File cabinets	Zeta Old to New	100,400
	Total Salvaged Material Value	$ 203,700
	Total Division 12 Material Value	$ 598,772
	% Salvaged [203,700 / 598,772]	34.0%
	34.0% > 30.0% MR 3.3 earned	

Equation 1: Salvage Rate for Furniture and Furnishings

$$\text{Salvage Rate [\%]} = \frac{\text{Replacement Value of Reused Furniture and Furnishings}}{\text{Total Value of New and Reused Furniture and Furnishings}}$$

Table 2: Division 12 Items

Construction Activity
Fabrics
Artwork (exclude from calculation)
Key cabinets
Hospital casework
Display casework
Window treatment
Panels and dividers
Furniture
Furniture systems
Furniture accessories
Floor mats and frames
Multiple seating
Chairs
Interior plants (exclude from calculation)
Planters

similar to **Table 1**. Include only furniture and furnishings, components typically found in CSI MasterFormat™ Division 12. See **Table 2**. These furniture and furnishings components are excluded from MR Credits 3.1 and 3.2. Artwork, interior plants and musical instruments also are to be excluded.

The items covered by this credit must have been previously used, but are not limited by where they were located prior to their reuse on the project. There is no requirement that they be modified or refurbished.

Calculations are based upon the replacement value of the reused furniture and furnishings. Replacement value is presumed to be greater than the market value; what would be paid for the reused product in the market place. With justification, the project team may use replacement values greater than the amount paid for newly acquired refurbished product. When the

determinations are being based on comparable new products, consider using the discounted contract prices as opposed to the published list price.

The replacement values used in MR Credit 3.3 are part of the total Division 12 material value, which is also used in the calculations of MR Credits 4.1, 4.2, 5.1, 5.2 and 6.

Considerations

For commercial interiors projects, furniture often is the largest single purchase made. Reusing furniture and furnishings lessens the environmental impacts associated with disposal and additional manufacturing.

Definitions

Replacement Value is the estimated cost that the project team establishes for the inventory of product reused on the project. It may be equal to the cost of the same quantity of new product. When the exact product is no longer available, establish cost based upon the use of products with comparable features.

Market Value, presumed to be less than replacement value, equating either to the amount that was or would have been paid for the actual reused materials.

Recycled Content
10% (post-consumer + 1/2 pre-consumer)

Intent

Increase demand for building products that incorporate recycled content materials, therefore reducing impacts resulting from extraction and processing of virgin materials.

Requirements

Use materials, including furniture and furnishings, with recycled content such that the sum of post-consumer recycled content plus 1/2 (one-half) of the pre-consumer content constitutes at least 10% of the total value of the materials in the project.

The value of the recycled content portion of a material or furnishing shall be determined by dividing the weight of recycled content in the item by the total weight of all material in the item, then multiplying the resulting percentage by the total cost ($) of the item.

Mechanical and electrical components shall not be included in this calculation. Plumbing products however may be included. Recycled content materials shall be defined in accordance with the Federal Trade Commission document, *Guides for the Use of Environmental Marketing Claims, 16 CFR 260.7 (e)*, available at www.ftc.gov/bcp/grnrule/guides980427.htm.

Submittals

Provide the LEED for Commercial Interiors Submittal Template, signed by the architect, interior designer, tenant or other responsible party, declaring that the above requirements have been met and listing the recycled content products used. Include details demonstrating that the project incorporates the required percentage of recycled content materials and products and showing their cost and percentage(s) of post-consumer and/or pre-consumer content, and the total cost of all materials for the project (excluding mechanical and electrical equipment).

Potential Technologies and Strategies

Establish a project goal for recycled content materials and identify material suppliers that can achieve this goal. During construction, ensure that the specified recycled content materials are installed and quantify the total percentage of recycled content materials installed.

1 point
in addition to
MR 4.1

Recycled Content
20% (post-consumer + 1/2 pre-consumer)

Intent

Increase demand for building products that have incorporated recycled content material, reducing the impacts resulting from extraction and processing of virgin materials.

Requirements

Use materials, including furniture and furnishings, with recycled content such that the sum of post-consumer recycled content plus 1/2 (one-half) of the pre-consumer content constitutes at least 20% of the total value of the materials in the project.

The value of the recycled content portion of a material or furnishing shall be determined by dividing the weight of recycled content in the item by the total weight of all material in the item, then multiplying the resulting percentage by the total cost ($) of the item.

Mechanical and electrical components shall not be included in this calculation. Plumbing products however may be included. Recycled content materials shall be defined in accordance with the Federal Trade Commission document, *Guides for the Use of Environmental Marketing Claims, 16 CFR 260.7 (e)*, available at www.ftc.gov/bcp/grn-rule/guides980427.htm.

Submittals

Provide the LEED for Commercial Interiors Submittal Template, signed by the architect, interior designer, tenant or other responsible party, declaring that the above requirements have been met and listing the recycled content products used. Include details demonstrating that the project incorporates the required percentage of recycled content materials and products and showing their cost and percentage(s) of post-consumer and/or pre-consumer content, and the total cost of all materials for the project (excluding mechanical and electrical equipment).

Potential Technologies and Strategies

Establish a project goal for recycled content materials and identify material suppliers that can achieve this goal. During construction, ensure that the specified recycled content materials are installed and quantify the total percentage of recycled content materials installed.

Summary of Referenced Standard

FTC Guides for the Use of Environmental Marketing Claims, 16 CFR 260.7 (e)

www.ftc.gov/bcp/grnrule/guides980427.htm

According to the guide: "A recycled content claim may be made only for materials that have been recovered or otherwise diverted from the solid waste stream, either during the manufacturing process (pre-consumer), or after consumer use (post-consumer). To the extent the source of recycled content includes pre-consumer materials, the manufacturer or advertiser must have substantiation for concluding that the pre-consumer material would otherwise have entered the solid waste stream. In asserting a recycled content claim, distinctions may be made between pre-consumer and post-consumer materials. Where such distinctions are asserted, any express or implied claim about the specific pre-consumer or post-consumer content of a product or package must be substantiated.

"It is deceptive to misrepresent, directly or by implication, that a product or package is made of recycled material, which includes recycled raw material, as well as used, reconditioned and remanufactured components. Unqualified claims of recycled content may be made if the entire product or package, excluding minor, incidental components, is made from recycled material. For products or packages that are only partially made of recycled material, a recycled claim should be adequately qualified to avoid consumer deception about the amount, by weight, of recycled content in the finished product or package. Additionally, for products that contain used, reconditioned or remanufactured components, a recycled claim should be adequately qualified to avoid consumer deception about the nature of such components. No such qualification would be necessary in cases where it would be clear to consumers from the context that a product's recycled content consists of used, reconditioned or remanufactured components."

See the FTC document for illustrative examples.

Credit Interpretation Rulings

In addition to LEED for Commercial Interiors Credit Interpretation Rulings (CIRs), applicable LEED for New Construction CIRs may also apply to LEED for Commercial Interiors projects.

Note that materials included in CSI MasterFormat™ Division 12 (Furniture) are to be included in the credit determination. More information is provided in LEED for Commercial Interiors MR Credit 3.3.

Approach and Implementation

Strategies

Establish a project goal for recycled content materials and identify material suppliers that can achieve this goal. During construction, ensure that the specified recycled content materials are the ones actually purchased and installed. Use the construction submittal process to confirm compliance: coordinate supplier and subcontractor material costs with the recycled content indicated on the submittals.

Submittal Documentation

Use the LEED for Commercial Interiors Submittal Template, making the declaration and completing the table similar to **Table 3**. Indicate the source of the recycled values used.

Additional Documentation

Documentation that may be requested to demonstrate credit achievement may in-

SS	WE	EA	**MR**	EQ	ID
Credit 4.1					

SS	WE	EA	**MR**	EQ	ID
Credit 4.2					

SS	WE	EA	**MR**	EQ	ID

Credit 4.1

SS	WE	EA	**MR**	EQ	ID

Credit 4.2

clude manufacturers' information indicating the percentages of post-consumer and pre-consumer content. The confirmation may take the form of cut sheets, product literature, brochures or an official statement from the manufacturer.

The Submittal Template calculations are expected to include a summary of the recycled content of furniture. To support this calculation, it is suggested that the project team request and maintain a detailed accounting of the components; please see **Table 2** for an example.

Exemplary Performance

Project teams may earn an Innovation in Design point for exemplary performance when the requirements reach the next incremental step. For recycled content, the credit calculation must be 30% or greater.

Calculations

Overview

The credit is based on the sum of post-consumer content plus 1/2 (one-half) the pre-consumer content. To obtain these two values, the material cost of the separate products in the project is multiplied by its percentage of post-consumer and pre-consumer content. The overall project recycled content rate is determined using **Equation 1**.

Post-Consumer Recycled Content

The post-consumer recycled content comes from consumer waste, much of which comes from residential curbside recycling programs for aluminum, glass, plastic and paper. To be a feedstock the raw materials need to have served a useful purpose in the consumer market before being used again. Other post-consumer

feedstock is generated when construction and demolition debris is recycled.

Pre-Consumer Recycled Content

By contrast pre-consumer (or post-industrial) recycled content comes from process waste that one industry has sold or traded with another through the marketplace. For instance, a composite board manufacturer may purchase (or haul away for free) sawdust from a lumber mill or waste straw from a wheat farm. This definition does not include in-house industrial scrap or trimmings, which are normally fed back into the same manufacturing process.

Assembly Recycled Content

Assemblies include all products that are made of multiple materials, either in reaching a formulation for a material (i.e., concrete), or of all the sub-components (i.e., a workstation). The determination of the recycled contents of an assembly should not be confused with the calculation that is shown in **Equation 1**, where the final value is expressed in dollars. For assembly recycled contents, the two values are the percents by weight of the post-consumer recycled content and the pre-consumer recycled content. When there are sub-components, the final two percentages must be determined by only using the weights of the smaller elements. No consideration is given to relative costs of the materials or the sub-components. In the example of the workstation, a pound of steel in a storage unit is of equal significance as a pound of fabric on a panel.

Table 1 shows a sample calculation of the assembly recycled contents for a hypothetical concrete mix. The cement type selected includes a small amount of pre-consumer content. The fly ash is a by-

Equation 1: Project Recycled Content Rate

$$\text{Recycled Content Value } [\$] = \text{Material or Product Cost } [\$] \times \text{Recycled Content \%}$$

Table 1: Sample Assembly Recycled Contents Calculation for Concrete

Components	Weight [lbs]	Post-Consumer %	Post-Consumer Weight [lbs]	Pre-Consumer %	Pre-Consumer Weight [lbs]
Cement	282			10%	28
Fly Ash	282			100%	282
Water	275				
Slag	750			100%	750
Recycled Concrete Aggregate	1000	100%	1000		
Sand	1200				
Sample Totals	3789		1000		1060

Post-Consumer Content [1000 / 3789]   26.4%
Pre-Consumer Content [1060 / 3789]   28.0%

SS | WE | EA | **MR** | EQ | ID

Credit 4.1

SS | WE | EA | **MR** | EQ | ID

Credit 4.2

Table 2: Sample Assembly Recycled Content for a BIFMA Typical Workstation Configuration

Manufacturer	Lambda Furniture
Product Line	High End Workstations
BIFMA Typical Configuration	Wkstn Configuration 0010

Component	Component Weight [lbs]	Post-Consumer %	Post-Consumer Weight [lbs]	Pre-Consumer %	Pre-Consumer Weight [lbs]
Aluminum	25.0	53%	13.3	47%	11.8
Wood	35.0	3%	1.1	87%	30.5
Steel	650.0	22%	143.0	5%	32.5
Textile	20.0	100%	20.0	0%	0.0
Other	23.0	0%	0.0	0%	0.0
	753.0		177.4		74.7

Post-Consumer Content [177.4 / 753.0]   23.4%
Pre-Consumer Content [74.7 / 753.0]   9.9%

product of coal-fired electrical generation, and slag from steel production. The aggregate comes from concrete demolition that has been recycled, ground and washed. Even though the patch plant recaptures the water it uses in cleaning the trucks and bins, unfortunately this environmentally responsible practice cannot be counted as being pre-consumer.

Systems Furniture

In LEED for Commercial Interiors, those materials listed in CSI MasterFormat[TM] Division 12 (Furniture) are to be in-

SS	WE	EA	**MR**	EQ	ID

Credit 4.1

SS	WE	EA	**MR**	EQ	ID

Credit 4.2

cluded in the calculation of MR Credits 4.1 and 4.2. This CSI category includes systems furniture. To facilitate the credit calculation, the applicant may use the percentages of post-consumer and pre-consumer recycled content determined by the product manufacturer for the typical workstation configuration that best represents their project installation. This approach also may be used in calculating MR Credits 6 and 7.

For use in this credit, The Business and Institutional Furniture Manufacturer's Association (BIFMA) International has defined typical workstation configurations for both open plan and private offices. They are available at www.bifma. org. Using these typical configurations, the individual manufacturers have determined the recycled content percentages for their individual product lines. **Table 2** is an example of a manufacturer's calculation. Project teams should obtain this documentation from the manufacturer should the credit be audited.

Project teams, most likely in conjunction with their furniture supplier, will need to segregate their total new furniture costs into segments that correspond to the industry typical configurations for each manufacturer and product line. These segment values are then multiplied by the manufacturer's recycled content percentages for the credit calculation. See **Table 3**.

This approach was developed so project teams would not have to build the credit values starting from individual workstation component counts, costs and recycled content percentages. However, when a project team has purchased components that have recycled contents outside a 5% range of those used in manufacturer's published percentages for the typical configurations, they will need to obtain project specific detail. This may occur when special green materials have been specified. In this case, request that the manufacturer prepare an assembly recy-

cled content calculation, similar to **Table 2**, for the actual products purchased.

Other products, such as seating, storage and conference tables, are not included in the typical configurations. For some of these items there are consistent attributes across a product line: the recycled content of a steel three-drawer file will be the same as that in the five-drawer variety. When this is the case, identify the dollar amount for all those products used on the project within the product line and multiply by the recycled content percentages. When this is not the case, individual products must be addressed separately. **Table 3** shows examples of both situations.

Default Recycled Content

For steel products where no recycled content information is provided, assume the recycled content to be 25% post-consumer. No other material has been recognized as having a similar consistent minimum recycled content.

Exclusions

Mechanical and electrical systems components are not to be included in this credit calculation. Plumbing products however may be included at the discretion of the project team. If plumbing products are included for this credit, they must also be included in the denominator for MR Credit 5, Regional Materials.

Also excluded from the credit calculation is the salvaged and refurbished material value of "reused resources," those that meet the definitions found in LEED for Commercial Interiors MR Credits 3.1, 3.2 and 3.3.

No default materials value

In the LEED for Commercial Interiors Rating System there is no default relationship between the value ($) of materials and total construction costs: nothing similar to the 45% used in LEED for New Construction has been found consistent for commercial interior projects.

Considerations

Building products with recycled content are beneficial to the environment because they reduce virgin material use and solid waste volumes. Success breeds future success: as the number of building products containing recycled content grows, the marketplace for recycled materials develops. Many commonly used products are now available with recycled content, including metals, concrete, masonry, acoustic tile, carpet, ceramic tile and insulation. Most recycled content products exhibit performance similar to products containing only virgin materials and can be incorporated into building projects with ease and minimal to no cost premium.

Resources

Please see the USGBC Web site at www.usgbc.org/resources for more specific resources on materials sources and other technical information.

Web Sites

Recycled Content Product Directory

California Integrated Waste Management Board

www.ciwmb.ca.gov/rcp

(916) 341-6606

A searchable database for recycled content products, developed by the California Integrated Waste Management Board.

Government Resources

Check with the solid waste and natural resources departments in your city or county. Many local governments provide information on recyclers and recycled content product manufacturers within their region.

GreenSpec

BuildingGreen, Inc.

www.buildinggreen.com/menus/index.cfm

(802) 257-7300

Detailed listings for more than 1,500 green building products, including environmental data, manufacturer information and links to additional resources.

Guide to Resource-Efficient Building Elements

www.crbt.org/index.html

The Center for Resourceful Building Technology Directory of environmentally responsible building products. This resource provides introductory discussions per topic and contact information for specific products, including salvaged materials. (The CRBT project is no longer active, and the CRBT Web site is no longer updated. The National Center for Appropriate Technology is providing this Web site for archival purposes only).

Oikos

www.oikos.com

A searchable directory of resource-efficient building products and sustainable design educational resources.

U.S. EPA Comprehensive Procurement Guidelines Program

www.epa.gov/cpg/products.htm

Contains EPA information on recycled content materials with guidelines for recycled percentages. Includes a searchable database of suppliers.

Definitions

Assembly Recycled Content includes the percentages of post-consumer and pre-consumer content. The determination is made by dividing the weight of the recycled content by the overall weight of the assembly.

The **Net Project Material Value** is determined for a credit based on those material components to be considered in determining the percentage earned. It is the denominator of the calculation. For LEED for Commercial Interiors MR Credits 4.1 and 4.2 the Net Project Mate-

SS	WE	EA	**MR**	EQ	ID
Credit 4.1					

SS	WE	EA	**MR**	EQ	ID
Credit 4.2					

rial Value includes the Construction Material Value and the Division 12 (Furniture & Furnishings) Material Value, less the material value of mechanical and electric components, and the salvage value identified in LEED for Commercial Interiors MR Credits 3.1, 3.2 and 3.3. The material value of plumbing, to the extent included in the numerator, must be included in the Net Project Material Value.

Post-Consumer recycled content is consumer waste that has become a raw material (feedstock) for another product. It originates from products that have served a useful purpose in the consumer market. Much of this feedstock comes from residential and commercial (office) recycling programs for aluminum, glass, plastic and paper. Other post-consumer feedstock is supplied by businesses that recycle construction and demolition debris.

Pre-Consumer content, previously referred to as Post-Industrial Content, is output from a process that has not been used as part of a consumer product, that is sold, traded, or exchanged under commercial terms (including auditable transactions between profit centers within an organization) as feedstock for another industrial process, and that would otherwise be landfilled, incinerated or somehow disposed of as a waste, as defined by the Federal Trade Commission. For instance, a composite board manufacturer may purchase (or haul away for free) sawdust from a lumber mill or waste straw from a wheat farm. Wood chips would not fit this definition.

Table 3: Sample MR 4.1 and 4.2 Recycled Content Spreadsheet

Product	Company	Product Cost	% Post-Consumer	Post Consumer Value	% Pre-Consumer	Pre-Consumer Value	Recycled content information source
Steel lintel	Alpha Steel	$ 400	25.0%	$ 100	0%	$ 0	25% rule for steel
Wheatboard shelving	Beta Mills	1,950	0%	0	100.0%	1,950	Cut sheet
Fireproofing	Gamma Insulation	3,300	25.0%	825	0%	0	Product brochure
Metal doors and frames	Delta Doors	920	59.0%	543	31.9%	293	Product brochure
Rolling service door	Epsilon Specials	2,100	55.0%	1,155	27.9%	586	Product brochure
Glass side lights	Zeta Glaze	4,500	10.0%	450	5.8%	261	Cut sheet
Gypsum wall board	Eta Wall	9,900	20.0%	1,980	0%	0	Letter from factory
Acoustic ceilings	Theta Tiles	3,680	42.4%	1,560	20.6%	758	Product brochure
Acoustic insulation	Iota Insulates	2,340	0%	0	75.0%	1,755	Letter from factory
Carpet tile	Kappa Karpet	63,293	45.0%	24,051	6.8%	4,304	Product brochure
Systems Furniture, new	Lambda Furniture	288,366	23.6%	68,054	9.9%	28,548	Manufacturer's typical
Seating	Lambda Furniture	59,253	26.0%	15,406	11.7%	6,933	Manufacturer's detail
Conference Tables	Mu Mills	19,751	2.8%	553	81.0%	15,998	Product brochure
File Cabinets	Mu Mills	27,652	22.0%	6,083	5.0%	1,383	Product brochure
			Subtotals	$ 120,760		$ 62,769	

Total Construction Material Value	$ 341,214
Less Mechanical and Electrical Material Value	-158,180
Less MR 3.1 and 3.2 Value (no MEP Salvage)	-12,640
Net Construction Material Value	$ 170,394
Division 12 Material Value	598,772
Less MR 3.3 Value	-203,700
Net Project Material Value	$ 565,466
% Post-Consumer + 1/2 Post-Industrial [(120,760 + 0.5 x 62,769) / 565,466]	26.9% MR 4.1 and MR 4.2 earned 26.9% > 20%

Regional Materials

20% Manufactured Regionally

Intent

Increase demand for building materials and products that are extracted and manufactured within the region, thereby supporting the regional economy and reducing the environmental impacts resulting from transportation.

Requirements

Use a minimum of 20% of the combined value of construction and Division 12 (Furniture) materials and products that are manufactured regionally within a radius of 500 miles.

Manufacturing refers to the final assembly of components into the building product that is furnished and installed by the tradesmen. For example, if the hardware comes from Dallas, Texas, the lumber from Vancouver, British Columbia and the joist is assembled in Kent, Washington; then the location of the final assembly is Kent, Washington.

Submittals

Provide the LEED for Commercial Interiors Submittal Template, signed by the architect, interior designer, owner or responsible party, declaring that the credit requirements have been met. Include calculations demonstrating that the project incorporates the required percentage of regional materials/products. Show their cost, percentage of regional components, distance from project to manufacturer, and the total cost of all materials for the project.

Potential Technologies and Strategies

Establish a project goal for locally sourced materials and identify materials and material suppliers that can achieve this goal. During construction, ensure that the specified local materials are installed and quantify the total percentage of local materials installed.

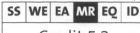
Regional Materials

10% Extracted and Manufactured Regionally

Intent

Increase demand for building materials and products that are extracted and manufactured within the region, thereby supporting the regional economy and reducing the environmental impacts resulting from transportation.

Requirements

In addition to the requirements of MR Credit 5.1, use a minimum of 10% of the combined value of construction and Division 12 (Furniture) materials and products extracted, harvested, recovered, or manufactured within 500 miles of the project.

Submittals

Provide the LEED Submittal Template, signed by the architect, interior designer, owner or responsible party, declaring that the credit requirements have been met. Include calculations demonstrating that the project incorporates the required percentage of regionally extracted and manufactured materials/products. Show their cost, percentage of regional components, distance from project to the points of extraction and manufacture, and the total cost of all materials for the project.

Potential Technologies and Strategies

Establish a project goal for locally sourced materials and identify materials and material suppliers that can achieve this goal. During construction, ensure that the specified local materials are installed and quantify the total percentage of local materials installed.

Credit Interpretation Rulings

In addition to LEED for Commercial Interiors Credit Interpretation Rulings (CIRs), applicable LEED for New Construction CIRs may also apply to LEED for Commercial Interiors projects.

Note that materials included in CSI MasterFormat™ Division 12 (Furniture) are to be included in the credit determination. More information is provided in LEED for Commercial Interiors MR Credit 3.3.

Approach and Implementation

Strategy

Establish a project goal for locally sourced materials and identify materials and material suppliers that can achieve this goal. During construction, ensure that the specified local materials are installed, and quantify the total percentage of local materials installed.

Synergies and Trade-Offs

Material values used in MR Credits 3.1, 3.2, 3.3, 4.1, 4.2, 6 and 7 may also be used in these credits.

Submittal Documentation

Use the LEED for Commercial Interiors Submittal Template, declaring compliance and completing the table that matches **Table 2**.

Additional Documentation

Documentation requested to demonstrate credit achievement may include a copy of the information confirming regional content. Confirmation may take the form of cut sheets, product literature, brochures or an official statement from the manufacturer.

Exemplary Performance

For regionally manufactured materials, the credit calculation must be 40% or greater. For regionally extracted materials, the calculation must be 20% or greater.

Calculations

Use the LEED for Commercial Interiors Submittal Templates to list those products that satisfy the requirements of the credits. Indicate the name of the manufacturer, the distance between the project site and the manufacturer, the product cost, and the distance between the project site and the extraction site for each product.

In LEED for Commercial Interiors, furniture and furnishings (CSI Division 12 components) must be included in the calculations for this credit. Additional information is included under LEED for Commercial Interiors MR Credit 3.3.

Exclusions

Mechanical and electrical systems components are not included in this credit calculation. Plumbing products however may be included at the discretion of the project team. If plumbing products are included for this credit, they must also be included in the denominator for MR Credit 4, Recycled Content.

No Default Materials Value

In the LEED for Commercial Interiors Rating System, there is no default value for the cost of materials relative to total construction cost: nothing similar to the 45% relationship used in LEED for New Construction has been found consistent for commercial interior projects.

Reused and Salvaged Materials

Reused and salvaged materials that satisfy the requirements of MR Credits 3.1, 3.2 and 3.3, may also contribute to MR Credits 5.1 and 5.2. The location from which they were salvaged may be used as the point of manufacture, and the location

SS	WE	EA	MR	EQ	ID
			Credit 5.1		

SS	WE	EA	MR	EQ	ID
			Credit 5.2		

where they were originally manufactured may be used as the point of extraction.

For a material with more than one point of manufacture or extraction, all within the 500-mile radius, list a single item with the greatest distance. If a portion of the material was either manufactured or extracted beyond the 500-mile radius, list only that portion satisfying the credit requirement.

For assemblies or products manufactured within the 500-mile radius but containing only some components that also were extracted within the 500-mile radius, use multiple lines in the Submittal Template. Base the proportionality of such products' costs on the weight of their various components, as clarified by the example for concrete shown in **Table 1** and **Table 2**.

Considerations

By purchasing regionally manufactured building materials, the local economy is supported, transportation costs and environmental impacts are reduced, and money paid for these materials is retained in the region, supporting the regional economy. The availability of regionally manufactured building materials is dependent on the project location. In some areas, the majority of products needed for the project can be obtained within a 500-mile radius. In other areas, only a small portion or none of the building materials can be sourced locally. It also is important to address the source of raw materials used to manufacture building products. Raw materials for some building products are harvested or extracted far from the point of manufacture, contributing to air and water pollution due to environmental impacts associated with transportation between point of extraction and point of manufacture.

Environmental Issues

The use of regional building materials reduces transportation activities and the accompanying pollution associated with delivering materials to the job site. Trucks, trains, ships and other vehicles deplete finite reserves of fossil fuels and generate air pollution. By selecting building materials that are produced from regional materials, transportation impacts are further reduced.

Economic Issues

Regional building materials are more cost effective for projects due to reduced transportation costs. Also, the support of regional manufacturers and labor forces

Table 1: Sample Assembly Percent Regionally Extracted Calculation for Concrete

Components	Weight [lbs]	Distance Between Project & Extraction Site [miles]	Weight Contributing to Regional Extraction [lbs]
Cement	282	1,250	0
Fly Ash	282	125	282
Water	275	1	275
Slag	750	370	750
Recycled Concrete Aggregate	1000	8	1000
Sand	1200	18	1200
Component Totals	3,789		3,507
Percent Regionally Extracted Materials [3,507 / 3,789]			92.6%

retains capital for the community, contributing to a more stable tax base and a healthier local economy.

Community Issues

Regional building materials are often consistent with regional design aesthetics and are sometimes more responsive to the local climate when compared with materials from other regions. The use of regional building materials supports the regional economy, helping to strengthen the local community and contribute to a high quality of life.

Resources

Please see the USGBC Web site at www. usgbc.org/resources for more specific resources on materials sources and other technical information.

Check with your local Chamber of Commerce and regional and state economic development agencies for building materials manufacturers in your area.

Definitions

Regionally Manufactured Materials, for use in this credit, must be assembled as a finished product within a 500-mile radius of the project site. Assembly, as used for this credit definition, does not include on-site assembly, erection or installation of finished components, as in structural steel, miscellaneous iron or systems furniture.

Regionally Extracted Materials, for use in this credit, must have their source as a raw material from within a 500-mile radius of the project site.

Table 2: Sample MR 5.1 and 5.2 Regional Materials Spreadsheet

Product	Manufacturer	Distance between project & manufacturer (in miles)	Product Cost [$]	Distance Between project & extraction site (in miles)	Product Cost [$]	Regional content information source
Concrete (manufactured and extracted)	Omega Mix	5	$ 926	370	$ 926	Letter from supplier
Concrete (just manufactured)	Omega Mix	5	74			
Wood Paneling	Zeta Panels	25	6,000			Contractor submittal
Casework	Chi Casework	20	30,000			Letter from fabricator
Gypsum wall	Nu Gyps	320	9,900	312	$ 9,900	Letter from fabricator
Wood flooring, salvaged	Xi Floors	20	2,640			Cut sheet
Ceiling light fixtures	Omicron Luminaire	275	21,000			Product brochure
Furniture, reused	Pi Works	45	203,700			Letter from prior owner
			$ 274,240		$ 10,826	

Total Construction Material Value	$	341,214
Division 12 Material Value	$	598,772
Total Project Material Value	$	939,986

% Manufactured Regionally [274,240 / 939,986]	29.2%	29.2% > 20.0% MR 5.1 earned
% Both Manufactured Regionally & Extracted Regionally [10,826 / 939,986]	1.2%	1.1% < 10.0% MR 5.2 not earned

SS	WE	EA	MR	EQ	ID
Credit 5.1					

SS	WE	EA	MR	EQ	ID
Credit 5.2					

Rapidly Renewable Materials

Intent

Reduce the use and depletion of finite raw materials and long-cycle renewable materials by replacing them with rapidly renewable materials.

Requirements

Use rapidly renewable construction, (Division 12, Furniture and Furnishings) materials and products, made from plants that are typically harvested within a 10-year or shorter cycle, for 5% of the total value ($) of all building materials and products used in the project.

Submittals

Provide the LEED for Commercial Interiors Submittal Template, signed by the architect, interior designer, tenant, landlord or other responsible party, declaring that the credit requirements have been met. Include calculations demonstrating that the project incorporates the required percentage of rapidly renewable products. Show their cost and percentage of rapidly renewable components, and the total cost of all materials for the project.

Potential Technologies and Strategies

Establish a project goal for rapidly renewable materials and identify materials and suppliers that can achieve this goal. Consider materials such as bamboo flooring, wool carpets, straw board, cotton batt insulation, linoleum flooring, poplar OSB, sun flower seed board, wheatgrass cabinetry and others. During construction, ensure that the specified rapidly renewable materials are installed.

Credit Interpretation Rulings

In addition to LEED for Commercial Interiors Credit Interpretation Rulings (CIRs), applicable LEED for New Construction CIRs may also apply to LEED for Commercial Interiors projects.

Note that materials included in CSI MasterFormat™ Division 12 (Furniture) are to be included in the credit determination. More information is provided in LEED for Commercial Interiors MR Credit 3.3.

Approach and Implementation

Strategies

Begin by establishing a project goal for the use of rapidly renewable materials. Incorporate into project specifications and plans. Then identify the materials and suppliers that meet the stated criteria and that can achieve this goal. See examples of the materials in **Table 1**. During construction, ensure that the specified rapidly renewable materials are installed and quantify the total percentage of these materials.

Synergies and Trade-Offs

Because some products made from rapidly renewable resources are relatively new, their long-term performance characteristics may be unknown. For example, the performance and stability of bamboo flooring has improved in recent years through the use of laminated layers of the material. Therefore it is important to evaluate a product's performance history prior to specifying.

Rapidly renewable materials costs can also be applied to MR Credits 5 and 7 if the materials meet the credit requirements. Some products made from rapidly renewable materials contain adhesives that may off-gas contaminants and have a negative impact on indoor air quality.

Submittal Documentation

Use the LEED for Commercial Interiors Submittal Template, making the declaration and completing the table similar to **Table 3**.

Additional Documentation

Documentation that may be requested to demonstrate credit achievement may include manufacturers' information indicating the rapidly renewable content. The confirmation may take the form of cut sheets, product literature, brochures or an official statement from the manufacturer.

When the Submittal Template table does not provide adequate lines to itemize all the systems furniture components it is

Table 1: Rapidly Renewable Materials

Examples of Rapidly Renewable Materials
Bamboo flooring
Cotton batt insulation
Linoleum flooring
Sunflower seed board
Wheatgrass cabinetry
Wool carpet

Equation 1: Rapidly Renewable Material Portion

$$\text{Rapidly Renewable Material Portion [\%]} = \frac{\sum \text{Rapidly Renewable Material Costs [\$]}}{\text{Total Project Material Value [\$]}}$$

recommended that a separate spreadsheet be developed: the results may then be entered as a single line in the Submittal Template.

Exemplary Performance

Project teams may earn an Innovation in Design point for exemplary performance when the requirements reach the next incremental step. For rapidly renewable materials, the credit calculation must be 10% or greater.

Calculations

Identify those products that are considered to be rapidly renewable. Sum all rapidly renewable materials costs and divide by the total project material value ($), as shown in **Equation 1**.

Assembly Rapidly Renewable Content

Assemblies include all products that are made of multiple materials, either in reaching a formulation for a material (i.e., particle board), or of all the sub-components (i.e., a worksurface). The determination of the rapidly renewable content of an assembly should not be confused with the calculation that is shown in **Equation 1**, where the final value is expressed in dollars. For assembly rapidly renewable content, the value is the percent by weight. **Table 2** is an example of a manufacturer's workstation product lines using one of the BIFMA typical workstation configurations.

When there are sub-components, the final percentage must be determined by only using the weights of the smaller elements. No consideration is given to relative costs of the sub-components. In the example shown in **Table 2**, only 75% by weight of the top veneer is bamboo and counts toward the rapidly renewable content.

Systems Furniture

In LEED for Commercial Interiors, those materials listed in CSI MasterFormat™ Division 12 (Furniture) are to be included in the calculation of MR Credit 6. This CSI category includes systems furniture. To facilitate the credit calculation, the applicant may use the percentages of rapidly renewable content determined by the product manufacturer for the typical workstation configuration that best

Table 2: Sample Assembly Rapidly Renewable Content for a BIFMA Typical Configuration

Manufacturer	Lambda Furniture		
Product Line	High End Workstations		
BIFMA Typical Configuration	Wkstn Configuration 0010		
Component	Weight [lbs]	Percent Rapidly Renewable	Weight Contributing to Rapidly Renewable Content [lbs]
Wheat Board	28.0	100%	28.0
Top Veneer, Bamboo	4.0	75%	3.0
Other	721.0	0%	0.0
	753.0		31.0
Percent Rapidly Renewable [31.0 / 753.0]			**4.1%**

Credit 6

represents their project installation. This approach also may be used in calculating MR Credits 4 and 7.

For use in this credit, BIFMA International has defined typical workstation configurations for both open plan and private offices. They are available at www.bifma.org. Using these typical configurations, the individual manufacturers have determined the rapidly renewable content percentages for their individual product lines. **Table 2** is an example of a manufacturer's calculation. Project teams should have this documentation from the manufacturer available should the credit be audited.

Project teams, most likely in conjunction with their furniture supplier, will need to segregate their total new furniture costs into segments that correspond to the industry-typical configurations for each manufacturer and product line. These segment values are then multiplied by the manufacturer's rapidly renewable content percentages for the credit calculation. See **Table 3**.

This approach was developed so project teams would not have to build the credit values starting from individual workstation component counts, costs and rapidly renewable content percentages. However, when a project team has purchased components that have rapidly renewable contents outside a 5% range of those used in the manufacturer's published percentages for the typical configurations, they will need to obtain project specific detail. This may occur when special green materials have been specified. In this case, request that the manufacturer prepare an assembly rapidly renewable content calculation, similar to **Table 2**, for the actual products purchased.

Other products, such as seating, storage and conference tables, are not included in the typical configurations. For some of these items there are consistent attributes across a product line: the rapidly renew-

Table 3: Spreadsheet Example for Rapidly Renewable Materials

Product name	Company	Product	% Renewable	Renewable Value	Rapidly renewable content information source
Countertops - wheatboard	Rho Tops	$ 6,700	30.0%	$ 2,010	Letter
Casework	Sigma Mill	30,000	50.0%	15,000	Letter
Linoleum flooring	Tau Floors	882	60.0%	529	Cut sheet
Bamboo window blinds	Upsilon Shades	14,079	75.0%	10,559	Product literature
Systems Furniture, new	Lambda Cubicles	228,366	4.1%	9,363	Manufacturer's typical
Tables, new	Mu Mills	19,751	88.4%	17,460	Manufacturer's detail

Rapidly Renewable Materials Subtotal	$	54,921
Total Construction Material Value	$	341,214
Division 12 Material Value		598,772
Total Project Material Value		939,986
% Rapidly Renewable Value [54,921 / 939,986]		5.8%

5.8% > 5.0%
MR 6 earned

able content of a 36" diameter table will be the same as that in the 72" variety. When this is the case, identify the dollar amount for all those products used on the project within the product line and multiply by the rapidly renewable percentages. When this is not the case, individual products must be addressed separately. **Table 3** shows examples of both situations.

Exclusions

Mechanical, electrical, and plumbing systems components are not to be included in this credit calculation. Note that the denominator for this credit will differ from that of MR Credit 4, Recycled Content, and MR Credit 5, Regional Materials, if plumbing products are included for those two credits.

No default materials value

In the LEED for Commercial Interiors Rating System there is no default relationship between the value of materials and total construction: nothing similar to the 45% relationship used in LEED for New Construction has been found consistent for commercial interior projects.

Considerations

Many conventional building materials require large inputs of land, natural resources, capital and time. Conversely, rapidly renewable materials generally require less of these inputs and are therefore likely to be more environmentally responsible. Rapidly renewable resources are those materials that substantially replenish themselves faster than traditional extraction demand (i.e., planted and harvested in less than a 10-year cycle).

Environmental Issues

Rapidly renewable resources sometimes provide the opportunity to displace raw materials that have greater environmental impacts. Common examples include composite panels that are made from agricultural fiber such as wheat, substituting for composite wood panels. Irresponsible forestry practices cause ecosystem and habitat destruction, soil erosion and stream sedimentation. Rapidly renewable crops require significantly less land—often due to higher density and shorter growing cycles—to produce the same amount of end product, and are often by-products that are otherwise considered waste.

Bio-based plastics (e.g., from corn starch) and other rapidly renewable resources are beginning to provide alternatives to some petroleum-based plastics.

Economic Issues

Because rapidly renewable resources may be harvested more quickly, they tend to give a faster payback on investment for manufacturers. As demand increases, they are expected to become cost-competitive with conventional materials.

Community Issues

The land saved from the production requirements of rapidly renewable resources may be used for a variety of other uses, including open space and other agricultural products. Rapidly renewable materials, by virtue of a more consistent harvesting cycle, may sustain a community over a longer period than the steady and eventual depletion of finite resources or the degradation of a productive ecosystem.

Resources

Please see the USGBC Web site at www.usgbc.org/resources for more specific resources on materials sources and other technical information.

Web Sites

Environmental Building News

BuildingGreen, Inc.

www.buildinggreen.com/products/bamboo.html

(802) 257-7300

An article in Environmental Building News on bamboo flooring, including a listing of bamboo flooring suppliers.

Environmental Design + Construction

www.edcmag.com (search for Highlights of Environmental Flooring)

An Environmental Design & Construction article providing information on bamboo flooring, linoleum and wool carpeting.

GreenSpec

BuildingGreen, Inc.

www.buildinggreen.com/menus/index.cfm

(802) 257-7300

Detailed listings for more than 1,500 green building products, including environmental data, manufacturer information, and links to additional resources.

Guide to Resource-Efficient Building Elements

www.crbt.org/index.html

The Center for Resourceful Building Technology Directory of environmentally responsible building products. This resource provides introductory discussions per topic and contact information for specific products, including salvaged materials. (The CRBT project is no longer active, and the CRBT Web site is no longer updated. The National Center for Appropriate Technology is providing this Web site for archival purposes only).

Oikos

www.oikos.com

A searchable directory of resource-efficient building products and sustainable design educational resources.

Definitions

Rapidly Renewable materials are considered to be an agricultural product, both fiber and animal, that takes 10 years or less to grow or raise, and to harvest in an ongoing and sustainable fashion.

Certified Wood

1 point

Intent

Encourage environmentally responsible forest management.

Requirements

When using new wood-based products and materials, use a minimum of 50% that are certified in accordance with the Forest Stewardship Council's Principles and Criteria. Division 12 (Furniture) material value is included in the determination of the certified wood content.

Submittals

Provide the LEED for Commercial Interiors Submittal Template, signed by the architect, interior designer, owner or other responsible party, declaring that the credit requirements have been met and listing the FSC-certified materials and products used. Include calculations demonstrating that the project incorporates the required percentage of FSC-certified materials/products and their cost together with the total cost of all materials for the project. For each material/product used to meet these requirements, provide the vendor's or manufacturer's Forest Stewardship Council chain-of-custody certificate number.

Potential Technologies and Strategies

Establish a project goal for FSC-certified wood products and identify suppliers that can achieve this goal. During construction, ensure that the FSC-certified wood products are installed and quantify the total percentage of FSC-certified wood products installed.

Summary of Referenced Standard

Forest Stewardship Council's Principles and Criteria

www.fscus.org

(877) 372-5646

Certification is a "seal of approval" awarded to forest managers who adopt environmentally and socially responsible forest management practices and to companies that manufacture and sell products made from certified wood. Certification enables consumers, including architects and specifiers, to identify and procure wood products from well-managed sources and thereby use their purchasing power to influence and reward improved forest management activities around the world.

LEED accepts certification established by the internationally recognized Forest Stewardship Council (FSC). FSC was created in 1993 to establish international forest management standards (known as the FSC Principles and Criteria) to assure that forestry practices are environmentally responsible, socially beneficial and economically viable. These Principles and Criteria ensure the long-term health and productivity of forests for timber production, wildlife habitat, clean air and water supplies, climate stabilization, spiritual renewal and social benefit, such as lasting community employment derived from stable forestry operations. FSC also accredits and monitors certification organizations. These "certifiers" are independent, third-party auditors that are qualified to annually evaluate compliance with FSC standards and to award certifications. There are two types of certification:

Forest Management Certification is awarded to responsible forest managers after their operations successfully complete audits of forestry practices and plans.

Chain of Custody Certification is awarded after companies that process, manufacture and/or sell products made of certified wood successfully complete audits to ensure proper use of the FSC name and logo, segregation of certified and non-certified materials in manufacturing and distribution systems, and observation of other relevant FSC rules (i.e., meeting minimum requirements for FSC fiber content in assembled and composite wood products).

The majority of FSC certification audits performed in North America are conducted by SmartWood and Scientific Certification Systems (SCS), which are based in the United States. A limited number are performed by SGS, which is based in Europe.

Credit Interpretation Rulings

In addition to LEED for Commercial Interiors Credit Interpretation Rulings (CIRs), applicable LEED for New Construction CIRs may also apply to LEED for Commercial Interiors projects.

Note that materials included in CSI MasterFormat™ Division 12 (Furniture) are to be included in the credit determination. More information is provided in LEED for Commercial Interiors MR Credit 3.3.

Credit Interpretation LEED for New Construction v2 MRc7 dated 6/3/2002 makes the following amendment: "The calculations for certified wood shall exclude the value of any post-consumer recycled wood fiber content of a product that qualifies to be counted under Credit 4, Recycled Content Materials."

Approach and Implementation

Establish a project goal for FSC-certified wood products and identify suppliers that can achieve this goal. Using the contacts and materials listed in the Resources section below, research the availability of the wood species and products to ensure that they are available from FSC-certified sources.

Another method for lowering the impact of wood resources is to research and specify quality grades that are most readily available from well-managed forests. Using lower grades of wood can dramatically reduce pressure on forests, which produce only limited quantities of top-grade timber (i.e., Architectural Woodwork Institute [AWI] Grades 2 or 3 for lumber or veneer rather than Grade 1; Select And Better rather than First And Second [FAS] for hardwood lumber graded to National Hardwood Lumber Association [NHLA] rules; or 2 and Better rather than Select Structural for softwood lumber graded to Western Wood Product Association [WWPA] rules). As an example, the typical yield of FAS-grade lumber in a deciduous forest is 5% – 20% of all hardwood lumber cut depending on many variables, i.e. thickness, length. In structural applications, specify the lowest grade that will meet the project's performance and engineering requirements. In interior finishes and other exposed surfaces, consider specifying "character" grades that highlight the uniqueness of wood as a natural material.

At the earliest opportunity make contact with local vendors, suppliers and manufacturers that are certified for FSC chain-of-custody. The FSC's referral service is an essential sourcing tool (offered through www.fscus.org/green_building). Provide project bidders with a list of certified vendors and encourage them to make contact early in the project to establish product availability and pricing. As the availability of certain certified wood products may vary over the life of a project, consider having the owner pre-purchase, store and supply particular items to the contractor ("Furnished by the Owner, Installed by the Contractor," or FOIC). Finding a storage location that best mimics the final ambient moisture of the project's space

will ensure proper installation. Because of the typically high ambient moisture present during construction, a job site is not the best location to store wood if FOIC is being implemented.

Synergies and Trade-Offs

Certified wood products can be applied to other MR Credits if these products comply with requirements for those credits. Like their non-certified counterparts, some FSC-certified products contain adhesives and chemicals that have off-gassing characteristics that may affect indoor air quality, and may conflict with eligibility for IEQ Credit 4.4 (e.g. urea formaldehyde).

Submittal Documentation

Use the LEED for Commercial Interiors Submittal Template, declaring compliance and completing the spreadsheet. See **Table 2** for an example.

Enter the value of new wood in all products containing wood. Indicate the percentage of wood that is FSC-certified for each individual product type and provide the relevant chain-of-custody certification number.

When the Submittal Template does not provide adequate lines to itemize all the systems furniture components it is recommended that a separate spreadsheet be developed. When this is done, the results may then be entered as a single line in the Submittal Template; see **Table 2**.

Chain-of-custody (CoC) certification is required to different extents based on two scenarios: products with and without the on-product FSC label. If a manufacturer places its FSC CoC label on the product or product packaging used for individual sale (generally applying to fabricated products), then subsequent entities in the supply chain are not required to have CoC certification unless the product's packaging or form is changed before it reaches

the end consumer. (Note: this instruction is meant for LEED compliance only; it varies from FSC rules). For LEED documentation, a wholesaler or retailer does not need CoC for a packaged product that is labeled with the manufacturer's CoC number. This number is to be supplied in the LEED submittal. A fabricator using a labeled product as a component of a larger assembly will need to have CoC certification since it is altering the product's packaging, and possibly its form.

For FSC certified products that are not individually packaged for sale, the vendor to the consumer is required to have CoC certification, and this is the sole CoC number for the product entered in the LEED submittal. Contractors and subcontractors are considered the end consumers; they can demonstrate with copies of invoices (if requested) the quantity purchased for the job and their suppliers' CoC numbers. For example, a contractor or subcontractor that installs non-labeled FSC wood panels is not required to have CoC certification; its supplier must have CoC certification. A manufacturer that installs its own product (e.g. custom casework) is not required to have CoC certification.

Additional Documentation

For potential use during submittal review, it is suggested that the project team compile and maintain copies of vendor invoices for each product used to meet the requirements. Per Forest Stewardship Council rules, each invoice should include the vendor's chain-of-custody certificate number and should also identify certified products on an item-by-item basis. If the product is individually labeled for distribution and sale, retain an invoice or other document that indicates the manufacturer's CoC number.

Exemplary Performance

Project teams may earn an Innovation in Design point for exemplary performance when the requirements reach the next incremental step. For certified wood,

Table 1: Sample Assembly Percent Wood-Based Content for a BIFMA Typical Configuration

Manufacturer	Lambda Furniture		
Product Line	**High End Workstations**		
BIFMA Typical Configuration	**Wkstn Configuration 0010**		
Component	**Weight [lbs]**	**Less Post-Consumer Weight [lbs]**	**Wood-based Component Weight [lbs]**	**FSC Certified Wood Weight [lbs]**
Wheat Board	28.0		28.0	28.0
Top Veneer	4.0		4.0	0.0
Other Wood	3.0	-1.1	1.9	1.5
Non-wood content	718.0		0.0	0.0
	753.0		33.9	29.5

Percent Wood [33.9 / 753.0]		**4.5%**
Percent FSC Certified Wood [29.5 / 753.0]		**3.9%**

Equation 1: Certified Wood Material Portion

$$\text{Certified Wood Material Portion [\%]} = \frac{\sum \text{FSC Certified Wood Material Value [\$]}}{\sum \text{Total New Wood Material Value [\$]}}$$

the credit calculation must yield 95% or greater.

Calculations

Use the LEED for Commercial Interiors Submittal Templates to list those products that satisfy the requirements of the credits. This credit compares the percent of FSC-certified wood to the total new wood used in the project. See **Equation 1**. The Submittal Template automatically performs the calculations based on the data entered, as shown in **Table 2**.

Assemblies

For assemblies, it is helpful to develop a working spreadsheet to calculate the value of FSC-certified wood as a percentage of new wood, by weight. Recycled and salvaged wood content is subtracted so as not to conflict with the intent of other LEED MR credits. See the example shown in **Table 1**. The summation may be entered as a single line in the Submittal Template. See **Table 2**.

Furniture and Furnishings

The wood content of newly purchased furniture and furnishings is to be included in this calculation. Because of its potential contribution to both the overall new wood content, and the FSC-certified wood content, it is prudent to consider it in the selection and purchasing process. Furniture and furnishings are not limited to what is supplied by the contractor, but also includes owner purchases.

Systems Furniture

To facilitate the credit calculation, the applicant may use the percentages of wood content and FSC-certified wood content determined by the product manufacturer for the typical workstation configuration that best represents their project installation. This approach also may be used in calculating MR Credits 4 and 6.

For use in this credit, BIFMA International has defined typical workstation configurations for both open plan and

Table 2: MR 7 Certified Wood Example Spreadsheet

Wood Product	Vendor	Material Value	Percent Wood (by Weight)	Value of Wood	Percent Certified Wood (by Weight)	Value of Certified Wood	Forest Stewardship Council chain-of-custody certificate number
Carpentry	Phi Woods	$19,800	92.1%	$ 18,240	92.1%	$ 18,240	SW-COC-013
Door bucks	Chi Bucks	720	100%	720	46.0%	331	SCS-COC-00067
Moldings	Psi Trim	1,710	100%	1,710	100.0%	1,710	SCS-COC-00094
Shelving	Psi Trim	2,407	77%	1,853	0.0%	0	n/a
Countertops	Beta Mills	6,347	95%	6,030	0.0%	0	n/a
Casework	Beta Mills	34,875	80%	27,900	58.50%	20,402	SW-COC-675
Wood doors and frames	Beta Mills	383	100%	383	100.0%	383	SCS-COC-00122
Furniture systems, new	Lambda Cubicles	288,366	4.5%	12,976	3.9%	11,297	Manufacturer's detail
Tables, new	Mu Mills	19,751	93.0%	18,974	11.0%	2,173	Manufacturer's detail
			Subtotal	$ 88,786		$ 54,536	
		% Certified Wood [54,536 / 88,786]		61.4%		61.4% > 50.0% MR 7 earned	

private offices. They are available at www.bifma.org. Using these typical configurations, the individual manufacturers have determined the wood content and the FSC-certified wood content percentages for their individual product lines. **Table 1** is an example of a manufacturer's calculation. Project teams should have this documentation from the manufacturer should the credit be audited.

Project teams, most likely in conjunction with their furniture supplier, will need to segregate their total new furniture costs into segments that correspond to the industry-typical configurations for each manufacturer and product line. These segment values are then multiplied by the manufacturer's wood content and FSC-certified wood content percentages for the credit calculation. See **Table 2**.

This approach was developed so project teams would not have to build the credit values starting from individual workstation component counts, costs and wood content percentages. However, when a project team has purchased components that have wood contents outside a 5% range of those used in the manufacturer's published percentages for the typical configurations, they will need to obtain project specific detail. This may occur when FSC-certified materials have been specified. In this case, request that the manufacturer prepare an assembly content calculation, similar to **Table 1**, for the actual products purchased.

Other products, such as seating, storage and conference tables, are not included in the typical configurations. For some of these items there are consistent attributes across a product line: the wood content and FSC-certified wood content of a 36" diameter table will be the same as that in the 72" variety. When this is the case, identify the dollar amount for all those products used on the project within the product line and multiply by the wood content and FSC-certified wood content

percentages. When this is not the case, individual products must be addressed separately.

Considerations

Wood has the potential to be a truly sustainable resource because it is renewable, biodegradable, non-toxic, energy efficient and recyclable. Too often, however, wood is linked to the degradation or destruction of ecologically important forest ecosystems, such as old-growth forests. Thus, responsible forestry practices aim to minimize or eliminate these problems. Responsible forestry seeks to meet the long-term forest product needs of humans while maintaining the function and biodiversity of forested landscapes. The primary goal is to restore, enhance and sustain a full range of forest values while producing a perpetual yield of quality forest products.

Environmental Issues

The negative environmental impacts of irresponsible forest practices can include destruction of forests, loss of wildlife habitat, soil erosion and stream sedimentation, water and air pollution, and waste generation. The FSC Standard incorporates many criteria that contribute to the long-term health and integrity of forest ecosystems. From an environmental perspective, the elements of responsible FSC-certified forestry include sustainable timber harvesting (i.e., not removing more timber volume than replaces itself over the cutting interval or rotation), preserving wildlife habitat and biodiversity, maintaining soil and water quality, minimizing the use of harmful chemicals, and conserving high conservation value forests (e.g., endangered and old-growth forests).

Economic Issues

World trade in forest products has increased dramatically in the last 30 years, from $47 billion in 1970 to $139 billion in 1998. As more developing countries embrace world forest product markets and their growing economies encourage domestic consumption, the protection of forests will become a critical issue. Currently, the costs of FSC-certified wood products are equal to or higher than conventional wood products and availability varies by region. The price of FSC-certified wood products is expected to be more competitive with conventional wood products in future years as the world's forest resources are depleted and the forest industry embraces more widespread adoption of sustainable business principles.

Community Issues

Irresponsible logging practices can have negative social impacts. Thus, the socioeconomic and political components to FSC certification include respecting indigenous people's rights and adhering to all applicable laws and treaties. Certification also involves forest workers and forest-dependent communities as stakeholders and beneficiaries of responsible forest management. Through the encouragement of responsible forest practices local timber economies are stabilized and forestland ecosystems are preserved for future generations.

Resources

Web Sites

Forest Certification Resource Center

www.certifiedwood.org

(503) 224-2205

Contains a searchable database of FSC products and a variety of resources including comparative information on forest certification systems.

Forest Stewardship Council

www.fscus.org/green_building

(202) 342-0413

A primary resource for information and practical tools such as databases of certified product suppliers, referral service, specification language, and the "Designing & Building with FSC" guide and forms.

GreenSpec

BuildingGreen, Inc.

www.buildinggreen.com/menus/index.cfm

(802) 257-7300

Detailed listings for more than 1,500 green building products, including environmental data, manufacturer information and links to additional resources.

Scientific Certification Systems' Forest Conservation Program

http://www.scscertified.com/forestry/

Scientific Certification System's Forest Conservation Program is a third-party certifier that is accredited to conduct forest management and chain-of-custody audits in the United States and internationally according to the rules of the FSC.

Smartwood

Rainforest Alliance

http://www.rainforest-alliance.org/programs/forestry/smartwood/

(802) 434-5491

SmartWood is a third-party certifier that is accredited to conduct forest management and chain-of-custody audits in the United States and globally according to the rules of the FSC. It is a nonprofit program of the Rainforest Alliance and is based in the United States.

Print Media

Sustainable Forestry: Philosophy, Science, and Economics, by Chris Maser, DelRay Beach: St. Lucie Press, 1994.

The Business of Sustainable Forestry: Strategies for an Industry in Transition, by Michael B. Jenkins and Emily T. Smith, Island Press, 1999.

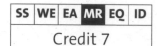

Definitions

Chain-of-Custody is a document that tracks the movement of a wood product from the forest to a vendor and is used to verify compliance with FSC guidelines. A "vendor" is defined as the company that supplies wood products to project contractors or subcontractors for on-site installation.

Sustainable Forestry is the practice of managing forest resources to meet the long-term forest product needs of humans while maintaining the biodiversity of forested landscapes. The primary goal is to restore, enhance and sustain a full range of forest values—economic, social and ecological.

Indoor Environmental Quality

Overview

Americans spend on average 90% of their time indoors where the U.S. Environmental Protection Agency reports that levels of pollutants may run two to five times—and occasionally more than 100 times—higher than outdoor levels. Similarly, the World Health Organization reported in its 1999 Air Quality Guidelines that most of an individual's exposure to many air pollutants comes through inhalation of this indoor air. Many of these pollutants can cause health reactions in the estimated 17 million Americans who suffer from asthma and 40 million who have allergies, thus contributing to millions of days absent from school and work. Outbreaks of Legionnaires' disease and sick building syndrome confirm the relationship of indoor air quality to the occupant health.

Over the past twenty years, research and experience has improved our understanding of what is involved in attaining high Indoor Environmental Quality (IEQ), and revealed manufacturing and construction practices that can prevent many IEQ problems from arising. The use of better products and practices has reduced potential liability for design team members and building owners. The results are increased market value for buildings with exemplary IEQ and greater productivity for the occupants. In a case study included in the 1994 publication Greening the Building and the Bottom Line, the Rocky Mountain Institute cites how improved indoor environmental quality improved worker productivity by 16%, netting a rapid payback on the increased capital investment.

Preventing IEQ problems is generally much less expensive than identifying and solving them after they occur. One practical way to prevent IEQ problems from arising is to specify materials that release fewer and less harmful chemical compounds. Evaluation of the properties of the adhesives, paints, carpets, composite wood products and furniture and specifying those materials with low levels of potentially irritating off-gas can reduce occupant exposure. Scheduling of deliveries and sequencing construction activities can reduce material exposure to moisture and absorption of off-gassed contaminants. Protection of air handling systems during construction and a building flush-out prior to occupancy further reduces potential for problems arising during the operational life of a project.

Using higher ratios of filtered outside air, increasing ventilation rates, managing moisture, and controlling the level of contaminants in the cleaning substances used can provide optimal air quality for building occupants. Installation of automatic HVAC sensors and controls to maintain proper temperature, humidity, and rates of outdoor air introduced to occupied spaces also plays a key role in maintaining optimal air quality. Use of sensors to alert building maintenance staff to potential Indoor Air Quality (IAQ) problems such as carbon dioxide (CO_2) build-up in occupied space can also effectively balance energy and IEQ issues.

Occupant wellbeing can be improved by providing views to the exterior and by providing daylighting. In addition, providing occupants with the ability to control their personal thermal environment can reduce hot/cold complaint calls and generally raise occupant satisfaction levels which can lead to increases in productivity.

The joint efforts of the building selection and interior design teams, contractors, subcontractors and suppliers are integral to providing a quality indoor environment. **Table 1** lists the LEED for Com-

---

Overview of LEED® Prerequisites and Credits

EQ Prerequisite 1
Minimum IAQ Performance

EQ Prerequisite 2
Environmental Tobacco Smoke (ETS) Control

EQ Credit 1
Outdoor Air Delivery Monitoring

EQ Credit 2
Increased Ventilation

EQ Credit 3.1
Construction IAQ Management Plan, During Construction

EQ Credit 3.2
Construction IAQ Management Plan, Before Occupancy

EQ Credit 4.1
Low-Emitting Materials, Adhesives and Sealants

EQ Credit 4.2
Low-Emitting Materials, Paints and Coatings

EQ Credit 4.3
Low-Emitting Materials, Carpet Systems

EQ Credit 4.4
Low-Emitting Materials, Composite Wood and Laminate Adhesives

EQ Credit 4.5
Low-Emitting Materials, Furniture and Seating

EQ Credit 5
Indoor Chemical and Pollutant Source Control

EQ Credit 6.1
Controllability of Systems, Lighting

EQ Credit 6.2
Controllability of Systems, Temperature and Ventilation

**Overview of LEED®
Prerequisites and
Credits cont'd**

EQ Credit 7.1
Thermal Comfort,
Compliance

EQ Credit 7.2
Thermal Comfort,
Monitoring

EQ Credit 8.1
Daylight and Views,
Daylight 75% of Spaces

EQ Credit 8.2
Daylight and Views,
Daylight 90% of Spaces

EQ Credit 8.3
Daylight and Views, Views
for 90% of Seated Spaces

mercial Interiors EQ Credits and shows
when attention must be given to each.

Table 1: Timing on Credit Decisions and Actions

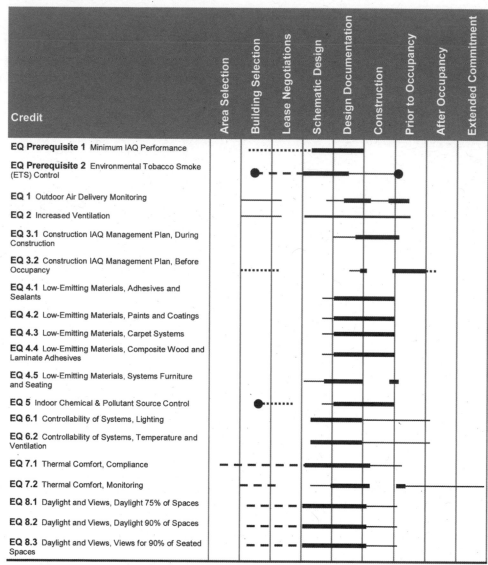

Key to symbols
● Critical decision point
━━━ Period of critical activity
─── Period of activity
- - - - Period of possible activity

Minimum IAQ Performance

Intent

Establish minimum indoor air quality (IAQ) performance to enhance indoor air quality in the occupant space, thus contributing to the comfort and wellbeing of the occupants.

Requirements

- Meet the minimum requirements of the voluntary consensus standard ASHRAE 62.1-2004, Ventilation for Acceptable Indoor Air Quality Mechanical ventilation systems shall perform according to the Ventilation Rate Procedure.

- Naturally ventilated buildings must comply with ASHRAE 62.1-2004 Section 5.1.

- Modify or maintain existing building outside-air (OA) ventilation distribution system to supply at least the outdoor air ventilation rate required by ASHRAE Standard 62.1-2004.

- If the project cannot meet the outside air requirements of ASHRAE 62.1-2004 (all other requirements must be met), it must document the space and system constraints that make it not possible, and complete an engineering assessment of the system's maximum cu.ft. per minute (cfm) capability towards meeting the requirements of ASHRAE 62.1-2004, and achieve those levels, with an absolute minimum of 10 cfm per person.

Submittals

- Provide the LEED for Commercial Interiors Submittal Template, signed by the responsible design professional, declaring that the project is fully compliant with Sections 4, 5, 6 and 7 of ASHRAE 62.1 2004 and all accepted Addenda. Provide a summary of calculations used to determine outdoor air ventilation rates, documenting all assumptions including occupancy category, occupant density, and multiple zone analysis.

- For existing buildings that cannot meet the ASHRAE 62.1-2004 minimum requirements, the engineer must certify in a letter that they have in hand and will deliver to the client: photographs/specs or cut-sheet of mechanical equipment as-built Mechanical plans; or single line drawings as-builts of all space constrained aspects in system (e.g., vertical riser/horizontal chase space).

Potential Technologies & Strategies

Design the HVAC system to meet the ventilation requirements of Sections 4, 5, 6 and 7 of the referenced standard. Identify potential IAQ problems on the site.

Summary of Referenced Standard

ANSI/ASHRAE Standard 62.1-2004: Ventilation for Acceptable Indoor Air Quality

American Society of Heating, Refrigerating and Air-Conditioning Engineers

www.ashrae.org

(800) 527-4723

This standard specifies minimum ventilation rates and indoor air quality (IAQ) levels to reduce the potential for adverse health effects. The standard specifies that mechanical or natural ventilation systems be designed to prevent uptake of contaminants, minimize the opportunity for growth and dissemination of microorganisms, and filter particulates, if necessary. Makeup air inlets should be located away from contaminant sources such as cooling towers; sanitary vents; and vehicular exhaust from parking garages, loading docks and street traffic.

A Ventilation Rate Procedure and an Indoor Air Quality Procedure are outlined to achieve compliance with the standard. The Ventilation Rate Procedure prescribes outdoor air quality acceptable for ventilation; outdoor air treatment measures; and ventilation rates for residential, commercial, institutional, vehicular, and industrial spaces. The procedure also includes criteria for the reduction of outdoor air quantities when recirculated air is treated by contaminant-removal equipment and criteria for variable ventilation when the air volume in the space is used as a reservoir to dilute contaminants. The Indoor Air Quality Procedure incorporates both quantitative and subjective evaluation and restricts contaminant concentrations to acceptable levels.

Credit Interpretation Rulings

In addition to LEED for Commercial Interiors Credit Interpretation Rulings (CIRs), applicable LEED for New Construction CIRs concerning this prerequisite may also apply to LEED for Commercial Interiors projects.

Approach and Implementation

As human beings inhale, our bodies consume oxygen (O_2); as we exhale, we give off carbon dioxide (CO_2). Mechanical HVAC system designs seek to ensure that fresh air is available for occupants in the space. Mechanical HVAC systems use air to add and remove heat from the building and provide an acceptable thermal environment. In addition, these systems are designed to provide adequate ventilation to ensure acceptable IEQ. ASHRAE 62.1-2004 establishes minimum guidelines for the rates that outdoor (fresh) air should be introduced into building spaces. ASHRAE 62.1-2004 guidelines take into account the density of people within an area, and the type of activity that will occur in the space (i.e., the amount of exertion).

Application

This prerequisite requires project teams to verify that the building HVAC system has the capability to supply ventilation at rates sufficient to provide acceptable indoor air quality. Several other credits in LEED for Commercial Interiors are predicated on the project space meeting the minimum outdoor air flow rates determined in the referenced standard. For this reason, EQ Prerequisite 1 is not limited to the project scope of work. Many of the provisions of ASHRAE 62.1-2004, such as the location of air intakes, apply to functional aspects of the HVAC system most commonly located in parts of the building outside the project space. When a project space is to be served by a central HVAC system, or an existing system, the project team should confirm as early as possible that the system will adequately function so the provisions of the standard can be met within the project space.

During the energy crisis in the mid-70s, fuel and power cost spikes pushed many building owners to build buildings with outdoor air rates well below the current standards in an effort to maximize energy efficiency; for project teams doing tenant fit-out work in one of these buildings, an alternative compliance path is provided.

Strategies

Prior to leasing or acquisition, evaluate the building in which the project plans to locate. This evaluation could logically be combined with the evaluation undertaken to confirm compliance with EA Prerequisite 2.

In determining outside air quality, potential problems may include heavy traffic areas, nearby industrial sites, or neighboring waste management sites. In the evaluation consider possible future uses of nearby sites that may impact outdoor air quality. Obtain ambient air quality data and local wind patterns from the U.S. EPA or local entities to determine if there are sources of pollution affecting the site.

After the building has been chosen, identify site activities that may have a negative impact on air quality such as construction activities, materials installed in the building, and chemical handling activities during occupancy. Establish air quality standards early in the design process. Clearly state these design criteria in plans and specifications.

If the project scope of work allows, design the fresh air intakes away from possible sources of contamination or confirm that the existing fresh air intakes are at least 25 feet from sources of contamination. Possible sources of contamination include loading areas, building exhaust fans, cooling towers, street traffic, idling vehicles, standing water, parking garages, sanitary vents, dumpsters and outside smoking areas.

Ensure that the outside air capacity for the ventilation system can meet the requirements of the referenced standard in all modes of operation. Remember to consider the potential occupancy load when calculating outside air needs in all spaces. Assess changes in occupant loads for renovation or retrofit projects and, where possible, allow flexibility to accommodate future changes to these loads. Avoid over- or under-design of the ventilation systems and plan for future retrofits where possible.

Consider including operational testing in the building commissioning report. Implement an operations and maintenance plan based on the ASHRAE 62.1-2004 Section 8 to maintain an uncontaminated HVAC system.

Synergies and Tradeoffs

Increased ventilation rates can solve some indoor air quality problems by diluting contaminant concentration but this strategy may affect indoor thermal comfort and may increase energy use. Building commissioning and Measurement & Verification processes are tools that can be used to improve indoor air quality while minimizing energy efficiency losses. Site location and landscape design affect the outdoor air volumes that can be circulated through the building. Dense neighborhoods, adjacent transportation facilities, and existing site contamination can adversely affect the quality of outside air available for ventilation purposes.

During construction and building fit-out, protect building materials from moisture. To reduce the detrimental effects some materials have on IAQ, specify materials and furnishings that do not release harmful or irritating chemicals, such as Volatile Organic Compounds (VOCs) from paints and solvents. Occupant activities such as chemical handling and smoking affect air quality.

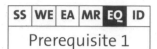

Submittal Documentation

Mechanically ventilated projects meeting ASHRAE 62.1-2004

Provide the declaration included in the LEED for Commercial Interiors Submittal Templates indicating that the building in which the project is located complies with Sections 4, 5, 6 and 7 of ASHRAE 62.1-2004. Follow the Ventilation Rate procedure found in Section 6.2 of ASHRAE 62.1-2004. The breathing zone outdoor airflow is equal to the sum of the outdoor airflow rate required per person times the zone population, plus the outdoor airflow rate required per unit area times the zone floor area. The standard's Table 6-1 "Minimum Ventilation Rates in Breathing Zone" provides information by occupancy category to determine both the amount of outdoor air needed to ventilate people-related source contaminants and area-related source contaminants. The people-related-sources portion of the outdoor air rate addressed actual occupancy density and activity. The area-related-sources portion accounts for background off-gassing from building materials, furniture and materials typically found in that particular occupancy. Finally, the required zone outdoor airflow is the breathing zone outdoor airflow adjusted to reflect the efficiency of the actual air distribution configuration. Complete the calculations and submit a spreadsheet similar to **Table 1**.

When one air handler supplies a mixture of outdoor air and recirculated return air to more than one zone, provide its multiple zone analysis. Indicate if Table 6-3 or Appendix A of ASHRAE 62.1-2004 has been used to determine system ventilation efficiency for multiple zone recirculating systems.

Naturally ventilated projects meeting ASHRAE 62.1-2004

Provide the LEED for Commercial Interiors Submittal Template indicating that the naturally ventilated space meets the requirements of ASHRAE 62.1-2004. Demonstrate through plans and tables that the ratio of operable opening area to floor area meets the required standard, and that the occupied areas are all within the allowable distance from the openings. Complete the calculations and submit a spreadsheet similar to **Table 2**.

Table 1: Sample Summary Calculations Used to Determine Outdoor Air Ventilation Rates

Zone Identification	Occupancy Category	Outdoor Airflow Rate Required per Person R_p [CFM / Person]	Zone Population P_z	Outdoor Airflow Rate Required per Unit Area R_a [CFM / SF]	Zone Floor Area A_z [SF]	Zone Air Distribution Effectiveness E_z	Standard Zone Outdoor Airflow V_{oz} [CFM / SF]	Design Zone Outdoor Airflow V_{oz} [CFM / SF]
General Office	Office Space	5	45	0.06	8,000	1.0	0.088	0.115
Training Room	Lecture hall	7.5	40	0.06	750	1.0	0.460	0.600
Break Room	Conf. / meeting	5	12	0.06	216	1.0	0.338	0.440

Breathing Zone Outdoor Airflow

$$V_{bz} = R_p \times P_z + R_a \times A_z$$

Zone Outdoor Airflow

$$V_{oz} = V_{bz} / E_z$$

U.S. Green Building Council

Project areas mechanically ventilated but not meeting ASHRAE 62.1-2004

Complete the LEED for Commercial Interiors Submittal Template indicating that the minimum Combined Outdoor Air Rate (per person) is 10 cfm or greater and that all other requirements of the standard are met. Submit the documentation on the determination of the minimum flow rate, and a copy of the letter to the client with the supporting information (i.e., photographs, spec or cut sheet of mechanical equipment, as-built mechanical plans or single line drawing as-builts of all space constrained aspects in the system, such as vertical riser and horizontal chase space).

In addition, provide the information required of those mechanically ventilated projects that are in compliance—the spreadsheet following the format of **Table 1**. When one air handler supplies a mixture of outdoor air and recirculated return air to more than one zone, provide its multiple zone analysis and ventilation system efficiency. Indicate if Table 6-3 or Appendix A of ASHRAE 62.1-2004 has been used.

Combinations

For projects that use both mechanical and natural ventilation in combination, provide the information requested for both conditions. Include an explanation and possibly a simple plan to accompany the other submittal information.

Considerations

Optimal IAQ performance in buildings yields improved occupant comfort, well-being and productivity. Key components for maintaining superior indoor air quality include using high-quality outdoor air and providing adequate ventilation rates. ASHRAE 62.1-2004 describes procedures for avoiding the introduction of contaminants; the criterion includes location of air intakes as they relate to potential sources of contamination. The referenced standard also outlines general ventilation rates for a variety of building types and occupancy categories.

Environmental Issues

Higher ventilation rates are sometimes necessary to improve IAQ, and this can result in higher energy use to operate the HVAC system. The additional energy cost may be offset by improved occupant productivity and lower absentee rates. Poor indoor air quality can cause occupant illness. Any premium associated with ensuring indoor air quality, when compared to the personnel costs of the occupants,

Table 2: Sample Summary Calculations Used for Naturally Ventilated Spaces

Zone Identification	Floor Area [SF]	Natural Ventilation Opening Area [SF]	Opening Area as % of Floor Area	Distance to Opening 25 ft or Less [Yes or No]
General Office	8,000	336	4.2%	Yes
Training Room	750	32	4.3%	Yes
Break Room	216	12	5.6%	Yes

is insignificant. Review the USGBC Web site (www.usgbc.org) for links to recent studies on this issue.

Because ASHRAE 62.1-2004 is standard ventilation design practice for many areas, no additional design effort or cost may be needed to meet this prerequisite. Its successful implementation reduces potential liability for architects, builders, owners, building operators and occupants.

Resources

Please see the USGBC Web site at www.usgbc.org/resources for more specific resources on materials sources and other technical information.

Web Sites

American Society of Heating, Refrigerating and Air-Conditioning Engineers (ASHRAE)

www.ashrae.org

(404) 636-8400

Advances the science of heating, ventilation, air conditioning and refrigeration for the public's benefit through research, standards writing, continuing education and publications.

U.S. Environmental Protection Agency's Indoor Air Quality Web Site

www.epa.gov/iaq

(800) 438-4318

Includes a wide variety of tools, publications and links to address IAQ concerns in schools and large buildings. The downloadable *IAQ Building Education and Assessment Model (I-BEAM)* software program provides comprehensive IAQ management guidance and calculates the cost, revenue, and productivity impacts of planned IAQ activities. Publications include the *Energy Cost and IAQ Performance of Ventilation Systems and Controls Modeling Study*; the *Building Assessment, Survey and Evaluation Study*; and the *Building Air Quality Action Plan*.

Definitions

Indoor Air Quality is the nature of air inside the space that affects the health and wellbeing of building occupants.

Mechanical Ventilation is provided by mechanical powered equipment, such as motor-driven fans and blowers, but not by devices such as wind-driven turbine ventilators and mechanically operated windows. (ASHRAE 62.1-2004)

Natural Ventilation is provided by thermal, wind or diffusion effects through doors, windows or other intentional openings in the building. (ASHRAE 62.1-2004)

Ventilation is the process of supplying and removing air to and from a space for the purpose of controlling air contaminant levels, humidity or temperature within the space.

Environmental Tobacco Smoke (ETS) Control

Intent

Prevent or minimize exposure of tenant space occupants, indoor surfaces and systems to Environmental Tobacco Smoke (ETS).

Requirements

Minimize exposure of non-smokers to ETS by one of the following options:

A. Locating tenant space in a building that prohibits smoking by all occupants and users and maintains any exterior designated smoking areas at least 25 feet away from entries, outdoor air intakes and operable windows,

OR

B. In buildings where smoking is permitted, confirming that smoking is prohibited in the portions of the tenant space not designated as a smoking space, in all other building areas served by the same HVAC system, and in the common areas used by tenant's occupants, and that there is no migration of ETS by either mechanical or natural ventilation from other areas of the building.

AND

If the tenant's occupants are permitted to smoke, providing one or more designated smoking rooms designed to effectively contain, capture and remove ETS from the building. At a minimum, each smoking room must be directly exhausted to the outdoors with no recirculation of ETS-containing air to the non-smoking area of a building, enclosed with impermeable deck-to-deck partitions and operated at a negative pressure compared to surrounding spaces of at least an average of 5 PA (0.02 inches of water gauge) and with a minimum of 1 PA (0.004 inches of water gauge) when the doors to the smoking room are closed.

Performance of the smoking rooms differential air pressure shall be verified by conducting 15 minutes of measurement, with a minimum of one measurement every 10 seconds, of the differential pressure in the smoking room with respect to each adjacent area and in each adjacent vertical chase with the doors to the smoking rooms closed. The testing will be conducted with each space configured for worst case conditions of transport of air from the smoking rooms to adjacent spaces.

OR

C. For multi-unit residential buildings, minimizing uncontrolled pathways for ETS transfer between individual residential units by sealing penetrations in walls, ceilings, and floors in the residential units, and by sealing vertical chases adjacent to the units. In addition, all doors in the residential units leading to common hallways shall be weather-stripped to minimize air leakage into the hallway. Acceptable sealing of residential units shall be demonstrated by blower door tests conducted in accordance with ANSI/ASTM-779-03, Standard Test Method for Determining Air Leakage Rate By Fan Pressurization, AND using the progressive sampling methodology defined in Chapter 7 "Home Energy Rating Systems (HERS) Required Verification And Diagnostic Testing" of the California Low Rise Residential Alternative Calculation Method Approval Manual (www.energy.ca.gov/title24_1998_standards/residential_acm/CHAPTER07.

PDF). Residential units must demonstrate less than 1.25 sq.in. leakage area per 100 sq.ft. of enclosure area (i.e., sum of all wall, ceiling and floor areas).

Submittals

Provide the LEED for Commercial Interiors Submittal Template, signed by the tenant or responsible party, declaring that the building will be operated under a policy prohibiting smoking, and the exterior designated smoking areas are at least 25 feet away from entries and operable windows.

OR

Provide the LEED for Commercial Interiors Submittal Template, signed by the tenant or responsible party, declaring and demonstrating that smoking is prohibited in that portion of the tenant space not designated as a smoking space and all other areas of the building serviced by the same HVAC system, plus common areas used by tenant occupants. If the tenant's occupants are permitted to smoke, declare and demonstrate that designated smoking rooms have met the design criteria described in the credit requirements and that performance has been verified using the method described in the credit requirements.

OR

Provide the LEED for Commercial Interiors Submittal Template, signed by the tenant or responsible party, declaring and demonstrating that the credit requirements for ETS transfer between individual residential units have been satisfied.

Potential Technologies & Strategies

Prohibit smoking in the building or provide negative pressure smoking rooms. For residential buildings, a third option is to provide very tight construction to minimize ETS transfer among dwelling units.

Summary of Referenced Standards

ANSI/ASTM-779-03, Standard Test Method for Determining Air Leakage Rate by Fan Pressurization

"Home Energy Rating Systems (HERS) Required Verification and Diagnostic Testing", California Low Rise Residential Alternative Calculation Method Approval Manual

www.energy.ca.gov/title24/residential_manual/res_manual_chapter4.pdf

Credit Interpretation Rulings

In addition to LEED for Commercial Interiors Credit Interpretation Rulings (CIRs), applicable LEED for New Construction CIRs concerning this prerequisite may also apply to LEED for Commercial Interiors projects.

Approach and Implementation

Strategies

Occupy a building in which smoking is prohibited. For those who smoke, provide appropriately located designated smoking areas outside the building away from building entrances, operable windows and ventilation system fresh air intakes. Post information on the non-smoking policy for occupants to read.

If interior smoking areas are designed within the building, separate ventilation systems must be installed, and their effectiveness must be tested to ensure that they are isolated from non-smoking portions of the building.

Submittal Documentation

The submittal documentation follows the three options provided in the prerequisite requirements. Option A and B apply to all spaces other than residential.

Option A only requires the LEED for Commercial Interiors Submittal Template declaration that the building will be operated under a policy that prohibits smoking, and that all exterior designated smoking areas are at least 25 feet away from entries, outdoor air intakes and operable windows.

For projects located in leased facilities, it is suggested that the project teams obtain and retain the supporting documentation that demonstrates the commitment of the building operator. It may take the form of a letter or the lease.

Option B addresses buildings where smoking may occur in designated smoking rooms. First, provide the Submittal Template declaration that no smoking is to occur in the non-smoking areas of the project. Second, the certification submittal must demonstrate that no smoking is permitted in common areas of the building used by the tenant occupants; this document must include the hallways and elevators used for ingress and egress, restrooms and service areas such as an indoor recycling collection location. Third, if smoking is permitted in portions of the building beyond the area occupied by the certifying project, the certification documentation needs to demonstrate how smoke from those areas is isolated from the project area. Documentation must demonstrate that there is no migration by either mechanical or natural ventilation. This may be accomplished using mechanical systems drawings. Fourth, if smoking is permitted in a designated smoking room constructed as part of the project, the Submittal Template needs to include a declaration that the design and construction of the designated smoking room meets the design criteria described in the credit requirement. Submit documentation of the design and the test report documenting compliance.

Option C addresses multi-unit residential buildings. First, provide the Submittal

Template declaration that this portion of the requirement has been met. Demonstration of compliance may include a narrative indicating the means employed to minimize uncontrolled pathways for ETS transfer between individual residential units. Consider providing photographs showing the sealing of penetrations in walls, ceilings and floors, and weather stripping on doors leading to common hallways. Complete and report the results of blower door tests that have been conducted in accordance with ANSI/ASTM-779-03 and the progressive sampling methodology defined in Chapter 7 "Home Energy Rating System (HERS)" of the California Low Rise Residential Alternative Calculation Method Approval Manual. Effective leakage area must be less than 1.25 sq.in. per 100 sq.ft. of enclosure area.

Considerations

The relationship between smoking and various health risks, including lung disease, cancer, and heart disease, has been well documented. A strong link between Environmental Tobacco Smoke (ETS) or "secondhand smoke" and health risks has also been demonstrated.

The most effective way to avoid health problems associated with ETS is to prohibit smoking indoors. If this cannot be accomplished, indoor smoking areas should be isolated from non-smoking areas and have separate ventilation systems to avoid the introduction of tobacco smoke contaminants to non-smoking areas.

Environmental Issues

Separate smoking areas occupy space in the building and may result in a larger building, additional material use and increased energy for ventilation. However, these environmental impacts can be offset by building occupants who are more comfortable, have higher productivity rates, and have lower absenteeism and illnesses.

Economics Issues

Separate smoking areas add to the design and construction costs of most projects. Maintenance of designated smoking areas also adds to lease and operating costs. Prohibition of indoor smoking can increase the useful life of interior fixtures and furnishings.

Smoking within a building contaminates indoor air and can cause occupant reactions ranging from irritation and illness to decreased productivity. These problems increase expenses and liability for building owners, tenants, operators and insurance companies.

Community Issues

Air is a community natural resource, and promoting clean air benefits everyone. Strict no-smoking policies improve the health of the community as a whole, resulting in lower health care and insurance costs.

Resources

Please see the USGBC Web site at www.usgbc.org/resources for more specific resources on materials sources and other technical information.

Web Sites

Secondhand Smoke: What You Can Do About Secondhand Smoke as Parents, Decision Makers, and Building Occupants

U.S. Environmental Protection Agency

www.epa.gov/smokefree/pubs/etsbro.html

(800) 438-4318

An EPA document on the effects of ETS and measures to reduce human exposure to it.

Setting the Record Straight: Secondhand Smoke Is a Preventable Health Risk

U.S. Environmental Protection Agency

www.epa.gov/iaq/pubs/strsfs.html

An EPA document with a discussion of laboratory research on ETS and federal legislation aimed at curbing ETS problems.

Print Media

The Chemistry of Environmental Tobacco Smoke: Composition and Measurement, Second Edition by R.A. Jenkins, B.A. Tomkins, et al., CRC Press & Lewis Publishers, 2000.

The Smoke-Free Guide: How to Eliminate Tobacco Smoke from Your Environment, by Arlene Galloway, Gordon Soules Book Publishers, 1988.

Definitions

Environmental Tobacco Smoke (ETS), or secondhand smoke, consists of airborne particles emitted from the burning end of cigarettes, pipes, and cigars, and exhaled by smokers. These particles contain about 4,000 different compounds, up to 40 of which are known to cause cancer.

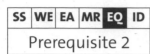

Outdoor Air Delivery Monitoring

1 point

Intent

Provide capacity for ventilation system monitoring to help sustain long-term occupant comfort and wellbeing.

Requirements

Install permanent monitoring and alarm systems that provide feedback on ventilation system performance to ensure that ventilation systems maintain design minimum ventilation requirements in a form that affords operational adjustments:

- For mechanical ventilation systems that predominantly serve densely occupied spaces (those with a design occupant density greater than or equal to 25 people per 1000 sq.ft.), install a CO_2 sensor within each densely occupied space.

- For all other mechanical ventilation systems, provide an outdoor airflow measurement device capable of measuring the minimum outdoor airflow rate at all expected system operating conditions within 15% of the design minimum outdoor air rate.

- For natural ventilation systems, install a CO_2 sensor within each naturally ventilated space.

Submittals

Provide the LEED for Commercial Interiors Submittal Template, signed by the responsible design professional, declaring and summarizing the installation, operational design and controls/zones for the carbon dioxide or outdoor airflow monitoring system.

Potential Technologies & Strategies

To ensure that sensors can reliably indicate that ventilation systems are operating as designed:

- CO_2 sensors should be located within the vertical constraints of breathing zone of the room as defined in ASHRAE Standard 62.1-2004.

- CO_2 sensors should be certified by the manufacturer to have an accuracy of no less than 75 ppm, factory calibrated or calibrated at start-up, and certified by the manufacturer to require calibration no more frequently than once every 5 years.

- Required CO_2 sensors and outdoor airflow monitors should be configured to generate an alarm if the indicated outdoor airflow rate drops more than 15% below the minimum outdoor air rate required by Standard 62.1 (see EQ Prerequisite 1) in one of the following ways:

  - A building automation system alarm visible to the system operator/engineer

  - An alert that is clearly visible to or audible by occupants.

  - CO_2 sensors may also be used for demand controlled ventilation provided the control strategy complies with ASHRAE Standard 62.1-2004 (see EQ Prerequisite 1), including maintaining the area-based component of the design ventilation rate.

- Space CO_2 alarms and demand controlled ventilation setpoints shall be based on the differential corresponding to the ventilation rates prescribed in ASHRAE

Standard 62.1 plus the outdoor air CO_2 concentration, which shall be determined by one of the following:

- Outdoor CO_2 concentration shall be assumed to be 400 ppm without any direct measurement; or

- Outdoor CO_2 concentration shall be dynamically measured using a CO_2 sensor located near the position of the outdoor air intake.

Summary of Referenced Standard

ANSI/ASHRAE Standard 62.1-2004: Ventilation for Acceptable Indoor Air Quality, American Society of Heating, Refrigerating and Air-Conditioning Engineers (ASHRAE)

www.ashrae.org

(800) 527-4723

This standard specifies minimum ventilation rates and indoor air quality (IAQ) levels to reduce the potential for adverse health effects. The standard specifies that mechanical or natural ventilation systems be designed to prevent uptake of contaminants, minimize the opportunity for growth and dissemination of microorganisms, and filter particulates, if necessary. Makeup air inlets should be located away from contaminant sources such as cooling towers; sanitary vents; and vehicular exhaust from parking garages, loading docks, and street traffic.

A Ventilation Rate Procedure and an Indoor Air Quality Procedure are outlined to achieve compliance with the standard. The Ventilation Rate Procedure prescribes outdoor air quality acceptable for ventilation; outdoor air treatment measures; and ventilation rates for residential, commercial, institutional, vehicular, and industrial spaces. The procedure also includes criteria for the reduction of outdoor air quantities when recirculated air is treated by contaminant-removal equipment and criteria for variable ventilation when the air volume in the space is used as a reservoir to dilute contaminants. The Indoor Air Quality Procedure incorporates both quantitative and subjective evaluation and restricts contaminant concentrations to acceptable levels.

Credit Interpretation Rulings

In addition to LEED for Commercial Interiors Credit Interpretation Rulings (CIRs), applicable LEED for New Construction CIRs concerning this credit may also apply to LEED for Commercial Interiors projects.

Carbon dioxide (CO_2) sensors at central locations near air handlers may report artificially low CO_2 readings from areas of high occupancy with adjacent areas of low occupancy. CO_2 sensors configured this way do not meet the intent of this credit.

When there are spaces with variable occupancies, such as dining rooms, nurse stations, conference rooms, and waiting rooms, the installation of CO_2 sensors in the air handlers have been found ineffective and therefore do not satisfy the requirements of this credit. In these situations, sensors should be located within the space and positioned in the breathing zone.

Though carbon monoxide (CO) monitoring in residential projects is an integral part of an indoor air quality monitoring program, the program must be robust and on-going. The data collected from air quality monitoring must be used to update and improve building operating procedures. If the IAQ program consists only of CO monitors it is failing to address the broader range of possible contaminants.

A system that provides 100% outside air but has no provision for indoor air quality monitoring does not meet the intent of the credit.

Approach and Implementation

Buildings' HVAC systems are designed to flush out indoor airborne contaminants by exhausting old air and replacing it with fresh outdoor air. The rate of exchange is based on space density and type of occupancy.

Many conventional systems do not directly measure the amount of outdoor air delivered. Air flow monitoring of the outdoor air rate insures that the HVAC equipment is delivering the design ventilation rate. Air balance control methodologies, such as fan tracking and building pressurization based strategies, do not satisfy the credit requirement. Outdoor air delivery can be measured at the intake using a variety of airflow devices including Pitot tubes, Venturi meters and rotating vane anemometers. The effectiveness of the ventilation system to deliver the needed outdoor air can be monitored using CO_2 sensors when properly located; a further discussion is found below. To satisfy the requirements of this credit, the measurement devices must detect when the system is 15% below the design minimum outdoor air rate. When the ventilation system fails to provide the required levels of fresh air, the monitoring system should be configured to deliver a visible or audible alert to the system operator. This alert will indicate to the system operator that operational adjustments may be necessary

The minimum outdoor air rate will change based on the design and modes of the HVAC system. Constant volume systems, with steady-state design occupancy conditions will have different outdoor air rates for weekdays and nighttime setback conditions. In variable-air-volume (VAV) systems, the rate of outdoor air needs to stay above the design minimum even when the supply air flow is reduced to partial-load conditions. Monitoring the outdoor air flow rate near the intake will confirm that the constrictions downstream have not compromised the delivery of fresh air.

In demand-controlled-ventilation (DCV) systems, where the outdoor air rate supplied to an area is based on readings taken by sensors located within the occupied spaces, the system-wide outdoor air rate will fluctuate. A DCV system, by virtue of its ability to conserve energy, might be logical in a large lecture hall where the number of people and times of use varies

significantly. In this type of operation, the monitoring system ideally confirms that the space—the lecture hall—is getting adequate outdoor air, and that the central system adjusts to match the changing requirement.

ASHRAE Standard 62.1-2004, Ventilation for Acceptable Indoor Air Quality, notes that: "Human occupants produce carbon dioxide, water vapor, and contaminants including particulate matter, biological aerosols, and volatile organic compounds. Comfort (odor) criteria with respect to human bioeffluents are likely to be satisfied if the ventilation results in indoor CO_2 concentrations less than 700 ppm above the outdoor air concentration." CO_2 sensors, when properly placed, are a practical means of confirming that a ventilation system is functioning properly. There are two typical system configurations that generally meet the requirements of this credit.

One approach to ensuring that appropriate levels of fresh air are being introduced into a space is the use of sensors to monitor indoor CO_2 concentration and provide an alert if design parameters are exceeded. As ambient outdoor air CO_2 concentrations typically vary between 300 to 500 ppm, an indoor concentration of 1000 ppm is commonly used as the setpoint for an alarm which notifies operations personnel that adjustments to the system may be required or that a malfunction has occurred. Increasing the supply of outdoor air delivered to the space will dilute indoor CO_2 concentrations and bring the space back into a range acceptable to occupants. Appendix C of ASHRAE Standard 62.1-2004 provides a further discussion of metabolic rate and other mitigating issues in the design of CO_2 based ventilation systems.

Another approach to ensuring delivery of fresh air is to modulate outdoor air based on the differential between indoor and outdoor CO_2 concentrations. Indoor CO_2 sensors are used to monitor building CO_2 concentrations. Readings from these sensors are compared to ambient outdoor CO_2 concentrations from sensors typically located in building fresh air intakes. The system is set to modulate fresh air delivery to maintain a defined differential between indoor and outdoor CO_2 concentrations—for typical office occupancies this differential is defined in ASHRAE 62.1-2004 as 530 ppm.

CO_2 sampling locations must be selected so that they provide representative readings of the CO_2 concentrations in occupied spaces. Providing multiple CO_2 monitoring stations throughout occupied spaces will provide better information and control than providing a single CO_2 monitor for the entire system. A single CO_2 monitor, typically installed in the return air duct, is less expensive and more straightforward to implement than proving multiple sensors but may be inaccurate and may not provide information which identifies areas within the building that are under ventilated.

CO_2 Monitoring in Densely Occupied Spaces

Within buildings that are mechanically ventilated, the CO_2 level within each densely occupied space needs to be monitored to satisfy the credit requirements. The density factor is 25 people per 1000 sq.ft.; for example, a 240 sq.ft conference room planned for 6 or more people would need to be monitored. These monitors need to be in the space and mounted within the vertical breathing zone—between 3 and 72 inches above the floor.

Monitoring in Naturally Ventilated Spaces

For naturally ventilated buildings, monitoring CO_2 levels in the occupied space, again with the sensor positioned in the breathing zone, provides feedback to building occupants and operators, so that they can make operational adjustments, such as opening windows.

CO_2 monitoring requires additional equipment to be installed and requires additional commissioning and maintenance attention.

Monitoring Existing HVAC Systems

For new outdoor air monitoring systems added to an existing building HVAC system, careful consideration may be required so that the design strategy will be compatible with the existing HVAC and automation systems. This situation may be the norm for commercial interior projects where there is a high likelihood the tenant space will share a central HVAC system with the balance of the building. Because the building owner may not allow modulation of the outside air based on feedback from CO_2 monitors located in one tenant space, the project team should consider including monitoring in the building selection criteria.

Prior to Occupancy

Leading up to air balancing and commissioning, confirm that the monitoring system is calibrated, and that the setpoints and control sequences meet specification. Provide the building owner, maintenance personnel and occupants with the information needed to understand, maintain and respond to the monitoring system. Maintenance personnel should make CO_2 monitor inspection part of routine O&M and preventive maintenance activities. Sensors should be recalibrated based on the manufacturers requirements. It is recommended to use CO_2 sensors that require recalibration intervals of at least 5 years. If a CO_2 monitor is allowed to fall out of calibration it may indicate that indoor CO_2 concentrations are lower or higher than they actually are, leading to under- or over-ventilation of the space. A permanent ventilation monitoring system assists in detecting indoor air quality problems quickly so that corrective actions can be taken. Under-ventilation of a space can lead to unsatisfactory indoor environmental conditions and occupant discomfort. Over-ventilation of a space may needlessly increase utility costs.

Submittal Documentation

The LEED for Commercial Interiors applicant should provide the LEED for Commercial Interiors Submittal Template, signed by the engineer or responsible party, declaring and summarizing the installation, operational design and controls/zones for the CO_2 or outdoor airflow monitoring system.

A brief narrative describing the CO_2 or outdoor airflow monitoring system is required. When applicable to the project, provide information on the following topics:

The area, use, and estimated maximum occupancy for each occupied zone; ASHRAE Standard 62.1-2004 ventilation rate requirements (in cfm/sq.ft. of cfm/person) for each occupied space; design ventilation rate (in cfm) for each occupied zone along with normalized design ventilation rate (cfm/sq.ft. or cfm/person); a brief description of the HVAC system type or other ventilation system designed to attain the design ventilation rate; description of the types of CO_2 and outdoor airflow monitoring systems employed in the control of ventilation rates and monitoring of air quality; description of the quantity, location, and setpoints for CO_2 sensors and outdoor airflow monitoring devices.

For innovative and unique approaches to providing outdoor air delivery monitoring, additional information should be provided: identify overall space plans with ventilation zones, ventilation equipment, registers, operable windows, CO_2 monitors and other ventilation air devices identified; provide information identifying areas within any zone that lie outside the ventilation system control areas or where people are permanently located.

Provide plans, controls schematics, and photographs, as necessary and appropriate, in support of the narrative. When a project incorporates more than one implementation strategy, the submittal will need to include the materials requested under each approach.

Considerations

Costs

CO_2 and ventilation rate monitoring systems increase initial construction costs compared to less efficiently and effectively controlled spaces. Capital costs and annual costs for air flow monitoring equipment maintenance and calibration procedures may be offset by reduced absenteeism, increased occupant productivity and reduced HVAC energy use.

Building Type

Air flow and CO_2 monitoring systems can be applied to any building or HVAC system type—including both mechanically and naturally ventilated buildings.

Demand controlled ventilation, which automatically adjusts ventilation rates based on measured CO_2 levels, is most beneficial in spaces with high occupant density and variable usage patterns, such as that found in conference rooms, classrooms, and assembly areas. The energy savings of DCV systems are generally greater in more extreme climates.

For naturally ventilated buildings and spaces served by HVAC systems that do not allow for active control of ventilation rates, CO_2 sensors in the occupied spaces can provide building occupants and operators with useful information that allows for operational adjustments, such as opening windows or adjusting fixed ventilation rates.

Regional Considerations

Ambient outdoor CO_2 concentrations may fluctuate based on local and regional factors, however high ambient concentrations are typically an indicator of combustion or other contaminant sources.

Resources

Please see the USGBC Web site at www. usgbc.org/resources for more specific resources on materials sources and other technical information.

Web Sites

American Society of Heating, Refrigerating and Air-Conditioning Engineers(ASHRAE)

www.ashrae.org

(404) 636-8400

Advances the science of heating, ventilation, air conditioning and refrigeration for the public's benefit through research, standards writing, continuing education and publications.

Building Air Quality: A Guide for Building Owners and Facility Managers

www.epa.gov/iaq/largebldgs

(800) 438-4318

An EPA publication on IAQ sources in buildings and methods to prevent and resolve IAQ problems.

Print Media

Air Handling Systems Design, by Tseng-Yao Sun, McGraw Hill, 1992.

ASHRAE Standard 55-2004: Thermal Environmental Conditions for Human Occupancy, ASHRAE, 2004

ASHRAE Standard 62.1-2004: Ventilation for Acceptable Indoor Air Quality, ASHRAE, 2004

ASTM D 6245-1998: Standard Guide for Using Indoor Carbon Dioxide Concentrations to Evaluate Indoor Air Quality and Ventilation, ASTM, 1998

Efficient Building Design Series, Volume 2: Heating, Ventilating, and Air Conditioning, by J. Trost and Frederick Trost, Prentice Hall, 1998

Definitions

CO_2 is carbon dioxide.

Mechanical Ventilation is ventilation provided by mechanically powered equipment, such as motor-driven fans and blowers, but not by devices such as wind-driven turbine ventilators and mechanically operated windows. (ASHRAE 62.1-2004)

Natural Ventilation is ventilation provided by thermal, wind, or diffusion effects through doors, windows, or other intentional openings in the building. (ASHRAE 62.1-2004)

ppm: parts per million

Ventilation is the process of supplying air to or removing air from a space for the purpose of controlling air contaminant levels, humidity, or temperature within the space. (ASHRAE 62.1-2004)

SS	WE	EA	MR	EQ	ID

Credit 1

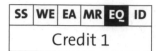

SS | WE | EA | MR | **EQ** | ID
Credit 1

Increased Ventilation

Intent

Provide additional air ventilation to improve indoor air quality for improved occupant comfort, wellbeing and productivity.

Requirements

For mechanically ventilated spaces:

Increase breathing zone outdoor air ventilation rates to all occupied spaces by at least 30% above the minimum rates required by ASHRAE 62.1-2004 as determined by EQ Prerequisite 1.

For naturally ventilated spaces:

Design natural ventilation systems for occupied spaces to meet the recommendations set forth in the Carbon Trust "Good Practice Guide 237" [1998]. Determine that natural ventilation is an effective strategy for the project by following the flow diagram process shown in Figure 1.18 of the CIBSE "Applications Manual 10: 2005, Natural ventilation in non-domestic buildings."

And either of the following;

Use diagrams and calculations to show that the design of the natural ventilation systems meets the recommendations set forth in the CIBSE "Applications Manual 10: 2005, "Natural ventilation in non-domestic buildings."

OR

Use a macroscopic, multi-zone, analytic model to predict that room-by-room airflows will effectively naturally ventilate at least 90% of occupied spaces.

Submittals

- For mechanical ventilation systems, provide the LEED for Commercial Interiors Submittal Templates, signed by the mechanical engineer or other responsible party, declaring that the outdoor air ventilation rates at the breathing zone of all occupied spaces are at least 30% above the minimum rates required by ASHRAE 62.1-2004, and provide the calculations demonstrating that design breathing zone ventilation rates exceed the minimum rates required by Standard 62.1 by at least 30%.

- For natural ventilation systems, provide the LEED for Commercial Interiors Submittal Templates, signed by the mechanical engineer or other responsible party, declaring that the project meets the natural ventilation requirements of the credit. Provide documentation that natural ventilation is an effective strategy for the project and follows the design recommendations established by CIBSE. Provide either of the following: diagrams and calculations based on CIBSE AM10, or diagrams and calculations based on results provided by a multi-zone analytical model.

Potential Technologies & Strategies

For Mechanically Ventilated Spaces: Design ventilation systems to provide breathing zone ventilation rates at least 30% larger than the minimum rates prescribed by the referenced standard.

For Naturally Ventilated Spaces: Follow the eight design steps described in Carbon Trust "Good Practice Guide 237" – 1) Develop design requirements, 2) Plan airflow paths, 3) Identify building uses and features that might require special attention, 4) Determine ventilation requirements, 5) Estimate external driving pressures, 6) Select types of ventilation devices, 7) Size ventilation devices, 8) Analyze the design. Some of the public domain software packages available to analytically predict room-by-room airflows include but are not limited to NIST's CONTAM, Multizone Modeling Software, along with LoopDA, Natural Ventilation Sizing Tool.

Summary of Referenced Standard

ANSI/ASHRAE Standard 62.1-2004: Ventilation for Acceptable Indoor Air Quality (Ventilation Rate Procedure), American Society of Heating, Refrigerating and Air-Conditioning Engineers (ASHRAE)

www.ashrae.org

(800) 527-4723

This standard specifies minimum ventilation rates and indoor air quality (IAQ) levels to reduce the potential for adverse health effects. The Ventilation Rate Procedure, as used in both this credit and EQ Prerequisite 1, outlines the process to achieve compliance with the standard and is the basis for demonstrating that a 30% increase over minimum rates have been achieved. The Ventilation Rate Procedure prescribes outdoor air quality acceptable for ventilation; outdoor air treatment measures; and ventilation rates for residential, commercial, institutional, vehicular, and industrial spaces. The procedure also includes criteria for the reduction of outdoor air quantities when recirculated air is treated by contaminant-removal equipment and criteria for variable ventilation when the air volume in the space is used as a reservoir to dilute contaminants.

Natural Ventilation in Non-Domestic Buildings, A Guide for Designers, Developers and Owners (Good Practice Guide G237)

The Carbon Trust

www.thecarbontrust.co.uk

The Good Practice Guide 237 is available for no charge but registration (also free) is required to get access to the guide. Under the Energy section of the Web site, search for "natural ventilation" to find the Guide. The Good Practice Guide 237 is based on an earlier version of the CIBSE AM10.

CIBSE Applications Manual 10: 2005, Natural Ventilation in Non-Domestic Buildings

The Chartered Institute of Building Services Engineers, London

www.CIBSE.co.uk

This manual sets out the various approaches to ventilation and cooling of buildings, summarizes the relative advantages and disadvantages of those approaches and gives guidance on the overall approach to design. The AM 10 (2005) provides detailed information on how to implement a decision to adopt natural ventilation, either as the sole servicing strategy for a building, or as an element in a mixed-mode design.

Credit Interpretation Rulings

EQ Credit 2 is new in LEED for Commercial Interiors v2.0, therefore rulings associated with the LEED for New Construction v2 CIRs most likely will have no bearing. Rulings issued for LEED for Commercial Interiors projects requests, and in other rating systems adopting similar credit requirements may apply.

Approach and Implementation

A green building should provide its occupants with superior indoor air quality to support a healthy lifestyle and work environment. A key component for maintaining superior indoor air quality is providing adequate ventilation rates. Under-ventilated buildings may be stuffy, odorous, uncomfortable and/or unhealthy for occupants.

Building ventilation systems, including both active HVAC systems and natural ventilation systems, are designed and installed to introduce fresh outside air into the building while exhausting an equal amount of building air. HVAC systems typically serve other functions as well, including providing thermal comfort for occupants. Building conditioning systems that provide enhanced ventilation air, as efficiently and effectively as possible, will help to maintain a high standard of indoor air quality in the building.

Strategies

There are two basic methods for ventilating buildings:

- Active Ventilation (i.e., mechanical ventilation)
- Passive Ventilation (i.e., natural ventilation)

ASHRAE Standard 62.1-2004 provides ventilation rate standards for different types of buildings and building uses. The LEED for Commercial Interiors credit is met for projects that exceed these standards by 30% for mechanically ventilated buildings.

The Good Practice Guide 237 and Applications Manual 10: 2005 "Natural Ventilation in Non-domestic Buildings" provide design guidance on appropriate natural ventilation design to provide for adequate fresh air exchange in a building. Naturally ventilated spaces should follow these guidelines in achieving credit compliance.

Projects employing both mechanical and natural ventilation (mixed mode ventilation) strategies will need to comply with ASHRAE 62.1-2004 for the mechanically ventilated portion and CIBSE AM10 for the naturally ventilation portion.

Synergies and Trade-Offs

In addition to designing the HVAC systems properly and selecting appropriate building materials, increasing ventilation rates beyond standard practice may be one strategy to provide superior indoor air quality. Managing indoor air quality concerns during construction and operations is also appropriate for many green building projects.

For mechanically ventilated and air-conditioned buildings, increasing ventilation rates will likely mean larger HVAC system capacity and greater energy use.

Natural ventilation systems can provide increased ventilation rates, good indoor air quality, and occupant control over thermal comfort and ventilation via operable windows.

Planning Phase

Most projects decide early on whether to have a mechanical ventilation system, a passive ventilation system, or a combination of both. This decision may be influenced by the building size and type, as well as climatic, economic and organizational influences. **Figure 1** from CIBSE AM10 provides a decision diagram to aid in making a knowledgeable evaluation. In addition to these considerations, project teams considering natural ventilation should evaluate site conditions and building design. Potential IAQ problems might result from heavy traffic, nearby polluting industries and neighboring waste management sites.

Mechanically Ventilated Spaces—Ventilation Rate Procedure

For mechanical ventilation systems, ASHRAE Standard 62.1-2004, Section 6, outlines guidelines for determining ventilation rates for various applications, using either the Ventilation Rate Procedure or the Indoor Air Quality Procedure. The Ventilation Rate Procedure is more straightforward to apply and much more common in practice. It is the prescribed approach used in EQ Prerequisite 1, Minimum IAQ Performance.

If the project team follows the Ventilation Rate Procedure, they need to use the methodology found in Section 6.2 of ASHRAE 62.1-2004. The breathing zone outdoor airflow is equal to the sum of the outdoor airflow rate required per person times the zone population, plus the outdoor airflow rate required per unit area times the zone floor area. The standard's Table 6-1 "Minimum Ventilation Rates in Breathing Zone" provides information by occupancy category to

Figure 1: Selecting a Strategy, from CIBSE Applications Manual AM10:2005, Natural ventilation in non-domestic buildings.

SS	WE	EA	MR	EQ	ID

Credit 2

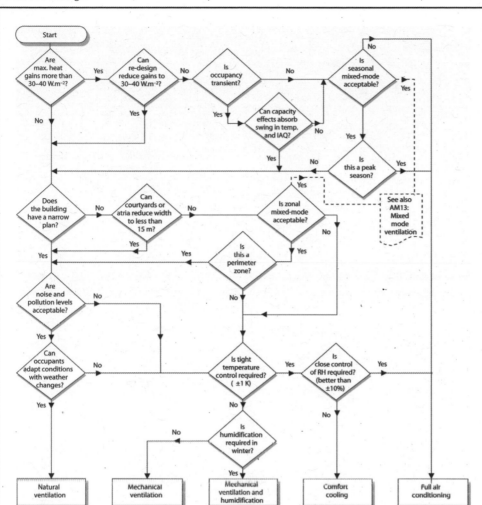

Reproduced with permission from The Chartered Institute of Building Services Engineers, London

determine both the amount of outdoor air needed to ventilate people-related source contaminants and area-related source contaminants. The people-related-sources portion of the outdoor air rate addresses actual occupancy density and activity. The area-related-sources portion accounts for background off-gassing from building materials, furniture and materials typically found in that particular occupancy. Finally, the required zone outdoor airflow is the breathing zone outdoor airflow adjusted to reflect the efficiency of the actual air distribution configuration.

This LEED for Commercial Interiors

credit requires that applicants demonstrate that the delivered zone outdoor airflow is at least 30% higher than what is required by ASHRAE Standard 62.1-2004 for each zone. **Table 1** in this section of the reference guide shows how the sample space used in EQ Prerequisite 1 has attained the 30% increase.

Naturally Ventilated Spaces

Project teams electing natural ventilation have two primary means of demonstrating credit compliance: the compliance path found in Chapter 2 of The CIBSE Applications Manual 10 (AM10), or

Table 1: Sample Summary Calculations—Increased Vantilation for Mechanical Ventilation using the Ventilation Rate Procedure

Zone Identification	Occupancy Category	Area [SF]	Standard Zone Outdoor Airflow V_{oz} [CFM / SF]	Design Zone Outdoor Airflow [CFM / SF]	Percent Increase [%]
General Office	Office space	8,000	0.088	0.115	30.7%
Training Room	Lecture hall	750	0.460	0.600	32.6%
Break Room	Conf. / meeting	216	0.338	0.440	30.2%

documentation using a macroscopic, multi-zone, analytic model that predicts room-by-room air flow rates.

Those using AM10 begin by establishing the required flow rates through each space. There is an acceptable average rate needed for IAQ and thermal comfort; over-sizing of this rate results in wasted energy during the heating seasons. There is also additional ventilation needed for the summer cooling requirements. There are several methods, either using a separate manual or simulation software, listed in AM10. Project teams should confirm their choice with justification. Submittals will need to include a narrative that includes information on the building, its orientation and the glazing ratios. Include a summary of the internal heat gains and weather conditions. Explain the ventilation strategy, including the airflow paths, the rates planned for different operational periods during the day and night, the peak internal temperatures, and means of shading for summer solar gains. Provide sample calculations on the determination of opening size for operable windows, trickle vents and louvers. Finally, include the calculations for the driving pressure showing the effects of both wind and stack-induced pressure differentials.

Project teams using a macroscopic, multi-zone, analytic model that predicts room-by-room air flow rates will need to provide a narrative providing the same information listed above. They will also need to demonstrate that 90% of the occupied areas meet the room-by-room airflow rates. Indicate the source of the standard being used, such as Volume A of the CIBSE Guide, ASHRAE 62.1-2004 Section 6.2 or other.

Submittal Documentation

Mechanical Ventilation. For mechanical ventilation systems, complete the LEED for Commercial Interiors Submittal Template declaring that the outdoor air ventilation rates at the breathing zone of all occupied spaces are at least 30% above the minimum rates required by the Ventilation Rate Procedure of ASHRAE 62.1-2004. Also develop a spreadsheet similar to **Table 1** that may be used to confirm the project's calculations. It may the same documentation used in EQ Prerequisite 1 when columns are provided that show both the required and designed outdoor air flow rates. Attention should be given to confirming compliance when multiple-zone systems are used; see Appendix A of the referenced ASHRAE standard.

Additional Documentation

It is recommended that the project team develop and maintain review plans showing the ventilation system for audit or clarification during submittal. A narrative is often needed to confirm compliance.

Natural Ventilation

Complete the LEED for Commercial Interiors Submittal Template declaration applicable to naturally ventilated spaces. Depending on the compliance path used, provide either the diagrams and calculations based on the CIBSE AM10, or diagrams and calculations based on results produced by the multi-zone analytical model. See the discussion above for additional detail.

Considerations

Operations Phase

For mechanical ventilation, the operating setpoints and parameters of the HVAC system will be the primary influence on ventilation rates in the building. Facility operators should periodically confirm that ventilation rates meet the design and the system controls related to ventilation are properly calibrated to help insure that chronic under-ventilation does not lead to indoor air quality problems in the building.

Occupants generally take a primary role in managing ventilation conditions in naturally ventilated buildings by opening and closing windows as necessary and appropriate. Naturally ventilated buildings generally have somewhat more variable ventilation rates than actively conditioned buildings, whose systems are often designed to maintain constant ventilation through all periods of occupancy.

Costs

Depending on the climate, increasing ventilation rates by 30% beyond ASHRAE Standard 62.1-2004 will yield higher HVAC energy costs and potentially greater HVAC capacity than associated with the minimum ventilation rates

established in the standard. This increase in HVAC capacity and energy use will be more pronounced in extreme climates than in mild, temperate climates.

Some organizations increase the outdoor air rate because they have found the resulting indoor air quality is associated with improved employee health, welfare, wellbeing, and productivity.

While the naturally ventilated building may have less invested in equipment, it may have higher quality windows and increased thermal mass. Power, fuel and maintenance costs of naturally ventilated buildings tend to be lower.

Regional Considerations

Additional ventilation is more practical for mild climates, where increasing ventilation rates beyond standard practice will not have as great an impact on HVAC systems capacity and energy consumption as in extremely hot, humid or cold climates.

Natural ventilation and passive conditioning approaches are also more typical in mild and temperate climates, although there are precedents for passively conditioned buildings in all climates.

Resources

Please see the USGBC Web site at www. usgbc.org/resources for more specific resources on materials sources and other technical information.

Web Sites

American Society of Heating, Refrigerating and Air-Conditioning Engineers (ASHRAE)

www.ashrae.org

(404) 636-8400

Advances the science of heating, ventilation, air conditioning and refrigeration for the public's benefit through research, standards writing, continuing education and publications. To purchase ASHRAE standards and guidelines, visit the bookstore on ASHRAE Web site and search for the desired publication.

Energy Cost and IAQ Performance of Ventilation Systems and Controls Modeling Study

U.S. Environmental Protection Agency

www.epa.gov/iaq/largebldgs/resources/(2)%20Energy%20Cost%20and%20IAQ/Executive%20Summary.PDF

Building Assessment, Survey and Evaluation Study

U.S. Environmental Protection Agency

www.epa.gov/iaq/largebldgs/base/base_publications.html

Building Air Quality Action Plan

U.S. Environmental Protection Agency

www.epa.gov/iaq/largebldgs/actionpl.html

The Chartered Institution of Building Services Engineers (CIBSE)

www.cibse.co.uk

This organization, located in London, on its own and in collaboration with other entities, publishes a full series of guides on the topic of ventilation, including natural ventilation.

The Carbon Trust

www.thecarbontrust.co.uk/thecarbontrust

This government funded business provides information on natural ventilation as a component on its mission to reduce carbon emissions associated with energy consumption. Its Web site makes the Good Practice Guide 237 available.

Definitions

Air Conditioning is the process of treating air to meet the requirements of a conditioned space by controlling its temperature, humidity, cleanliness and distribution. (ASHRAE 62.1-2004)

Breathing Zone is the region within an occupied space between planes 3 and 72 in. above the floor and more than 2 ft. from the walls or fixed air-conditioning equipment.

Conditioned Space is that part of a building that is heated or cooled, or both, for the comfort of occupants. (ASHRAE 62.1-2004)

Contaminant is an unwanted airborne constituent that may reduce acceptability of the air. (ASHRAE 62.1-2004)

Exfiltration is air leakage outward through cracks and interstices and through ceilings, floors and walls of a space or building.

Exhaust Air is the air removed from a space and discharged to outside the building by means of mechanical or natural ventilation systems.

Infiltration is air leakage inward through cracks and interstices and through ceilings, floors and walls of a space or building.

Makeup Air is any combination of outdoor and transfer air intended to replace exhaust air and exfiltration.

Mechanical Ventilation is ventilation provided by mechanically powered equipment, such as motor-driven fans and blowers, but not by devices such as wind-driven turbine ventilators and mechanically operated windows.

Natural Ventilation is ventilation provided by thermal, wind, or diffusion effects through doors, windows, or other intentional openings in the building.

Outdoor Air is the ambient air that enters a building through a ventilation system, through intentional openings for natural ventilation, or by infiltration. (ASHRAE 62.1-2004)

Recirculated Air is the air removed from a space and reused as supply air. (ASHRAE 62.1-2004)

Return Air is the air removed from a space to be then recirculated or exhausted. (ASHRAE 62.1-2004)

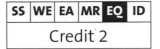

Supply Air is the air delivered by mechanical or natural ventilation to a space, composed of any combination of outdoor air, recirculated air, or transfer air. (ASHRAE 62.1-2004)

Ventilation is the process of supplying air to or removing air from a space for the purpose of controlling air contaminant levels, humidity or temperature within the space.

Refer to ASHRAE Standard 62.1-2004 and CIBSE Applications Manual 10 for additional definitions.

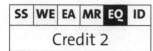

Construction IAQ Management Plan

During Construction

Intent

Prevent indoor air quality problems resulting from the construction/renovation process in order to help sustain the comfort and wellbeing of construction workers and building occupants.

Requirements

Develop and implement an Indoor Air Quality (IAQ) Management Plan for the construction and pre-occupancy phases of the tenant space as follows:

During construction meet or exceed the recommended Design Approaches of the Sheet Metal and Air Conditioning Contractors' National Association (SMACNA) IAQ Guidelines for Occupied Buildings Under Construction, 1995, Chapter 3.

Protect stored on-site and installed absorptive materials from moisture damage.

If air handlers must be used during construction, filtration media with a Minimum Efficiency Reporting Value (MERV) of 8 must be used at each return air grill, as determined by ASHRAE 52.2-1999.

Replace all filtration media immediately prior to occupancy. Coordinate with EQ Credits 3.2 and 5, installing only a single set of final filtration media.

Submittals

Provide the LEED for Commercial Interiors Submittal Template, signed by the general contractor or responsible party, declaring that a Construction IAQ Management Plan has been developed and implemented, and listing each air filter used during and at the end of construction. Include the MERV value, manufacturer name and model number.

AND EITHER

Provide 18 photographs—six photographs taken on three different occasions during construction—along with identification of the SMACNA approach featured by each photograph, in order to show consistent adherence to the credit requirements.

OR

Declare the five Design Approaches of SMACNA IAQ Guideline for Occupied Buildings under Construction, 1995, Chapter 3, which were used during building construction. Include a brief listing of some of the important design approaches employed.

Potential Technologies & Strategies

Adopt an IAQ management plan that minimizes the exposure of absorptive materials to moisture and airborne contaminants and that protects the HVAC system during construction. Sequence the installation of absorptive materials, such as insulation, carpeting, ceiling tile and gypsum wall board, to avoid contamination.

Summary of Referenced Standards

IAQ Guidelines for Occupied Buildings Under Construction

Sheet Metal and Air Conditioning Contractors' National Association (SMACNA)

www.smacna.org

(703) 803-2980

This standard provides an overview of air pollutants associated with construction, control measures, construction process management, quality control, communications with occupants, and case studies. Consult the referenced standard for measures to protect the building HVAC system and maintain acceptable indoor air quality during construction and demolition activities.

ANSI/ASHRAE 52.2-1999: Method of Testing General Ventilation Air-Cleaning Devices for Removal Efficiency by Particle Size

American Society of Heating, Refrigerating and Air-Conditioning Engineers (ASHRAE)

www.ashrae.org

(800) 527-4723

This standard presents methods for testing air cleaners for two performance characteristics: the ability of the device to remove particles from the air stream and the device's resistance to airflow. The minimum efficiency reporting value (MERV) is based on three composite average particle size removal efficiency (PSE) points. Consult the standard for a complete explanation of MERV value calculations.

Credit Interpretation Rulings

Credit Interpretation Rulings concerning EQ Credit 3.1 made to LEED for Commercial Interiors project requests, and unless inapplicable, to LEED for New Construction project requests apply to LEED for Commercial Interiors projects if adopted prior to project certification.

Because of the significant revisions to the credit requirements, LEED for New Construction v2.1 Credit Interpretation Rulings may be inapplicable. Below is a summary of CIRs that remain applicable.

Smaller-sized packaged HVAC systems are not excluded from compliance for the credit requirements.

Currently there is no ASHRAE approved testing methodology for dynamic air cleaners. Dynamic air cleaners are not an acceptable means of compliance. See LEED for New Construction v2.1 Credit Interpretation Ruling EQ Credit 3.1 dated 11/4/2003 for more detail.

Scheduling aspects of this credit are not related to time-of-day ("off hours") when materials are installed, but rather to the sequence in which they are installed over the course of construction. It is advantageous to install VOC-emitting products before installing absorbent materials (e.g. ceiling tiles, gypsum wall board, fabric furnishings, carpet and insulation).

Though the title of the SMACNA guidelines refers to occupied buildings, they constitute the same IAQ management methods to be used on new construction.

Utilizing temporary ventilation units is one strategy to meet the SMACNA control measure for HVAC protection, but does not on its own satisfy all the requirements of this credit.

Many of the LEED for New Construction v2.1 Credit Interpretation Rulings concerned the MERV rating of the filtration media to be installed following construction and just prior to occupancy. Though the requirement for the replacement of this filtration media remains a part of both EQ Credits 3.1 and 3.2, the MERV 13 standard is now a requirement of only EQ Credit 5. MERV 8 or better filters still must be used over return air grills if air handlers are operated during construction.

Approach and Implementation

Strategies

This credit hinges on performance by the general contractor. The development and implementation of a project specific IAQ Management Plan is key. The IAQ Management plan keeps the roles and responsibilities clear. The plan should be completed before construction begins and should include construction-related IAQ procedures in the pre-construction and construction progress meeting agendas. Education of subcontractors and all field personnel on the goals of the IAQ Management Plan and importance of following the plan's procedures ensures compliance and achievement. If warranted, select a member of the contractor's team to serve as the IAQ Manager who will have the responsibility to identify IAQ problems and their mitigation.

The referenced SMACNA standard recommends control measures in five areas: HVAC protection, source control, pathway interruption, housekeeping and scheduling. For each project, review the applicability of each control measure and include those that apply in the final IAQ Management Plan. The control measures are as follows:

HVAC Protection

Protect all HVAC equipment from both dust and odors. Ideally, do not use the system during construction, particularly during demolition. Seal all duct and equipment openings with plastic. If the system must be operated to maintain service to other occupied portions of the building or to protect finished work be sure to protect the return/negative pressure side of the system. If the returns cannot be closed off, install and maintain temporary filters over grills and openings. To comply with the credit requirements the filtration medium must be MERV 8 or better. If a plenum over the construction zone must be used, isolate it by having all ceiling tiles in place. Leaks in the return ducts and air handlers should be checked. Make needed repairs promptly. Avoid using the mechanical rooms for construction storage.

Source Control

Specify finish materials such as paints, carpet, composite wood, adhesives, and sealants that have low toxicity levels, or none at all. The selection of low-emitting materials is covered under EQ Credit 4. The IAQ Management Plan should specify the control measures for materials containing VOCs. Recover, isolate and ventilate containers housing toxic materials. Also, avoid exhaust fumes from idling vehicles and gasoline fueled tools.

Pathway Interruption

During construction, isolate areas of work to prevent contamination of clean or occupied spaces. Depending on the climate, ventilate using 100% outside air to exhaust contaminated air directly to the outside during installation of VOC-emitting materials. Depressurize the work area allowing the air pressure differential between construction and clean areas to contain dust and orders. Provide temporary barriers that contain the construction area.

Housekeeping

Institute cleaning activities designed to control contaminants in building spaces during construction and prior to occupancy. Porous building materials should be protected from exposure to moisture and stored in a clean area prior to installation. Some other strategies are using vacuum cleaners with high efficiency particulate filters, increasing the cleaning frequency and utilizing wetting agents for dust.

Scheduling

Coordinate construction activities to minimize or eliminate disruption of operations in the occupied portions of the building. Construction activities over the duration of the project should be sequenced carefully to minimize the impact on the indoor air quality. It may be necessary to conduct activities with high pollution potential during off-hours, such as on the weekends or in the evenings to allow time for new materials to air out. Plan adequate time to complete work so flush-out and IAQ test procedures can be completed prior to occupancy.

Upon completion of construction, replace all filtration media immediately prior to occupancy. This activity should be coordinated with the activities and requirements addressed in EQ Credit 3.2 and 5.

Submittal Documentation

The applicant must complete and submit the LEED for Commercial Interiors Submittal Template, signed by the general contractor or responsible party, declaring that a Construction IAQ Management Plan has been developed and implemented, and listing each air filter used during and at the end of construction. Include the MERV value, manufacturer name and model number. See **Table 1** on page 296.

The project team has two options to demonstrate compliance. The first approach requires at least 18 photographs, taken in groups of six, documenting three different occasions during construction. To demonstrate consistent adherence to the credit requirements, indicate on each photograph the SMACNA approach being employed. Consider date stamping the photographs.

The second approach requires a declaration indicating the five design approachs that were used during the construction, giving a brief listing of some of the im-

portant design approaches employed. Though an overview was provided above, Chapter 3 of SMACNA's IAQ Guidelines for Occupied Buildings Under Construction provides detailed explanations of the five methods and numerous strategies to incorporate into a project's IAQ plan.

Submitting a narrative may be appropriate for non-standard approaches to this credit; where applicable, provide a description of the HVAC system and how it was protected. Identify the housekeeping methods used. Indicate how natural ventilation was promoted and off-gassed toxins were evacuated. When illustrating the techniques used, provide a plan view identifying window locations and show the return air grill locations along with the means of protection.

The project team should develop and maintain a copy of its Construction IAQ Management Plan.

Note: The Resources and Definitions for EQ Credit 3.1 can be found at the end of the EQ Credit 3.2 section.

Construction IAQ Management Plan

Before Occupancy

Intent

Reduce indoor air quality problems resulting from the construction/renovation process, to sustain long-term worker and occupant comfort and wellbeing.

Requirements

Develop and implement an Indoor Air Quality (IAQ) Management Plan for the preoccupancy phases as follows:

OPTION A: Flush out procedure:

After construction ends and with all interior finishes installed, as described in this Reference Guide, install new filtration media and flush-out the building by supplying a total air volume of 14,000 cu.ft. of outdoor air per sq.ft. of floor area while maintaining an internal temperature of at least 60 °F and, where mechanical cooling is operated, relative humidity no higher than 60%.

The space may only be occupied following delivery of a minimum of 3,500 cu.ft. of outdoor air per sq.ft. of floor area to the space, and provided the space is ventilated at minimum rate of 0.30 cfm/sq.ft. of outside air or the design minimum outside air rate, whichever is greater, a minimum of three hours prior to occupancy and during occupancy, until the total of 14,000 cu.ft./sq.ft. of outside air has been delivered to the space.

OR

OPTION B: IAQ test procedure:

Conduct baseline IAQ testing, after construction ends and prior to occupancy, using testing protocols consistent with the United States Environmental Protection Agency "Compendium of Methods for the Determination of Air Pollutants in Indoor Air" and as additionally detailed in this Reference Guide.

Demonstrate that the contaminants concentration levels listed below are not exceeded:

Table 1: Maximum Contaminant Concentration Levels

Chemical Contaminate	Maximum Concentration
Formaldehyde	50 parts per billion
Particulates (PM 10)	50 micrograms per cubic meter
Total Volatile Organic Compounds (TVOC)	500 micrograms per cubic meter
* 4 - Phenylcyclohexene (4-PCH)	6.5 micrograms per cubic meter
Carbon Monoxide (CO)	9 parts per million and no greater than 2 parts per million above outdoor levels

* This test is only required only if carpets and fabrics with Styrene Butadiene (SB) latex backing material are installed as part of the base building systems.

For each sampling point where the maximum concentration limits are exceeded based on the table above, conduct additional flush out with outside air and retest the specific parameter(s) that were exceeded to indicate the requirements are achieved. Repeat the procedure until all requirements have been met. When retesting non-complying building areas, take samples from the same locations as in the first test.

The air sample testing shall be conducted as follows:

- All measurements shall be conducted prior to occupancy, but during normal occupied hours, and with the building ventilation system starting at the normal daily start time and operated at the minimum outside air flow rate for the occupied mode throughout the duration of the air testing.

- The building shall have all interior finishes installed, including but not limited to millwork, doors, paint, carpet and acoustic tiles. Non-fixed furnishings such as workstations and partitions are required to be in place for the testing.

- The number of sampling locations will vary depending upon the size of the building and number of ventilation systems. For each portion of the building served by a separate ventilation system, the number of sampling points shall not be less than one per 25,000 sq.ft., or for each contiguous floor area, whichever is larger, and include areas with the least ventilation and greatest presumed source strength.

- Air samples shall be collected between 4 feet and 7 feet from the floor over a minimum 4-hour period.

Submittals

OPTION A

Provide the LEED for Commercial Interiors Submittal Template, signed by the contractor or the responsible party, describing flush-out procedures and dates. Provide calculations to demonstrate that the required total air volumes and minimum ventilation volumes and rates have been delivered.

OR

OPTION B

Provide the LEED for Commercial Interiors Submittal Template, signed by the environmental consultant, or other responsible party, indicating that the air quality testing procedure has been conducted and that all areas tested do not exceed the maximum allowable concentration limits.

AND

Provide a copy of the IAQ testing results that includes documentation of the results and identifying the EPA testing method used. If alternative testing protocols are used, provide documentation and rationale justifying that the measured results meet the intent of the EPA testing methods.

Potential Technologies & Strategies

Prior to occupancy, perform a two week flush-out or test for contaminant levels in the tenant space.

For IAQ testing consider using a recognized measurement protocol such as the EPA "Compendium of Methods for the Determination of Air Pollutants in Indoor Air." If alternative testing protocols are used, provide justification that the measured test results meet the intent of the EPA testing methods.

Copies of the IAQ testing results should describe the contaminant sampling and analytical methods, the locations and duration of contaminant samples, the field sampling log sheets and laboratory analytical data and the methods and results utilized to determine that the ventilation system was started at the normal daily start time and operated at the minimum outside air flow rate for the occupied mode through the duration of the air testing.

SS	WE	EA	MR	**EQ**	ID
Credit 3.1					

SS	WE	EA	MR	**EQ**	ID
Credit 3.2					

Summary of Referenced Standards

United States Environmental Protection Agency "Compendium of Methods for the Determination of Air Pollutants in Indoor Air"

This standard is available from NTIS (800) 553-6847 with the ordering number PB90200288.

Credit Interpretation Rulings

Credit interpretation rulings concerning EQ Credit 3.2 made to LEED for Commercial Interiors project requests, and unless inapplicable, to LEED for New Construction project requests apply to LEED for Commercial Interiors projects.

Because of the significant revisions to the credit requirements, LEED for New Construction v2.1 Credit Interpretation Rulings may be inapplicable. Below is a summary of those that remain applicable.

Currently there is no ASHRAE-approved testing methodology for dynamic air cleaners. Dynamic air cleaners are not an acceptable means of compliance. See LEED for New Construction v2.1 Credit Interpretation Ruling EQ Credit 3.1 dated 11/4/2003 for more detail.

When core and shell projects are certifying using the LEED for New Construction Rating System, they are not eligible to earn either EQ Credit 3.1 or 3.2 until all interior construction has been completed. Because the intent of these credits is to eliminate indoor air quality problems that occur as a result of construction, architectural finishes used in tenant build-outs—a significant source of air pollutants—must be addressed. If significant build-outs remain to be completed at the time of a LEED for New Construction certification review, EQ Credit 3.2 is not applicable unless the project follows the guidance regarding build-out requirements for leases found in the LEED for New Construction v2.1 Administrative Credit Interpretation Ruling dated 5/17/2002 (located in the "Administrative Inquiries" section of LEED CIRs at www.usgbc.org).

IAQ testing of one floor should not be presumed to be representative of other floors within a building. Tenant build-outs invariably contain different types and amounts of materials.

When filtration media is replaced immediately prior to building flush-out, the replacement filtration media may be the same required to be installed following construction in EQ Credit 3.1. After flush-out, new filters must replace all filters except those solely processing outside air.

When there are multiple HVAC systems that can be operated independently, it is acceptable to flush-out portions of the building as they are completed but no additional construction work is to oc-

Table 1: Sample Documentation for EQ Credit 3.1

Filtration Media Used	Manufacturer	Model Number	MERV Value
Installed during construction:			
Roll, 36" wide	Iota Filters, Inc.	RF-36x1200-M08	8
Roll, 48" wide	Iota Filters, Inc.	RF-24x2400-M10	10
Installed at the end of construction:			
Air Handlers, return air	Chi Media	CM-48.48.2-13	13
Air Handlers, pre-coil	Chi Media	CM-36.24.3-13	13

cur once the flush-out of an area begins. Isolate completed areas from those under construction per SMACNA Guidelines for Occupied Buildings.

Punch-list items are part of construction and must be completed prior to building flush-out. Commissioning may occur during flush-out providing it does not introduce any additional contaminants into the building.

Many of the LEED for New Construction v2.1 Credit Interpretation Rulings concern the MERV rating of the filtration media to be installed following construction and just prior to occupancy. Though the requirement for the replacement of this filtration media remains a part of both EQ Credits 3.1 and 3.2, the MERV 13 standard is now a requirement of only EQ Credit 5. MERV 8 or better filters still must be used over return air grills if air handlers are operated during construction.

In LEED for Commercial Interiors EQ Credit 3.2, all furniture and furnishings are to be installed before either flush-out or baseline testing.

Flush-out Procedure

Approach and Implementation

This compliance path uses the building HVAC system to evacuate airborne contaminants. The flush-out may begin only after all construction work is completed, including punch-list items. All cleaning needs to be finalized and all furniture needs to be installed prior to flush-out. Final test and balancing should be completed and HVAC control should be functional, particularly if the occupants will be moving in during the second phase of flush-out.

The flush-out procedure discussed below assumes the use of the building's HVAC system, but alternatives are acceptable

providing they meet the air quantity, temperature and humidity requirements. One approach uses temporary supply and exhaust systems placed into windows or window openings. EPA's indoor air quality for schools Web site provides information on exhaust and spot ventilation during construction activities (see Web site information in the resources section of this credit) that can be helpful for design teams who are considering to use this approach.

Care must be taken to ensure the airflow is not short circuited, potentially leaving remote corners within the project spaces with less than adequate circulation, or other parts of the building with unanticipated increases, such as a stack effect up elevator shafts.

If the space's central HVAC system is being used, the next step is to remove any temporary filters and duct coverings installed as part of the Construction IAQ Management Plan. Replace the HVAC filtration media with new media; if the system is configured such that there are filters filtering only the outside air makeup, these outside air filters may remain unchanged. The new filters installed prior to the start of flush-out, as long as they meet the design specification, will satisfy the requirements of EQ Credit 3.1 as well. Note that these filters must be MERV 13 or better when a project plans to earn EQ Credit 5, Indoor Chemical and Pollution Source Control. Depending upon their condition following flush-out, some or all of the filters may be ready for replacement, but this is not a condition for satisfying the credit requirements.

Outside air is used to displace the off-gassed toxins. The quantity of outside air that must be introduced to the project space for the flush-out is 14,000 cu.ft. of air per sq.ft. of floor area. Occupants may move in earlier, after the point in the flush-out where 3,500 cu.ft. of air per sq. ft. has been reached. See **Graph 1**, and the example below. After the initial flush-out

SS	WE	EA	MR	EQ	ID
Credit 3.1					

SS	WE	EA	MR	EQ	ID
Credit 3.2					

Graph 1: Sample Flush-out Procedure Air Quantity Graph

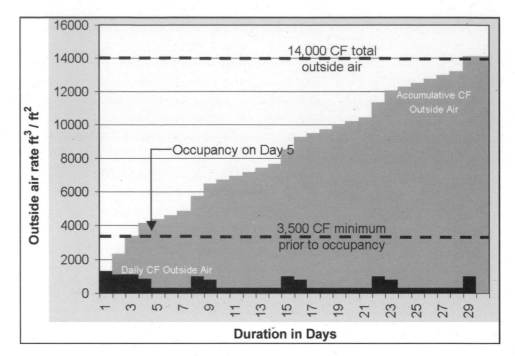

phase when 3,500 cu.ft. of outside air has been supplied per sq.ft. of floor area, the occupants may move in, but the flush-out is not complete. A total of 14,000 cu.ft. of outside air must be supplied per sq.ft of floor area before switching the HVAC system to its normal operational mode.

Not all outside air is equal. Depending upon geography and season it can be very cold or damp. Because of this, prudent limits have been set to ensure no harm comes to the building and potentially to the occupants. The rate of outside air should not cause the interior temperature to drop below 60°F. When mechanical cooling is operating, the relative humidity should not exceed 60%.

During an occupied flush-out phase, there is a minimum ventilation rate that must commence at least three hours prior to daily occupancy and continue while the space is occupied. The rate of outside air must be at least 0.30 cfm/sq.ft. or the design minimum outside air rate, whichever is greater. The design minimum outside air rate should be determined using ASHRAE 62.1-2004, the same criteria

for EQ Prerequisite 1, or the applicable local code if it is more stringent.

The 0.30 cfm/sq.ft. rate may be several times that required by ASHRAE 62.1-2004 for a project's planned occupancy. If the HVAC system is part of the project scope, plan ahead and design it to meet the flush-out rate minimum. If the project area will be served by an existing HVAC system, the system's outside air delivery capabilities ideally should be part of the building selection criteria, similar to the evaluation recommended to confirm compliance with EQ Prerequisite 1.

There are other thermal comfort, expense and operational considerations to evaluate in conjunction with occupying a space before the end of flush-out. Check to make sure the HVAC system is capable of maintaining temperatures within a range acceptable to the occupants; opinions formed during this period may last long after the system is operating normally.

There are numerous expense and operational issues to be considered such as the rent or lease details, and the existing

HVAC system capacity to accommodate the flush-out criteria. It is evident that input from nearly the entire project team is needed to determine the best approach. When completed, make the evaluation and the resulting flush-out strategy part of the project Construction IAQ Management Plan.

Submittal Documentation

Complete the declaration on the LEED for Commercial Interiors Submittal Template indicating that the flush-out procedure was used. Provide calculations indicating that the required total volume was reached, and that the minimum rate was maintained. See **Table 2** for a sample.

It is suggested that the project team develop and maintain an evaluation of how the HVAC system will be operated during the flush-out procedure. In addition, the team should make the flush-out part of its IAQ Management Plan and retain it through certification review.

Example

The 20,000 sq.ft. project is located on the entire third floor of a five-story office building that has a single common HVAC system. The organization moving in faced a $40,000 hold-over charge if it failed to vacate its former space by the last day of January. Rent in their new space was set to begin January 1, regardless of occupancy. When the client realized it would be too disruptive to move until after the first of the year, predictably the construction schedule adjusted accordingly to complete the move in January.

The old space was filled with computers, printers and copiers. There was no proper ventilation or office layout. Management was committed to improving the indoor air quality in its new space, enclosing the major sources in segregated areas with deck-to-deck partitions and separate

ventilation. They decided the flush-out was a critical part of their IEQ program, even if it delayed the move.

The project team explored their options. Fortunately, New Year's Day fell on a Tuesday, creating a four-day weekend when the entire building would not be occupied. The mechanical contractor and building operations team worked out a two-phased flush-out schedule that would not inconvenience the other building occupants and minimized the load on the building HVAC system.

The mechanical engineer's calculations showed that if they started by midnight Friday before New Year's, the system had the capacity to supply the 3,500 cu.ft. of outside air per sq.ft. of area by 10:00 a.m. New Year's Day, allowing move-in to start the next day. Space temperatures could be kept above 60°F as long as the outside air temperature didn't drop below freezing. Lower temperatures meant trimming the building's air handlers back from their maximum 60/40 split of outside to recirculated air thus making the system unable to supply the required minimum level of outside air to allow occupants to move in based on two-phased flush-out. Therefore, occupancy couldn't start on January 2nd.

As part of the planning, all parties involved agreed it was best to program the controls and complete the air balancing ahead of the flush-out.

By 6:00 p.m. Friday, December 28, the mechanical contractor and building operations crew trimmed down the dampers on the supply and return ducts located on all the other floors and confirmed that the controls were in night-time mode. For the project space, the primary supply and return louvers, which had been kept closed during demolition and much of the construction, were now wide open. Then MERV 13 filters were installed at 8:15 p.m. The controls engineer logged on to the building's energy management

SS	WE	EA	MR	EQ	ID
Credit 3.1					

SS	WE	EA	MR	EQ	ID
Credit 3.2					

SS | WE | EA | MR | **EQ** | ID

Credit 3.1

SS | WE | EA | MR | **EQ** | ID

Credit 3.2

Table 2: Sample Flush-out Outside Air Volume Summary

Day	Date	Run Hours / Day	Time-weighted Daily Average Outside Air Rate [cfm / ft²]	Minimum Outside Air Rate [cfm / ft²]	Volume Outside Air [ft³ / ft²]	Accumulative Volume Outside Air [ft³ / ft²]
Phase 1—Not Occupied						
1	Dec 28	4	0.72 cfm/sf	0.45 cfm/sf	172.8	172.8
2-4	Dec 29 — Dec 31	24	0.72 cfm/sf	0.72 cfm/sf	3,110.4 @ 1036.8/day	3,283.2
5	Jan 1	18	0.72 cfm/sf	0.72 cfm/sf	777.6	4,060.8
Phase 2—Occupied						
6 - 8	Jan 2– Jan 4 weekdays	13	0.3 cfm/sf	0.3 cfm/sf	702.0 @ 234.0/day	4,762.8
8	Jan 4 Friday evening	6	0.5 cfm/sf	0.3 cfm/sf	180.0 evening	4,942.8
9 - 10	Jan 5 - Jan 6 weekend	24	0.5 cfm/sf	0.3 cfm/sf	1,440.0 @ 720.0/day	6,382.8
11 - 15	Jan 7 - Jan 11 weekdays	13	0.3 cfm/sf	0.3 cfm/sf	1,170.0 @ 234.0/day	7,552.8
15	Jan 11 Friday evening	6	0.5 cfm/sf	0.3 cfm/sf	180.0 evening	7,732.8
16 - 17	Jan 12 - Jan 13 weekend	24	0.5 cfm/sf	0.3 cfm/sf	1,440.0 @ 720.0/day	9,172.9
18 - 22	Jan 14 - Jan 18 weekdays	13	0.3 cfm/sf	0.3 cfm/sf	1,170.0 @ 234.0/day	10,342.8
22	Jan 18 Friday evening	6	0.5 cfm/sf	0.3 cfm/sf	180.0 evening	10,522.8
23 - 24	Jan 19 - Jan 20 weekend	24	0.5 cfm/sf	0.3 cfm/sf	1,440.0 @ 720.0/day	11,962.8
25 - 29	Jan 21 - Jan 25 weekdays	13	0.3 cfm/sf	0.3 cfm/sf	1,170.0 @ 234.0/day	13,132.8
29	Jan 25 Friday evening	6	0.5 cfm/sf	0.3 cfm/sf	180.0 evening	13,312.8
30	Jan 26 Saturday	23	0.5 cfm/sf	0.3 cfm/sf	687.2	14,000.0
Flush-out Complete						

system and selected the flush-out mode. In this mode, which had previously been programmed, the VAV boxes within the project space fully opened and the central air handlers were turned back on, with dampers set to provide 60/40 outside to recirculated air, beginning the flush-out.

Temperatures were held, both inside and out. Spot checks of several of the diffusers showed air flow to the project area was uniformly exceeding the projected 0.6 cfm/sq.ft. rate by 20%. The 3,500 cu.ft. of outside air per sq.ft. of area criteria would be exceeded before switching to the occupied flush-out mode on the evening of New Year's Day.

So, at 6:00 p.m. January 1, phase one ended. The operations crew reset the manual dampers on all the floors. The energy management system was set to operate the building HVAC system on the second phase occupied flush-out mode. There would be a normal night-time set back without outside air; then at 5:00 am, three hours before the start of the daily occupancy, the systems would switch into a modified daytime mode. The minimum 0.30 cfm/sq.ft. would be delivered to the project space.

During the unoccupied phase over the holiday weekend, the system pumped outside air into the space at the rate of 0.72 cfm/sq.ft., satisfying the first 4,060 cu.ft./sq.ft. of the 14,000 total. During weekdays, when occupants were there, the rate was cut back to the minimum limit of 0.3 cfm/sq.ft. to eliminate thermal comfort problems throughout the building. Starting at the end of workday on Fridays, the rate was increased; this shortened the flush-out by two weeks and could be done without touching the supply and return dampers on the other floors.

Finally, on the 30th day the 14,000 cu.ft./sq.ft. mark was reached. The building air filters were checked and found to be in a condition satisfactory to continue using. Controls were switched to the normal

mode. The test and balance crew spot checked air distribution and found no major problems. Final commissioning was completed. The occupants had all moved out of their old space on time.

IAQ Test Procedure

Approach and Implementation

The baseline IAQ testing approach to credit compliance provides confirmation that major contaminants are below recognized acceptable levels prior to occupancy. While the list included in the credit is not intended to be all inclusive, together they approximate the major forms of airborne constituents found following construction. More explanation on the significance of each is provided below.

Favorable test results are strong indicators that the project has implemented a successful construction IAQ management plan, that low-emitting materials have been specified, that cleanup has been thorough, and that the HVAC system is providing adequate ventilation. They also can mean that occupancy can occur potentially sooner than what might be possible if the flush-out compliance path has been followed. Ideally the groundwork for baseline testing should occur during the design process, making sure the testing requirements are included in Division 1 of the project construction specifications. While the credit does not establish qualifications for the laboratory or those conducting the sampling, this work requires special knowledge. The project team should evaluate the capabilities of the IAQ specialist, industrial hygienist and testing facility being considered.

During construction, maintain vigilance to avoid substitutions of the specified low-emitting materials. Once both construction and the installation of furniture and furnishings are completed, which is a

SS	WE	EA	MR	EQ	ID
Credit 3.1					

SS	WE	EA	MR	EQ	ID
Credit 3.2					

SS	WE	EA	MR	**EQ**	ID
				Credit 3.1	

SS	WE	EA	MR	**EQ**	ID
				Credit 3.2	

credit requirement in the LEED for Commercial Interiors Rating System, complete the final cleaning. Use low-VOC cleaning supplies to prevent short-term high VOC levels that may affect test results. Use vacuum cleaners with HEPA filtration to capture particulates.

Projects also following the requirements of LEED for Commercial Interiors EQ Credit 3.1 should replace all filtration media at this point. Finally, complete the air test and balancing of the HVAC system before beginning the baseline IAQ testing. The IAQ maximum contaminant levels are dependent on the HVAC system operating under normal conditions with outdoor air flow rates at the minimum; this stipulation is made so that the air tested is as similar as possible to what the occupants will be breathing.

The protocols described in the referenced publication, US EPA's "Compendium of Methods for the Determination of Air Pollutants in Indoor Air" are recommended, but others may be used if valid justification can be provided. The sampling locations should be selected carefully to ascertain the concentrations in areas with the least ventilation with potentially the greatest presumed contaminant source strength.

Samples are to be taken in each portion of the building served by a separate ventilation system, and shall not be less then one per 25,000 sq.ft. For example, in a tenant space of 20,000 sq.ft. served by three rooftop units, one each for the north and south elevations (general office area), and the third for a training room and conference rooms, samples should be taken in at least three places, even though two of the units serve one general office area

The samples are to be taken in the breathing zone, between 4 feet and 7 feet above the floor. They are to be taken during normal occupied hours with the HVAC system operating with normal daily start times at the minimum outside air flow rate. Record the exact sample locations using Y and Z coordinates, since follow-up samples may be needed.

If a test sample exceeds the maximum concentration level, flush out the space by increasing the rate of outside air. While the credit requirements do not prescribe the duration of the flush-out, those responsible for testing should make an evaluation based on the contaminant, its concentration and the potential source. The off-gassing characteristics of sources differ; some deplete rapidly while others emit at a steady rate over an extended period of time. Resample and confirm compliance before allowing the space to be occupied. The retest may be limited to the chemical contaminants that produced excessive chemical concentration levels in the initial test of the spaces.

Submittal Documentation

Complete the declaration on the LEED for Commercial Interiors Submittal Template declaring that the baseline air quality testing procedure was conducted and that all areas tested are at or below the maximum concentrations. Provide the test results indicating the EPA protocol used. If an alternative testing protocol has been used, provide documentation and rationale justifying the results.

It is suggested that the project team develops and maintains a plan showing the locations of each sample, and the reasoning for its selection. For samples testing over the limits, document the probable cause and remediation.

Chemical Contaminants

Formaldehyde

Formaldehyde is a gas emitted from numerous indoor sources. These include many building materials (especially pressed wood products such as particleboard, plywood, oriented strand board, fiberboard), glues and adhesives, most carpets, composite wood furnishings, permanent pressed fabrics, and combustion sources. Materials containing formaldehyde release formaldehyde gas into the air. Short term effects include eye, nose, throat, and skin irritation; nausea; headache; allergic sensitization; and exacerbation of asthma. People vary substantially in their sensitivity to formaldehyde. For most individuals these effects occur at exposure levels ranging from 37 ppb and 3,000 ppb. In 2004, the International Agency for Research on Cancer (IARC) classified formaldehyde as a known carcinogen. The State of California recommended maximum indoor concentration for formaldehyde is "lowest feasible concentration" to reduce cancer and 27 ppb to avoid acute irritant effects.

Referenced Standard: For the test for formaldehyde, the concentration of 50 ppb is an adaptation of an 1989 architectural specification for a group of buildings in the State of Washington. This specification required that each material in the building not contribute more than 50 ppb to the indoor concentrations. For this credit the total emissions from all building materials must not result in an indoor concentration greater than 50 ppb with the building ventilation system operating in the minimum outside air mode.

Particulate Matter (PM10)

Airborne particulate matter often is generated in large quantities during construction. If dust control precautions are not undertaken during construction then reservoirs of construction dusts can remain on surfaces and especially within carpeted surfaces where the particles may be re-suspended into the air by occupant activities for many months following construction. The outdoor air which enters the building can also be a significant source of indoor airborne particulate matter. The test samples particles with an aerodynamic diameter less than or equal to a nominal 10 micrometers (PM10). Elevated indoor concentrations of PM10 have been associated with asthma and respiratory symptoms, for example cough, phlegm, chest pain, or wheeze, asthma exacerbation, and use of asthma medications.

Referenced Standard: For the test for PM10, the concentration of 50 µg/m3 is an adaptation of an 1989 architectural specification for a group of buildings in the State of Washington. This specification required that each material in the building not contribute more than 50 µg/m3 to the indoor concentrations. For this credit the total emissions from all building materials must not result in an indoor concentration greater than 50 µg/m3 with the building ventilation system operating in the minimum outside air mode.

TVOC, Total Volatile Organic Compounds

TVOC is the sum of all of the individual VOCs in the air. There are hundreds of individual VOCs emitted by materials in buildings. These include pressed wood products such as particleboard, plywood, oriented strand board, fiberboard, as well as glues and adhesives, paints, most carpets, composite wood furnishings, thermal insulation, and combustion sources. When in high concentrations, these compounds can cause health problems, including eye, nose, and respiratory irritation. In addition, many volatile organic compounds are carcinogenic.

Referenced Standard: For the test for TVOC, the concentration of 500 µg/m3 is an adaptation of an 1989 architectural specification for a group of buildings in the State of Washington. This specification required that each material in the building not contribute more than 500 µg/m3 to the indoor concentrations. For this credit the total emissions from all building materials must not result in an indoor concentration greater than 500 µg/m3 with the building ventilation system operating in the minimum outside air mode.

SS	WE	EA	MR	EQ	ID
Credit 3.1					

SS	WE	EA	MR	EQ	ID
Credit 3.2					

| SS | WE | EA | MR | **EQ** | ID |

Credit 3.1

| SS | WE | EA | MR | **EQ** | ID |

Credit 3.2

4-PCH, 4-phenylcyclohexene

This compound, whose odor is easily detectable at very low levels, is generally known as "new carpet" odor. It is emitted from the styrene butadiene rubber (SBR) binder that some manufacturers used to hold carpet fibers and backing together. This test may be waived if there are no carpets or fabrics containing SBR.

Referenced Standard. For the test for 4-PCH, the concentration of 6.5 micrograms per cubic meter is from the IAQ Standard developed by the State of Washington citing the threshold value of 6.5 micrograms per cubic meter .

Carbon Monoxide (CO)

Carbon monoxide is a colorless, odorless, and tasteless gas. It is a product of incomplete combustion, emitted from sources such as vehicle exhaust, gas and propane device exhaust, wood stoves, kerosene heaters, and cigarettes. Carbon monoxide can trigger acute health effects, even death, at very high concentrations, or flu-like symptoms and other health effects at lower concentrations over periods of time.

Referenced Standard. For the test for CO the concentration of 9 parts per million is from the EPA National Primary and Secondary Ambient Air Quality Standards, Code of Federal Regulations, Title 40 Part 50 (40CFR50), as amended July 1, 1987. A summary of the Primary Standards is included in ASHRAE 62-2001, Table 1. In addition, a concentration of no more than 2 parts per million over outdoor concentrations is required, as this indicates a source of this potentially lethal gas in the building.

Considerations

Building construction invariably introduces contaminates into the building. If unaddressed, the contamination can result in poor indoor air quality extending over the lifetime of the building. Fortunately there are IAQ management strategies, if instituted during construction and before occupancy, that will minimize potential problems. The strategies include protection of HVAC systems during construction, and IAQ testing or flush-out of the building prior to occupancy.

Environmental Issues

A ventilation flush-out prior to occupancy may require additional energy use, which is associated with air and water pollution. However, contaminant reduction is beneficial to building occupants, resulting in greater comfort, lower absenteeism and greater productivity.

Economic Issues

Superior indoor air quality is likely to increase worker productivity translating to greater profitability for companies. Additional time and labor may be required during and after construction to protect and clean ventilation systems. However, these actions can extend the lifetime of the ventilation system and improve ventilation system efficiency, resulting in reduced energy use. The sequencing of material installation may require additional time and could potentially delay the date of initial occupancy. Early coordination between the contractor and subcontractors can minimize or eliminate scheduling delays.

Community Issues

Contaminants from the construction process can affect the health of construction workers during construction and building users during occupancy. If contaminants remain after occupancy commences, they may lead to expensive and complicated clean-up procedures. Construction worker health is covered by federal and state regulations, primarily the Occupational Safety and Health Administration (OSHA). However, building occupants are not covered under these regulations.

Resources

Please see the USGBC Web site at www. usgbc.org/resources for more specific resources on materials sources and other technical information.

Web Sites

Compendium of Methods for the Determination of Inorganic Compounds in Ambient Air

U.S. Environmental Protection Agency

www.epa.gov/ttn/amtic/files/ambient/inorganic/iocompen.pdf

IAQ Design for Schools

U.S. Environmental Protection Agency

www.epa.gov/iaq/schooldesign/controlling.html

Detailed information on exhaust or spot ventilation practices during construction activity can be found towards the end of the Web page at the abovementioned URL address

IAQ Standards Program

State of Washington

www.aerias.org/kview.asp?DocId=85& sparrid=2&subid=13

This IAQ standard for the State of Washington was the first state-initiated program to ensure the design of buildings with acceptable indoor air quality.

Sheet Metal and Air Conditioning Contractors' National Association (SMACNA)

www.smacna.org

(703) 803-2980

SMACNA is a professional trade association that publishes the referenced standard as well as *Indoor Air Quality: A Systems Approach*, a comprehensive discussion of the sources of pollutants, measurement, methods of control, and management techniques.

Print Media

Indoor Air Quality, Construction Technology Centre Atlantic. Written as a comprehensive review of indoor air quality issues and solutions, the report is available for purchase from ctca.unb.ca/IAQ/index.htm or by calling (506) 453-5000.

Definitions

A **Construction IAQ Management Plan** is a document specific to a building project that outlines measures to minimize contamination in the building during construction and to flush the building of contaminants prior to occupancy.

HVAC Systems include heating, ventilating, and air-conditioning systems used to provide thermal comfort and ventilation for building interiors.

SS	WE	EA	MR	EQ	ID
				Credit 3.1	

SS	WE	EA	MR	EQ	ID
				Credit 3.2	

SS	WE	EA	MR	EQ	ID
Credit 3.1					

SS	WE	EA	MR	EQ	ID
Credit 3.2					

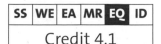
Low-Emitting Materials

Adhesives and Sealants

1 point

Intent

Reduce the quantity of indoor air contaminants that are odorous, potentially irritating and/or harmful to the comfort and wellbeing of installers and occupants.

Requirements

All adhesives and sealants used in the building interior, (i.e., inside of the exterior moisture barrier) must not exceed the VOC content limits of:

- Adhesives, Sealants and Sealant Primers: South Coast Air Quality Management District (SCAQMD) Rule #1168 requirements in effect on January 1, 2003 and rule amendment dated October 3, 2003.

- Aerosol Adhesives: Green Seal Standard GC-36 requirements in effect on October 19, 2000.

Submittals

Provide the LEED for Commercial Interiors Submittal Template, signed by the architect, interior designer or responsible party, listing the adhesives, sealants, sealant primers and aerosol adhesives used in the building and declaring that they meet the noted requirements. For each product in the listing, state the VOC level, the applicable standard, the classification of material and the VOC limit.

Potential Technologies & Strategies

Specify Low-VOC materials in construction documents. Ensure that VOC limits are clearly stated in each section of the specifications where adhesives and sealants are addressed. Review product cut sheets, MSD sheets, signed attestations or other official literature from the manufacturer clearly identifying the VOC contents or compliance with referenced standards.

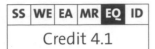
Summary of Referenced Standards

South Coast Rule #1168 by the South Coast Air Quality Management District

South Coast Air Quality Management District

www.aqmd.gov/rules/reg/reg11/r1168.pdf

(909) 396-2000

The South Coast Air Quality Management District is a governmental organization in Southern California with the mission to maintain healthful air quality for its residents. The organization established source specific standards to reduce air quality impacts. The South Coast Rule #1168 VOC limits for adhesives are summarized in the following table.

Table 1: South Coast Rule # 1168 VOC Limits, Less Water and Less Exempt Compounds

Architectural Adhesives Applications	VOC Limit [g/L]	Welding & Installation	VOC Limit [g/L]
Indoor Carpet Adhesives	50	PVC welding	510
Carpet Pad Adhesives	50	CPVC welding	490
Outdoor Carpet Adhesives	150	ABS welding	400
Wood Flooring Adhesives	100	Plastic cement welding	350
Rubber Floor Adhesives	60	Adhesive primer for plastic	650
Subfloor Adhesives	50	Contact Adhesive	80
Ceramic tile installation	65	Special Purpose Contact Adhesives	250
VCT and Asphalt Tile Adhesives	50	Structural Wood Member Adhesive	140
Dry Wall and Panel Adhesives	50	Sheet Applied Rubber Lining Operations	850
Cove base installation	50	Top and Trim Adhesive	250
Multipurpose Construction Adhesives	70	**Sealants**	
Structural Glazing Adhesives	100	Architectural	250
Substrates		Porous Architectural Sealant Primer	775
Metal to metal	30	Non-porous Architectural Sealant Primer	250
Plastic foams	50		
Porous material except wood	50		
Wood	30		
Fiberglass	80		

Table 2: Aerosol Adhesives VOC Limits

Aerosol Adhesives	VOC Limit
General purpose mist spray	65% VOCs by weight
General purpose web spray	55% VOCs by weight
Special purpose aerosol adhesives (all types)	70% VOCs by weight

Green Seal Standard 36 (GS-36)

www.greenseal.org/standards/commercialadhesives.htm

Green Seal is an independent nonprofit organization that promotes the manufacture and sale of environmentally responsible consumer products. GS-36 is a standard that sets VOC limits for commercial commercial adhesives.

Credit Interpretation Rulings

Credit Interpretation Rulings concerning EQ Credit 4.1 made to LEED for Commercial Interiors project requests, and unless inapplicable, to LEED for New Construction project requests apply to LEED for Commercial Interiors projects.

Duct sealants are included under this credit.

Adhesives and sealants applied to casework, doors or other interior prefabricated components manufactured off-site are not subject to the VOC requirements.

Cut sheets, brochures and testimonial letters from manufacturers are acceptable substitutes for MSDS sheets. Documentation must be authentic and must include the required data.

ALL adhesives used AT THE SITE must meet the LEED VOC limits. This would include the adhesive used for the wood doors only if the doors were built on-site. Products used at outside manufacturing facilities would not be subject to these limits.

Submittal Documentation

Make the declaration included with the LEED for Commercial Interiors Submittal Template. Complete the spreadsheet tab placing the products under the applicable standard and classification and indicate the products' VOC level. See sample **Table 2**. It is recommended that any conspicuous absences be explained in the submittal.

If a VOC Budget is being submitted, follow the direction provided later in the text. If the VOC Budget methodology is used, or if there are other non-standard approaches to this credit, a narrative may be appropriate as well.

Additional Documentation

For potential use during submittal review, it is suggested that the project team assemble and maintain the MSD sheets or other product information confirming the VOC levels of products shown in the Submittal Template listing. Consider highlighting this information if requested during the review process.

Resources

Please see the USGBC Web site at www.usgbc.org/resources for more specific resources on materials sources and other technical information.

Web Sites

South Coast Rule #1168 by the South Coast Air Quality Management District

South Coast Air Quality Management District

www.aqmd.gov/rules/reg/reg11/r1168.pdf

(909) 396-2000

The South Coast Air Quality Management District is a governmental organization in Southern California with the mission to maintain healthful air quality for its residents. The organization established source specific standards to reduce air quality impacts. The South Coast Rule #1168 VOC limits for adhesives are summarized in **Table 1**.

Green Seal Standard 36 (GS-36)

www.greenseal.org/standards/commercialadhesives.htm

Green Seal is an independent nonprofit organization that promotes the manu-

Table 2: Sample Submittal Information for Adhesives and Sealants

SCAQMD Rule 1168 Section		VOC Limit g/L
Product	Product VOC g/L	
Indoor Carpet Adhesives		50
ABCD Carpet Adhesives #00100	39	
Carpet Pad Adhesives		50
Wood Flooring Adhesives		100
EFGH Adhesives #00222	71	
Rubber Floor Adhesives		60
IJKL Adhesives #006377	46	
Subfloor Adhesives		50
Ceramic Tile Adhesives		65
VCT and Asphalt Tile Adhesives		50
Dry Wall and Panel Adhesives		50
MNOP Adhesives #AZ1118		
Cove Base Adhesives		50
Mutipurpose Construction Adhesives		70
QRST Adhesives #2266ss	48	
Structural Glazing Adhesives		100

facture and sale of environmentally responsible consumer products. GS-36 is a standard that sets VOC limits for commercial commercial adhesives.

Definitions

Adhesive is any substance that is used to bond one surface to another surface by attachment. Adhesives include adhesive bonding primers, adhesive primers, adhesive primers for plastics, and any other primer.

Aerosol Adhesive is an adhesive packaged as an aerosol product in which the spray mechanism is permanently housed in a non-refillable can designed for hand-held application without the need for ancillary hoses or spray equipment. Aerosol adhesives include special purpose spray adhesives, mist spray adhesives and web spray adhesives.

Indoor applies to all materials that have the potential to emit contaminants to indoor spaces; typically all materials inside the exterior moisture barrier.

Porous Sealant is a substance used as a sealant on porous materials. Porous materials have tiny openings, often microscopic, in which fluids may be absorbed or discharged. Such materials include, but are not limited to, wood, fabric, paper, corrugated paperboard and plastic foam.

Primer is a material applied to a substrate to improve adhesion of subsequently applied adhesive.

Non-porous Sealant is a substance used as a sealant on non-porous materials. Non-porous materials do not have openings in which fluids may be absorbed or discharged. Such materials include, but are not limited to, plastic and metal.

A **Sealant** is any material with adhesive properties that is formulated primarily to fill, seal, or waterproof gaps or joints between two surfaces. Sealants include sealant primers and caulks.

VOC (Volatile Organic Compounds) are carbon compounds that participate in atmospheric photochemical reactions (excluding carbon monoxide, carbon dioxide, carbonic acid, metallic carbides and carbonates, and ammonium carbonate). The compounds vaporize (become a gas) at normal room temperatures.

Note: Please see the end of EQc4.5 for more information on Approach and Implementation for EQ credit 4.1 and the other EQ credit 4 sections.

Low-Emitting Materials

Paints and Coatings

Intent

Reduce the quantity of indoor air contaminants that are odorous, potentially irritating and/or harmful to the comfort and wellbeing of installers and occupants.

Requirements

Interior paints and coating applied on-site must meet the limitations and restrictions concerning chemical components set by the following standards:

- "Topcoat Paints: Green Seal Standard GS-11, Paints", First Edition, May 20, 1993.

- "Anti-Corrosive and Anti-Rust Paints: Green Seal Standard GS-03, Anti-Corrosive Paints", Second Edition, January 7, 1997. For applications on ferrous metal substrates.

- "All Other Architectural Coatings, Primers and Undercoats: South Coast Air Quality Management District (SCAQMD) Rule 1113, Architectural Coatings", rules in effect on January 1, 2004.

Submittals

Provide the LEED for Commercial Interiors Submittal Template, signed by the architect, interior designer or responsible party, listing all the interior paints and coatings used in the building that are addressed by the referenced standards. State that they comply with the VOC and chemical component limits and the chemical component restrictions of each standard. For each product in the listing, state the VOC level, the applicable standard, the classification of material and the VOC limit.

Potential Technologies & Strategies

Specify Low-VOC paints and coatings in construction documents. Ensure that VOC limits are clearly stated in each section where paints and coatings are addressed.

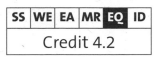

Summary of Referenced Standards

Green Seal Standard GS-11

http://www.greenseal.org/standards/paints.htm

(202) 872-6400

Green Seal is an independent nonprofit organization that promotes the manufacture and sale of environmentally responsible consumer products. GS-11 is a standard that sets VOC limits for commercial flat and non-flat paints.

Green Seal Standard GS-03

www.greenseal.org/standards/anti-corrosivepaints.htm

(202) 872-6400

GS-03 is a Green Seal standard that sets VOC limits for anti-corrosive and anti-rust paints.

Table 3: Green Seal GS-11 Limits for Interior Paints

Paint Type	VOC Limit [g/L]
Non-flat	150
Flat	50

Table 4: Green Seal GS-03 Limits for Anti-Corrosive and Anti-Rust Paint

Paint Type	VOC Limit* [g / L]
Gloss	250
Semi-gloss	250
Flat	250

Table 5: South Coast Rule # 1133 VOC Limits for Architectural Coatings

Applications	VOC Limit [g/L]	Applications	VOC Limit [g/L]
Bond Breakers	350	Mastic coatings	300
Clear Wood Finishes:		Metallic pigmented coatings	500
Varnish	350	Multi-color coatings	250
Sanding Sealers	350	Pigmented lacquer	550
Lacquer	550	Pre-treatment wash primers	420
Clear Brushing Lacquer	680	Primers, sealers and undercoaters	200
Concrete-curing compounds	350	Quick-dry enamels	250
Dry-fog coatings	400	Quick-dry primers, sealers and	
Fire-proofing exterior coatings	350	undercoaters	200
Fire-retardant coatings:		Recycled coatings	250
Clear	650	Rust preventative coatings	400
Pigmented	350	Shellac—Clear	730
Floor coatings	100	Shellac—Pigmented	550
Graphic arts (sign) coatings	500	Specialty primers	350
Industrial maintenance (IM) coat-	250	Stains	250
High temperature IM coatings	420	Waterproofing sealers	250
Zinc-rich IM primers 420 340	100	Waterproofing concrete/	
Japans / faux finishing coatings	350	masonry sealers	400
Magnesite cement coatings	450	Wood preservatives	350

South Coast Air Quality Management District (SCAQMD) Rule 1113, Architectural Coatings

www.aqmd.gov/rules/reg/reg11/r1113.pdf

The South Coast Air Quality Management District is a governmental organization in Southern California with the mission to maintain healthful air quality for its residents. The organization established source specific standards to reduce air quality impacts. The South Coast Rule #1113 VOC limits for architectural coatings are summarized in **Table 5**.

Credit Interpretation Rulings

Credit Interpretation Rulings concerning EQ Credit 4.2 made to LEED for Commercial Interiors project requests, and unless inapplicable, to LEED for New Construction project requests apply to LEED for Commercial Interiors projects.

Enamel is considered an interior top coat paint, with a limit of 50 g/L for a flat finish, and 150 g/L for a non-flat finish.

If the project is forced to use small quantities of non-complying paint, a VOC budget can be calculated to demonstrate that the overall average VOC of all products (based on gallons of each applied) is below the allowed limit, by category.

The Green Seal standard for low-VOC paints states, "The calculation of VOC shall exclude water and tinting color added at the point of sale."

Submittal Documentation

Make the declaration included with the LEED for Commercial Interiors Submittal Template. Complete the spreadsheet tab placing the products under the applicable standard and classification and indicate the products' VOC level (similar to **Table 2** for EQc4.1). It is recommended that any conspicuous absences be explained in the submittal.

If a VOC Budget is being submitted, follow the direction provided later in the text. If the VOC budget methodology is used, or if there are other non-standard approaches to this credit, a narrative may be appropriate as well.

Additional Documentation

For potential use during submittal review, it is suggested the project team assemble and maintain the MSD sheets or other product information confirming the VOC levels of products shown in the Submittal Template listing. Consider highlighting this information if requested during the review process.

Resources

Please see the USGBC Web site at www.usgbc.org/resources for more specific resources on materials sources and other technical information.

Web Sites

Green Seal

www.greenseal.org

South Coast Air Quality Management District

www.aqmd.gov

Definitions

Anti-corrosive Paints are coatings formulated and recommended for use in preventing the corrosion of ferrous metal substrates.

Paints are liquid, liquefiable or mastic composition that is converted to a solid protective, decorative, or functional adherent film after application as a thin layer. These coatings are intended for on-site application to interior or exterior surfaces of residential, commercial, institutional or industrial buildings.

Indoor refers to all materials that have the potential to emit contaminants to indoor spaces; typically all materials inside of the exterior moisture barrier.

Flat Coatings are coatings that register a gloss of less than 15 on an 85-degree meter or less than 5 on a 60-degree meter.

Non-flat Coatings are coatings that register a gloss of 5 or greater on a 60-degree meter and a gloss of 15 or greater on an 85-degree meter.

Primer is a material applied to a substrate to improve adhesion of subsequently applied adhesive.

VOCs (Volatile Organic Compounds) are carbon compounds that participate in atmospheric photochemical reactions (excluding carbon monoxide, carbon dioxide, carbonic acid, metallic carbides and carbonates, and ammonium carbonate). The compounds vaporize (become a gas) at normal room temperatures.

Note: Please see the end of EQc4.5 for more information on Approach and Implementation for EQ credit 4.2 and the other EQ credit 4 sections.

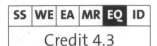

Low-Emitting Materials
Carpet Systems

Intent

Reduce the quantity of indoor air contaminants that are odorous, potentially irritating and/or harmful to the comfort and wellbeing of installers and occupants.

Requirements

Carpet must meet or exceed Carpet and Rug Institute's Green Label Plus testing and product requirements. (Green Label Plus does not address backer or adhesive.)

Carpet pad must meet or exceed CRI Green Label testing and product requirements.

Carpet adhesive must meet the requirements of EQ Credit 4.1

Submittals

Provide the LEED for Commercial Interiors Submittal Template, signed by the architect, interior designer or responsible party, listing all the carpet systems used in the tenant space and stating that they meet or exceed the applicable testing and product requirements.

Potential Technologies & Strategies

Specify Low-VOC carpet products and systems in construction documents. Provide product cut sheets, MSD sheets, signed attestations or other official literature from the manufacturer clearly identifying the affected products meet these requirements. Ensure that requirements are clearly stated in each section of the specifications where these materials are addressed.

Summary of Referenced Standard

Carpet and Rug Institute Green Label Plus Testing Program

Carpet and Rug Institute

www.carpet-rug.com

(800) 882-8846

The Carpet and Rug Institute is a trade organization representing the carpet and rug industry. Green Label Plus is an independent testing program that identifies carpets with very low emissions of volatile organic compounds (VOCs). The "Green Label Plus" program for carpets and its associated VOC emission criteria in micrograms per square meter per hour developed by the Carpet & Rug Institute (CRI) in coordination with California's Sustainable Building Task Force and the California Department of Health Services (DHS) are described on the CRI Web site. In the CRI Green Label Plus Program, emission rates must be verified by conducting annual testing. Valid/approved certification numbers can be reviewed on the CRI Web site under Indoor Air Quality/Green Label Plus/Approved companies. Approved products are listed under the company heading.

Testing Criteria

Carpet must not exceed the maximum target emission factors used in the CRI Green Label program and following the test protocol used by Green Label Plus. Test results submitted must be no more than 2 years old at the time of submission.

Standard Practice for the Testing of Volatile Organic Emissions from Various Sources using Small-Scale Environmental Chambers (State of California Standard 1350), Section 9

www.dhs.ca.gov/ps/deodc/ehlb/iaq/
VOCS/Section01350_7_15_2004_FINAL_
PLUS_ADDENDUM-2004-01.pdf

This standard practice document specifies testing criteria for carpet emissions that will satisfy the credit requirements.

Credit Interpretation Rulings

Credit Interpretation Rulings concerning EQ Credit 4.3 made to LEED for Commercial Interiors project requests, and unless inapplicable, to LEED for New Construction project requests apply to LEED for Commercial Interiors projects.

There is currently no point available for using hard surface flooring that is certified as low-emitting. The project could apply for an Innovation in Design Credit, provided that comprehensive, quantifiable and significant environmental benefit is documented.

Submittal Documentation

Make the declaration included with the LEED for Commercial Interiors Submittal Template and complete the spreadsheet tab placing the products under the applicable standard and classification and indicate the product's VOC level (similar to **Table 3**).

The VOC budget approach is not applicable to this credit.

Additional Documentation

For potential use during submittal review, it is suggested that the project team assemble and maintain the information that confirms CRI Green Label Plus compliance.

Resources

Please see the USGBC Web site at www.usgbc.org/resources for more specific resources on materials sources and other technical information.

Web Sites

Carpet and Rug Institute

www.carpet-rug.org

Note: Please see the end of EQc4.5 for more information on Approach and Implementation for EQ credit 4.3 and the other EQ credit 4 sections.

SS	WE	EA	MR	EQ	ID
				Credit 4.3	

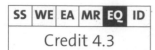
Table 3: Sample Submittal Information for Carpet Systems

Carpet and Rug Institute Green Label Testing Program	Approved "Green Label Plus" Product Identification Numbers
Product	
Carpets	
Cushions	

Low-Emitting Materials

Composite Wood and Laminate Adhesives

Intent

Reduce the quantity of indoor air contaminants that are odorous, potentially irritating and/or harmful to the comfort and wellbeing of installers and occupants.

Requirements

Composite wood and agrifiber products, including core materials, must contain no added urea-formaldehyde resins. Laminate Adhesives used to fabricate on-site and shop applied assemblies containing these laminate adhesives must contain no added urea formaldehyde. Products covered by EQ Credit 4.5, Low-Emitting Materials, System Furniture and Seating shall be excluded from these requirements.

Submittals

Provide the LEED for Commercial Interiors Submittal Template, signed by the architect, interior designer or responsible party, listing all the composite wood products used in the tenant space and stating that they contain no added urea-formaldehyde resins and listing all the laminating adhesives used in the tenant space and stating that they contain no added urea-formaldehyde.

Provide documentation that all core and laminate adhesive products used on the project contained no added urea-formaldehyde.

Potential Technologies & Strategies

Specify wood and agrifiber products that contain no added urea-formaldehyde resins. Specify laminating adhesives for field and shop applied assemblies that contain no urea-formaldehyde. Review product cut sheets, MSD sheets, signed attestations or other official literature from the manufacturer.

Credit Interpretation Rulings

Credit Interpretation Rulings concerning EQ Credit 4.4 made to LEED for Commercial Interiors project requests, and unless inapplicable, to LEED for New Construction project requests apply to LEED for Commercial Interiors projects.

There is no baseline level of formaldehyde that is permitted. Rather, it is the absence of urea-formaldehyde resins that is required. The language was intended to allow for background traces of formaldehyde that occur naturally in wood.

Submittal Documentation

Make the declaration included with the LEED for Commercial Interiors Submittal Template and complete a listing of all composite wood products used in the tenant space stating that they contain no added urea-formaldehyde resins. Complete a listing of all the laminating adhesives used in the tenant space stating that they contain no urea-formaldehyde. A spreadsheet tab is provided in the Submittal Templates.

Provide documentation that confirms that all core and adhesive products used on the project contain no added urea-formaldehyde. Please highlight the portion of the documentation making the claim. A narrative is not required but is recommended if there are special circumstances such as products that may not clearly meet the definition of a composite wood.

Note that products covered by EQ Credit 4.5 are excluded from the requirements of EQ Credit 4.4.

The VOC budget approach is not applicable to this credit.

Additional Documentation

If the submittal is complete, there should be no additional information required during review.

Resources

Please see the USGBC Web site at www.usgbc.org/resources for more specific resources on materials sources and other technical information.

Web Sites

Formaldehyde Update

Consumer Product Safety Commission

www.cpsc.gov/CPSCPUB/PUBS/725.html

An informational document from the Consumer Product Safety Commission.

Definitions

Composite Wood is a product consisting of wood or plant particles or fibers bonded together by a synthetic resin or binder. Examples: plywood, particleboard, OSB, MDF, strawboard, wheatboard, door cores. For the purposes of this credit, the following conditions describe which products must comply with the requirements:

1. The product is inside the exterior moisture protection. To elaborate: all materials that emit contaminants that have the potential to enter the indoor air will be considered as indoor sources of contaminants. Materials which have the potential to communicate their emissions to the indoor air include all indoor surfaces in contact with the indoor air including flooring; walls; ceilings; interior furnishings; suspended ceiling systems and the materials above those suspended ceilings; all ventilation system components in communication with the ventilation supply or return air; and all materials inside of wall cavities, ceiling cavities, floor cavities, or horizontal or vertical chases. These materials include the caulking materials for windows and insulation in ceilings or walls. Examples of materials that have little or no potential

for communicating with the indoor air are those siding and roofing materials that are on the exterior side of the waterproofing membrane.

2. Composite wood components used in assemblies are included (e.g., door cores, panel substrates, plywood sections of I-beams).

3. The product is part of the base building systems. If it is considered fit-out, furniture or equipment (FF&E) it is not controlled because it is not a base system.

Laminate Adhesive is an adhesive used in wood/agrifiber products (veneered panels, composite wood products contained in engineered lumber, door assemblies, etc.).

Formaldehyde is a naturally occurring VOC found in small amounts in animals and plants, but is carcinogenic and an irritant to most people when present in high concentrations—causing headaches, dizziness, mental impairment, and other symptoms. When present in the air at levels above 0.1 ppm (parts per million parts of air), it can cause watery eyes, burning sensations in the eyes, nose, and throat; nausea; coughing; chest tightness; wheezing; skin rashes; and asthmatic and allergic reactions.

Urea Formaldehyde is a combination of urea and formaldehyde that is used in some glues and may emit formaldehyde at room temperature.

Phenol Formaldehyde, which off-gasses only at high temperature, is used for exterior products, although many of those products are suitable for interior applications.

Note: Please see the end of EQc4.5 for more information on Approach and Implementation for EQ credit 4.4 and the other EQ credit 4 sections.

Low-Emitting Materials

Systems Furniture and Seating

Intent

Reduce the quantity of indoor air contaminants that are odorous, potentially irritating and/or harmful to the comfort and wellbeing of installers and occupants.

Requirements

All systems furniture and seating* introduced into the project space that has been manufactured, refurbished or refinished within one year prior to occupancy must meet one of the requirements below.

- Option A: Greenguard Indoor Air Quality Certified

OR

- Option B: Calculated indoor air concentrations that are less than or equal to those established in Table 1 for furniture systems and seating determined by a procedure based on the U.S. Environmental Protection Agency's Environmental Technology Verification (ETV) Large Chamber Test Protocol for Measuring Emissions of VOCs and Aldehydes (September 1999) testing protocol conducted in an independent air quality testing laboratory.

Table 1: Indoor Air Concentrations

Chemical Contaminant	Emission Limits Systems Furniture	Emission Limits Multiple Office Seating
TVOC	0.5 mg/m^3	0.25 mg/m^3
Formaldehyde	50 parts per billion	25 parts per billion
Total Aldehydes	100 parts per billion	50 parts per billion
4 - PC (as an odorant)	0.0065 mg/m^3	0.00325 mg/m^3

Systems furniture is defined as either a panel-based workstation comprised of modular interconnecting panels, hang-on components and drawer/filing components or a free-standing grouping of furniture items and their components that have been designed to work in concert.

Seating is defined as task and guest chairs used with systems furniture.

*Furniture other than systems furniture and task and guest chairs used with systems furniture is defined as occasional furniture and is excluded from the credit requirements.

Salvaged and used furniture that is more than one year old at time of occupancy is excluded from credit requirements.

Submittals

Provide the LEED for Commercial Interiors Submittal Template, signed by the architect, interior designer or responsible party, declaring that all systems furniture and seating covered by this credit is included in a listing that states the manufacturer and product line, item description, period of manufacture, form of compliance and the period for which the item is U.S. Environmental Protection Agency's Environmental Technology Verification (ETV) Large Chamber Test Protocol for Measuring Emissions of VOCs and Aldehydes (September 1999).

For Greenguard Air Quality Certified systems furniture and seating, a copy of the product certification, complete with the start and end dates of certification. The period covered must have begun before and extend through the actual manufacturing dates of the product used on the project.

For systems furniture and seating tested using a procedure based on the U.S. EPA ETV protocol, provide details of the procedure, and the emission factors from the large-chamber testing of the systems furniture and the calculations used in determining the emission limits, complete with the air exchange rate, demonstrating that emissions limits have not exceeded those shown in Table 1. Test results and supporting calculations must be dated and signed by an officer of the independent laboratory where the testing was conducted. Test results must represent the manufacturing practices employed for the product used on the project. Tests must have been completed before the start of manufacturing but no earlier than 24 months prior to the last manufacturing date.

Potential Technologies & Strategies

Specify low-VOC materials in construction documents. Ensure that VOC limits are clearly stated in each section where furniture assemblies are addressed.

Summary of Referenced Standards

Greenguard™ Certification Program

Greenguard Environmental Institute

www.greenguard.org

(800) 427-9681

U.S. Environmental Protection Agency's Environmental Technology Verification (ETV) Large Chamber Test Protocol for Measuring Emissions of VOCs and Aldehydes (September 1999).

Research Triangle Institute and U.S. EPA

www.epa.gov/etv/pdfs/vp/07_vp_furniture.pdf

The standards referenced were developed by a testing protocol committee under the leadership of the EPA. The protocol uses a climatically controlled test chamber in which the seating product or furniture assembly being tested is placed. A controlled quantity of conditioned air is drawn through the chamber with emission concentrations measured at set intervals over a four-day period.

Credit Interpretation Rulings

Credit Interpretation Rulings concerning EQ Credit 4.5 made to LEED for Commercial Interiors project requests, apply to LEED for Commercial Interiors projects. This credit is not found in other LEED rating systems.

Approach and Implementation

Office furniture, through the off-gassing of the materials and finishes used in its manufacture, can adversely impact indoor air quality. This credit provides the means of assuring that the furniture meets a minimum standard that provides for occupants' comfort and wellbeing.

In the selection of systems furniture and multiple office seating, the specifier should confirm that the desired product will meet the testing requirements at the time it is manufactured.

The Greenguard Environmental Institute provides a listing of the products it has certified. Additional manufacturers may also have met the testing requirements set out in this credit.

Performance-based emission limits

By satisfying the test results referenced in LEED for Commercial Interiors EQ Credit 4.5, the product should not cause the concentration of contaminants in the air around it to be increased by any more than the threshold limits; the values are expressed as either mg/m^3 or parts per billion.

The testing protocol that covers systems furniture uses a large chamber, approximately 10' x 10' x 8', where a full workstation is assembled. The workstation size, mix of components, types of materials, including fabrics and finishes, are intended to be representative of what is most commonly used in actual installations. Product specifiers may want to confer with the manufacturer when substitutions are being considered or the density of the components will be higher than in a normal application.

For the performance based standard used in this credit to be applicable at the project site, other considerations need to be satisfied. The air velocity and outdoor air rate introduced into the work place should meet ASHRAE Standard 62.1-2004, the same standard referenced in EQ Prerequisite 1. Adequate ventilation during installation helps dissipate early off-gassing. The flush-out period called for in EQ Credit 3.2 is not to begin until furniture installation is complete.

Remember that systems furniture may be either a panel-based workstation comprising modular interconnecting panels, hang-on components and drawer/filing components or a free-standing grouping of furniture items and their components that have been designed to work in concert. Seating covered by this credit is defined as task and guest chairs used with systems furniture.

Work tools often attached to systems furniture are not included in the credit requirement. Other furniture is considered as occasional furniture and need not be included in the credit documentation. Also, salvaged and used furniture that is more than one year old at the time of occupancy is excluded from the credit. Refurbishment of systems furniture or multiple office seating occurring within the 12-month period prior to occupancy must meet the credit requirements.

Submittal Documentation

Complete the LEED for Commercial Interiors Submittal Template indicating that all the systems furniture and seating covered by the credit have met one of the two compliance paths. Complete a listing of the materials in the table provided in the Submittal Templates similar to **Table 2**. This listing is used to confirm that either the certification was in effect at the time the project's product was manufactured, or the testing was done no more than 24 months prior to the manufacture date.

For Option A, Greenguard Indoor Air Quality Certified, provide a copy of the product certification, complete with the start and end dates of certification. This document

may be obtained from the Greenguard Web site. (See Resources section.)

For Option B, where the product has been tested using a procedure based on the U.S. EPA ETV protocol, provide the details required in the credit submittal section. The results must represent the manufacturing practices employed for the product used on the project and must have been completed before the start of manufacturing, but no earlier than 24 months prior to the last manufacturing date.

Note that products covered by EQ Credit 4.5 are excluded from the requirements of EQ Credit 4.4.

The VOC budget approach is not applicable to this credit.

Additional Documentation

If the submittal is complete, there should be no additional information required during review.

Resources

Please see the USGBC Web site at www. usgbc.org/resources for more specific resources on materials sources and other technical information.

Web Sites

Greenguard™ Certification Program

Greenguard Environmental Institute

www.greenguard.org

800) 427-9681

Table 2: Project Low-Emitting Systems Furniture and Seating Record

Manufacturer	Product Line	Description	Period of Manufacture [earliest date / latest date]	Form of Compliance	Test Date or Certification Period
Lambda Cubicles	Sine	Workstations	3/2/03—5/6/03	EPA ETV Large Chamber	7/15/02
Mu Seating Systems	Cosine	Chairs	4/8/03—4/22/03	Greenguard Registered	2/12/03—2/11/04
Nu Drawers	Tangent	File cabinets	3/12/03—3/25/03	EPA ETV Large Chamber	4/20/02
Xi Tops	Cotangent	Table	5/15/03—5/18/03	Greenguard Certified	6/15/02—9/15/03

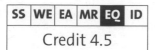
U.S. Environmental Protection Agency's Environmental Technology Verification (ETV) Large Chamber Test Protocol for Measuring Emissions of VOCs and Aldehydes (September 1999).

Research Triangle Institute and U.S. EPA

www.epa.gov/etv/pdfs/vp/07_vp_furniture.pdf

Definitions

Systems Furniture is defined as either a panel-based workstation comprised of modular interconnecting panels, hang-on components and drawer/filing components or a free-standing grouping of furniture items and their components that have been designed to work in concert.

Seating is defined as task and guest chairs used with systems furniture.

Occasional Furniture refers to furniture located in lobbies and in conference rooms.

Supplemental Information

All EQ Credit 4 Sections

Approach and Implementation

The five parts of LEED for Commercial Interiors EQ Credit 4 apply to products and installation processes that have the potential to adversely affect the indoor air quality (IAQ) of a project space and, in turn, those exposed to the contaminants these materials may off-gas.

Strategies

The requirements for products and activities covered in EQ Credit 4 should be noted in the project specifications and, ideally, within the specific section of the document applicable to a particular trade or supplier.

Synergies and Trade-Offs

Selecting materials that are low in VOCs helps reduce sources of pollutants during the construction process and in the finished building. There are typically multiple products available that meet these criteria for a wide variety of applications. However, these criteria must be balanced against other green building considerations, such as location of manufacture, durability and performance.

Planning Phase

Excellence in indoor air quality and elimination of sources of indoor pollutants should be established as a goal in early project phases.

Design Phase

In order to achieve this goal, credit requirements should be clearly stated in project specifications. Reference the credit requirements in both Division 1 and in the technical divisions. Indicate what must be provided in the way of cut sheets, material safety data sheets (MSD sheets), certificates and test reports. Consider making submittal of this compliance documentation a condition of product approval.

Construction Phase

Meeting the requirements set in EQ Credit 4 is not everyday practice for all construction teams and suppliers. Education is key to change. Think about asking the project owner to stress the importance of meeting the LEED requirements during pre-bid meetings and again at the time of contract award. During these sessions, have LEED Accredited Professionals available and ask for questions. Include requirements in subcontract and purchase order language.

Follow-up during construction

Place LEED project signage alongside the project safety signage. Take a few minutes during progress meetings to cover topics relevent to the current phase of work. Finally, provide leadership and ensure compliance.

LEED for Commercial Interiors EQ Credit 4 employs three approaches to limit off-gassing; those three approaches use composition limits, emission factors and performance-based standards.

Composition Limits

In this approach the formulation of a product is controlled. Limits are set on the amount of volatile organic compounds (VOCs) permitted in a given volume of the product. The threshold limits and the content within a particular product are generally expressed in grams per liter (g/L). EQ Credits 4.1 and 4.2 use this approach for adhesives, sealants, paints and coatings. EQ Credit 4.4 also controls formulation by setting a limit of zero added urea-formaldehyde resins.

Emission Factors

This type of standard, clearly more sophisticated, sets a limit on the rate that off-gassing may occur. The rate is stated as mass of contaminant that may be off-gassed by a given unit quantity of the product in a set period of time. This approach is used in EQ Credit 4.3 for carpet where the rate is expressed as micrograms of contaminant per square meter of carpet per hour. These tests, which are now being done on an array of product types, place samples of precise size in test chambers. Air samples are drawn off at set times, generally over several days, and analyzed. There are extensive protocols established to make the testing representative of actual conditions on a project site and consistent between similar products from multiple manufactures. The Carpet and Rug Institute (CRI) Green Label Plus program uses emission factor test results for its certifications.

Performance-Based Standards

This approach, yet most sophisticated, calculates the resultant concentrations of contaminants the products will add to the air being breathed. The protocols are very similar to those for emission factor testing, but are crafted to allow more complex assemblies, such as systems

furniture, to be tested. Again, groups of products are placed in a test chamber. Air is circulated in the chamber, simulating the conditions where the product would normally be used. At set intervals, samples of the air are taken and analyzed. The results are reported in the same units of measure established for air quality and used in the IAQ testing procedure of EQ Credit 3.2.—ppm, ppb, or micrograms per cubic meter of air. The performance-based standards approach is used in EQ Credit 4.5 for systems furniture and office seating. The Greenguard Institute testing program for systems furniture and office seating use performance-based standards. Using products listed as Greenguard certified is one means of compliance for EQ Credit 4.5. They are certified as having test results below the threshold contaminant amounts.

VOC Budgets

This alternative compliance path allows for specialty applications for which there is no low-VOC product option. It may be used with adhesives and sealants covered in EQ Credit 4.1 and with paints and coatings covered in EQ Credit 4.2. The documentation must demonstrate that the over-all low-VOC performance has been attained for paints and adhesives separately, not in combination.

The calculation is a comparison between a baseline case and the design case. See

Table 1: Sample VOC Budget Calculation for Paint

Location	Product	Quantity [gal.]	Threshold VOC Level [g/L]	Budget Total VOCs [gal. X g/L]	Design Product VOC Level [g/L]	Design Total VOCs [gal. X g/L]
Walls—Office Area	Alpha Primer	24	50	1,200	65	1,560
Walls—Office Area	Alpha Flat	30	50	1,500	36	1,080
				2,700		2,640

Budget Total VOCs > Design Total VOCs [2,700 > 2,640]

Table 1. When the design (or actual) is less than the baseline, the credit requirement is satisfied. The values used in the comparison are the total VOCs contained in the products (i.e., paint) used on the project. The total VOCs is determined by multiplying the volume of the product used by the threshold VOC level for the baseline case and actual product VOC level for the design case. The baseline application rate should not be greater than that used in the design case.

When submitting a VOC budget calculation, also provide the supporting documentation concerning the product—the name, application rate, class or use to confirm that the correct threshold VOC level has been used in determining the baseline case, and finally the actual VOC level of the product.

As the term "budget" implies, this compliance path should be a decision planned in advance. Occassionally, honest mistakes occur—even on LEED projects. If realized in time, this approach may be used to determine if credit compliance can be attained. A narrative explaining the situation should accompany the project submittal. Additional coats, even with products below the threshold limits, add to the overall level of off-gassed VOCs. It is not enough to meet the requirements; the intent also has to be met to earn the credit.

Considerations

A large number of building products contain compounds that have a negative impact on indoor air quality and the Earth's atmosphere. The most prominent of these compounds, volatile organic compounds (VOCs), contribute to smog generation and air pollution outdoors while having an adverse effect on the wellbeing of building occupants indoors. By selecting low-emitting materials, both outdoor and indoor air quality impacts can be reduced.

Environmental Issues

VOCs react with sunlight and nitrogen oxides in the atmosphere to form ground-level ozone, a chemical that has a detrimental effect on human health, agricultural crops, forests and ecosystems. Ozone damages lung tissue, reduces lung function, and sensitizes the lungs to other irritants. Ozone is also a major component of smog, which affects agricultural crops and forestland.

Economic Issues

Healthy occupants are more productive and have less illness-related absenteeism. Use of high-VOC content materials can cause illness and may decrease occupant productivity. These problems result in increased expenses and liability for building owners, operators and insurance companies. As a result, the construction market is driving product manufacturers to offer low-VOC alternatives to conventional building products. Costs for these low-VOC products are generally competitive with conventional materials. However, some low-VOC materials are more expensive than conventional materials, particularly when the products are first introduced to the marketplace. Low-VOC products may also be difficult to obtain for some product types. However, these problems will recede as application of low-VOC products become more commonplace.

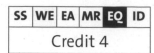

Indoor Chemical & Pollutant Source Control

Intent

Minimize exposure of building occupants to potentially hazardous particulates, biological contaminants and chemical pollutants that adversely impact air and water quality.

Requirements

Design to minimize and control pollutant or biological contaminant entry into the tenant space and later cross-contamination of regularly occupied areas:

- Employ permanent entryway systems (i.e., grills, grates, etc.) to capture dirt, particulates, etc. from entering the building at all high volume exterior entryways within the tenant area.

AND

- Where hazardous gasses or chemicals may be present or used (including housekeeping and laundry areas and copying and printing rooms), provide segregated areas with deck to deck partitions with separate outside exhausting at a rate of at least 0.5 cu.ft. per minute per square foot, no air recirculation and operated at a negative pressure compared with the surrounding spaces of at least an average of 5 PA (0.02 inches of water gauge) and with a minimum of 1 PA (0.004 inches of water gauge) when the doors to the rooms are closed.

AND

- Provide containment drains plumbed for appropriate disposal of hazardous liquid wastes in spaces where water and chemical concentrate mixing occurs for maintenance, or laboratory purposes.

AND

- Provide regularly occupied areas of the tenant space with new air filtration media prior to occupancy that provides a Minimum Efficiency Reporting Value (MERV) of 13 or better.

Submittals

- Provide the LEED for Commercial Interiors Submittal Template, signed by the architect, engineer, interior designer or responsible party, declaring that:

  Permanent entryway systems (i.e., grilles, grates, etc.) to capture dirt, particulates, etc. are provided at all high volume exterior entryways within the tenant area.

  - Chemical use areas and copy rooms have been physically separated with deck-to-deck partitions; independent exhaust ventilation has been installed at the required exhaust rate and negative pressure differential.

  - Drains in facility cleaning and maintenance areas within the tenant space are plumbed for environmentally appropriate disposal of hazardous liquid wastes.

  - Filters used meet the MERV requirements with new media installed prior to occupancy. Provide a listing of each filter installed including the MERV value, manufacturer name and model number.

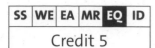

Credit 5

Potential Technologies & Strategies

Design separate exhaust and plumbing systems for rooms with contaminants to achieve physical isolation from the rest of the building. Where appropriate, install permanent architectural entryway systems such as grills or grates to prevent occupant-borne contaminants from entering the space.

Summary of Referenced Standard

ANSI/ASHRAE 52.2-1999: Method of Testing General Ventilation Air-Cleaning Devices for Removal Efficiency by Particle Size, American Society of Heating, Refrigerating and Air-Conditioning Engineers (ASHRAE)

www.ashrae.org

(800) 527-4723

This standard presents methods for testing air cleaners for two performance characteristics: the ability of the device to remove particles from the air stream and the device's resistance to airflow. The minimum efficiency reporting value (MERV) is based on three composite average particle size removal efficiency (PSE) points. Consult the standard for a complete explanation of MERV value calculations. Filtration media used during the construction process must have a MERV of 13. **Table 1** summarizes the requirements for a MERV value of 13.

Credit Interpretation Rulings

In addition to LEED for Commercial Interiors Credit Interpretation Rulings (CIRs), applicable LEED for New Construction CIRs concerning this credit may also apply to LEED for Commercial Interiors projects.

Permanent Entryway Systems

The determination of need should be based on frequency of use, as opposed to percentage of building occupants served. Doors providing only egress to the exterior, and those infrequently used

may be excluded. Walk-off areas within a vestibule or within a building and exterior walk-off for areas protected from weather are all acceptable.

Segregated Chemical Areas

Drywall ceilings may be used in place of full-height partitions, but acoustical lay-in ceilings are not adequate.

The definition of convenience printers and copiers, which are not required to be segregated into a chemical area, may be left to the discretion of the design team, but they are generally the smaller units shared by many office personnel for short print and copy jobs.

Battery banks used to provide temporary back-up power—in a data center for example—must be segregated to satisfy credit requirements.

Housekeeping facilities that are part of a common laundry room in residential buildings must meet the chemical storage requirements.

Rooms where chemicals are mixed and disposed of should be isolated and should include sinks and/or drains in appropriate locations to ensure these chemicals are disposed of properly and not dumped into inadequate spaces (i.e. restrooms); local codes requiring separate drain lines are to be followed.

Approach and Implementation

The indoor air quality of buildings is adversely affected by seemingly benign activities of daily occupancy and operations. Occupants and building visitors

Table 1: Requirements for a MERV Value 13

Composite Average Particle Size Efficiency [%]				Minimum Final Resistance	
0.30 - 0.10 μm	1.0 - 3.0 μm	3.0 - 10.0 μm	[Pa]	[in. of water]	
< 75%	≥ 90%	≥ 90%	350	1.4	

contribute to IAQ issues within buildings by tracking in contaminants on their shoes and clothing. Daily copier, fax, and printer operations add contaminants to the building's interior environment. Additionally, the storage, mixing, and disposal of housekeeping liquids may adversely affect the health and productivity of building occupants. This credit strives to improve indoor environmental conditions by mitigating the amount of particulate, chemical and biological contaminants that occupants are exposed to inside buildings.

Scope of Work

Not all commercial interior projects will have the need to satisfy all the requirements of this credit. When the project space does not have direct access to the exterior, the requirement for a permanent entryway system may be waived. When local code does not require separate plumbing for the sink located within the segregated area for hazardous gasses or chemicals, the separate plumbing may be waived.

However, to earn this credit, the project team must demonstrate that if there is a need for a segregated area for hazardous gasses or chemicals, the requirements for its construction and ventilation are met. Finally, the project team must demonstrate that new air filtration media has been installed prior to occupancy with a MERV 13 or better rating.

Strategies

Incorporate permanent entryway systems, which remove debris from shoes, at all high-traffic exterior access points to reduce the amount of contaminants tracked into the occupied space by people. The entryway systems should be designed to capture and remove particles from shoes without allowing build-up of contaminants. Open grates/grilles or other entryway systems that have a recessed collection area are generally thought to be most effective. (Carpeted systems are not regarded as providing the same effectiveness in particulate removal as open grid type systems and require continuous cleaning/maintenance to avoid build-up of dirt and debris.)

Locate high-volume copy, print and fax equipment away from occupant work spaces in enclosed rooms. In order to effectively remove airborne contaminants generated by this type of equipment, the rooms must be physically separated from adjacent spaces. This may be accomplished through installation of deck to deck partitions or sealed gypsum board enclosures. Rooms with large openings but no doors will not be able to meet the credit requirement. Installation of a self closing door is an option to such spaces. To remove airborne contaminants, and prevent cross-contamination into occupied spaces, copy, print and/or fax rooms must be equipped with a dedicated exhaust system (no return air) that creates a negative pressure within the room meeting the requirements of this credit. Convenience (small) copier and printer use should be minimized where possible. Although encouraged, designing exhaust systems that account for convenience copier and printer use is not a required part of this credit.

Chemical storage and mixing areas, such as janitor's closets and photo labs should also be located away from occupant work areas. Additionally, these rooms must be physically separated from adjacent spaces via installation of deck-to-deck partitions or sealed gypsum board enclosures. Rooms must be equipped with a dedicated exhaust system (no return air) that creates the required negative pressurization to ensure that cross contamination into adjacent occupied spaces will not occur.

All building HVAC systems must be designed to accommodate filtration systems with a minimum MERV 13 rating.

Synergies and Trade-Offs

Additional ventilation systems to mitigate contaminating space activities may affect building energy performance and require commissioning and Measurement & Verification attention. Ventilation system design will also be affected to ensure that installed systems are capable of accommodating filtration media required for credit compliance. This may be difficult to achieve for spaces with low capacity, packaged air handling systems, due to the size of these type of filters and their associated pressure drop. The selected space layout may prohibit deck-to-deck separation and separate ventilation systems for chemical use areas. Storage areas for recyclable materials may also be considered to be contaminant sources, depending on the items recycled. Janitorial supplies may impact indoor air quality if not wisely chosen.

Planning Phase

During the early planning stage of a project, it is important to ask questions that will enable the design team to understand the client's equipment requirements and usage patterns. This information will be critical in determining if dedicated, isolated, equipment rooms are going to be required to house copy, fax and print equipment.

Design Phase

Identify locations for entryway systems and incorporate project specific details to ensure proper performance of the selected system. It is also critical at this phase of the project to confirm the locations of chemical use areas and high-volume copy, fax and print equipment rooms. It may be possible to locate such rooms above or adjacent to one another to minimize the need for individual exhaust systems and to reduce the amount of exhaust ductwork and drainage piping required. It is also critical during this phase to confirm that chemical and equipment rooms are properly isolated from adjacent spaces.

Construction Phase

Indoor chemical and pollutant source control is primarily a planning, design and operations issue. In the construction phase the space exhaust systems are installed and commissioned to ensure that they meet the owner's requirements and the design intent.

Submittal Documentation

Complete the declaration in the LEED for Commercial Interiors Submittal Template, indicating that the credit requirements have been met. Provide a listing of each filter installed including the MERV value, manufacturer name and model number on the Submittal Template. Include with the initial submittal a narrative explaining when the project scope has not included the need for either a permanent entryway system or separate plumbing from sinks used for disposal of hazardous liquid wastes. Also, consider providing a narrative when the project team has employed non-standard approaches to satisfying the credit requirements.

Additional Documentation

For potential use during submittal review, it is suggested that the project team assemble and retain highlighted copy of the final construction drawings showing the location of installed permanent entryway systems, full height separation walls, dedicated exhaust systems, and applicable drains. Additional confirmation may be requested in the form of the contractor's submittals for installed entryway systems, and contractor's submittals and manufacturer's product data for installed filtration media clearly showing the Minimum Efficiency Reporting Value, MERV, rating for each filter (a MERV of 13 minimum is required).

Be prepared to explain the choice of exterior entrances not provided with permanent entryway systems.

Considerations

Cost

Additional sinks, drains, room separations, and separate exhausts for copying and housekeeping areas can increase the project's overall initial cost. Also, dedicated ventilation and exhaust systems may require additional ductwork and associated installation costs. However, effective cleaning spaces and systems coupled with good human health initiatives should prove economically sound over the lifetime of the building. Clean air can help support worker productivity, and this translates into increased profitability for the company. Reducing the potential for spills can avoid costly environmental cleanups.

Regional Considerations

Local weather conditions should be factored into determining the location and type of entryway systems. For example, in areas that are prone to large amounts of rain or snow, it may be prudent to locate entryway systems in an enclosed vestibule or inside the building. A floor drain beneath the grille may also be necessary to remove collected moisture.

Environmental Issues

Additional materials and energy may be required to provide entryway systems and isolated chemical use areas. This can increase natural resource consumption as well as air and water pollution. However, through proper management of hazardous chemicals used for building operations and maintenance, chemical spills and accidents can be avoided that would otherwise harm wildlife and ecosystems.

Community Issues

Good housekeeping benefits the community by reducing the potential for chemical spills that can impact neighboring properties. An environmentally sound building also supports the wellbeing of occupants, which may contribute to lowering health insurance rates and healthcare costs.

Resources

Please see the USGBC Web site at www. usgbc.org/resources for more specific resources on materials sources and other technical information.

Web Sites

Green Seal

www.greenseal.org/recommendations. htm

(202) 872-6400

Green Seal is an independent nonprofit organization that promotes the manufacture and sale of environmentally responsible consumer products. This Web site should contain product recommendations for general purpose cleaning solutions.

Janitorial Products Pollution Prevention Project

www.westp2net.org/janitorial/jp4.htm

A governmental and nonprofit project that researches issues and provides fact sheets, tools and links.

EPA Environmentally Preferable Product Information

www.epa.gov/opptintr/epp/tools/ toolsuite.htm

This list of tools includes links to cleaning product information and a database of environmental information on over 600 products, including janitorial and pest control products.

Print Media

Clean and Green: The Complete Guide to Non-Toxic and Environmentally Safe Housekeeping, by Annie Berthold-Bond, Ceres Press, 1994.

Controllability of Systems

Lighting

Intent

Provide a high level of lighting system control for individual occupants, and specific groups in multi-occupant spaces (e.g. classrooms and conference areas) to promote the productivity, comfort and wellbeing of building occupants.

Requirements

Provide lighting controls, for:

- At least 90% of occupants, enabling adjustments to suit individual task needs and preferences

AND

- All shared multi-occupant spaces where transient groups must share lighting controls.

Submittals

Provide the LEED for Commercial Interiors Submittal Template, signed by the architect or responsible party, demonstrating and declaring that the required lighting controls are provided.

Potential Technologies & Strategies

Design the tenant space with occupant controls for lighting. Strategies to consider include lighting controls and task lighting.

Credit Interpretation Rulings

In addition to LEED for Commercial Interiors Credit Interpretation Rulings (CIRs), applicable LEED for New Construction CIRs concerning this credit may also apply to LEED for Commercial Interiors projects.

Shared multi-occupant spaces include gymnasiums, cafeterias, conference rooms and libraries.

For LEED for Commercial Interiors registered projects, hardwiring of task lighting is not necessary to satisfy the credit requirements. Fixtures such as desktop lamps, which are not attached to a workstation, may be used.

Approach and Implementation

Conventional buildings too frequently only have fixed-intensity general lighting systems which illuminate indoor spaces without consideration of specific tasks and individual occupant comfort. A more desirable approach provides uniform general ambient lighting, augmented with individually controlled task fixtures.

Planning Phase

During the early planning phase of a project, it is important to ask questions that will enable the design team to understand the client's lighting needs and desires. Determine the tasks that will be accomplished in each space and the specific tools and equipment that will be used by occupants. A lighting strategy that is appropriate for a computer data entry area may not provide the functionality needed for other occupant functions.

When developing a task-ambient approach, the designer should investigate methods for providing uniform ambient illumination. Increased uniformity will reduce the perception of decreased footcandle levels in open spaces by minimizing high contrast areas. Designers should investigate the benefits of direct/indirect or pendant mounted systems coupled with high reflectance ceiling surfaces and finishes. Integration of surface materials selection and lighting design may create opportunities to reduce the number of installed lighting fixtures, resulting in potential energy savings.

To comply and be consistent with ANSI/ASHRAE/IESNA 90.1-2004, task lighting must be included in the lighting allowance for EA Prerequisite 2 and EA Credit 1.2. Also daylighting can be integrated with this credit by using daylighting technologies and strategies to compensate for the reduced footcandle levels in the space as detailed in EQ Credits 8.1 and 8.2. Credit intent is to keep the ambient lighting even, whether by electrical lighting or daylighting.

Design Phase

Identify lighting fixtures, controls, and finishes that will meet the intent of your chosen lighting design strategy. It is important to determine if any installed lighting systems or controls will require special calibration and commissioning prior to occupancy. The office equipment and layout should be carefully analyzed to ensure that 90% of the occupants have the lighting controls.

Task lights come in several varieties, from desk-top lamps to fixtures that are permanently attached to workstations. Ideally they will have multiple lighting levels and automatic shutoff switching.

Construction Phase

The operation of occupancy sensors, daylight monitors and other lighting controls may be adversely affected by items that are installed during and following construction, such as office equipment and furnishings. It is important to coordinate the final calibration of these items with the installer and commissioning agent early in the construction phase to ensure the system operates as design intended providing lighting controls to 90% of the occupants.

Calculations

Adjustable Task Lighting

To satisfy this portion of the requirement, start by identifying those workstation locations intended for individual use. The count should include private offices, open plan workstations, reception stations, ticket booths, etc.

Confirm that 90% or more of these occupants have task lighting that enables adjustment to suit individual task needs. Adjustability, at a minimum, must allow the workstation occupant the ability to turn the fixture on and off. Ideally the fixture can be easily repositioned by the occupant and has multiple light levels. The fixture should be appropriate for the occupant's task. In LEED for Commercial Interiors, task lights need not be permanently wired.

Shared Multi-Occupant Spaces

These spaces include conference rooms, classrooms and other indoor spaces used as a place of congregation for functions such as presentations and training. In these spaces, the work group should have access to adequate controls to provide the functionality to suit their activities. Meeting spaces that can be subdivided, as with a movable wall in a convention hall, must be designed so occupants in each area have control of their individual area.

When natural daylighting is used as a component of an ambient lighting scheme, in either type of space, there should be glare control, lighting level controls and possibly room-darkening shades.

Submittal Documentation

Complete the LEED for Commercial Interiors Submittal Template declaring

that the required lighting controls are provided. Demonstrate through the use of a floor plan and schedule that adjustable task lighting has been provided for at least 90% of the occupants.

Demonstrate through the use of a floor plan the location of shared multi-occupant spaces, indicating the activities and types of lighting controls.

Additional Documentation

For potential use during submittal review, it is suggested that the project team obtain and retain information on the task lighting and sensors and lighting controls. A narrative may be needed to confirm credit compliance.

Considerations

Cost

Additional task lights and lighting controls may increase first-time costs for the building. However, these costs are generally offset by reduced heat load and reduced footcandle levels. Conversely, abuse of personal controls, such as leaving task lights on when not in the office, has the potential to increase energy costs. Therefore, it is important to educate occupants on the design and function of system controls. Integrating individual controls with occupancy sensors give the project teams opportunity to lower the energy cost.

Environmental Issues

Provision of individual controls for lighting can lead to increased occupant comfort by enabling occupants to tailor the workspace to their individual needs. Additionally, by reducing ambient space footcandle levels and providing user controlled, flexible, task-specific lighting, the project may reduce lighting energy costs and reduce heat loads associated with high footcandle levels of indoor lighting.

SS | WE | EA | MR | **EQ** | ID
Credit 6.1

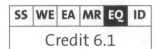

Resources

Please see the USGBC Web site at www. usgbc.org/resources for more specific resources on materials sources and other technical information.

Web Sites

A Field Study of PEM (Personal Environmental Module) Performance in Bank of America's San Francisco Office Buildings

www.cbe.berkeley.edu/research/pdf_files/ bauman1998_bofa.pdf

This University of California, Berkeley research center provides information on underfloor air distribution technologies and other topics.

"Do Green Buildings Enhance the Wellbeing of Workers? Yes,"

Environmental Design + Construction

www.edcmag.com/CDA/ ArticleInformation/coverstory/ BNPCoverStoryItem/0,4118,19794,00. html

This article by Judith Heerwagen in the July/August 2000 edition of Environmental Design + Construction, quantifies the effects of green building environments on productivity.

Print Media

Controls and Automation for Facilities Managers: Applications Engineering, by Viktor Boed, CRC Press, 1998.

Definitions

Shared (Group) Multi-Occupant Spaces include conference rooms, classrooms and other indoor spaces used as a place of congregation for presentations, trainings, etc. Individuals using these spaces share the lighting and temperature controls and they should have, at a minimum, a separate zone with accessible thermostat and an air-flow control.

Individual Occupant Spaces are typically private offices and open office plans with workstations.

Non-Occupied Spaces include all rooms used by maintenance personnel that are not open for use by occupants. Included in this category are janitorial, storage and equipment rooms, and closets.

Non-Regularly Occupied Spaces include corridors, hallways, lobbies, break rooms, copy rooms, storage rooms, kitchens, restrooms, stairwells, etc.

Controllability of Systems

Temperature and Ventilation

Intent

Provide a high level of thermal and ventilation control for individual occupants or specific groups in multi-occupant spaces (i.e. classrooms and conference areas) to promote the productivity, comfort and wellbeing of building occupants.

Requirements

Provide thermal and ventilation controls for:

- At least 50% of the space occupants that enable adjustment to suit individual needs and preferences,

AND

- All shared multi-occupant spaces where transient groups must share controls.

Operable windows may be used in lieu of individual controls for occupants near windows (20 feet inside of and 10 feet to either side of the operable part of the window), and where the operable windows meet the requirements of ASHRAE Standard 62.1-2004 Section 5.1 Natural Ventilation.

Submittals

- Provide the LEED for Commercial Interiors Submittal Template, signed by the architect or responsible party, demonstrating and declaring that the required ventilation and temperature controls are provided.

Potential Technologies & Strategies

Design the tenant space with occupant controls for airflow and temperature. Natural ventilated spaces must include strategies for control of temperature and ventilation.

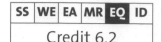
Summary of Referenced Standard

ANSI/ASHRAE Standard 62.1-2004: Ventilation for Acceptable Indoor Air Quality, American Society of Heating, Refrigerating and Air-Conditioning Engineers (ASHRAE)

www.ashrae.org

(800) 527-4723

Section 5.1 of the standard provides minimum requirements for operable openings. The portion of the window that can be opened must be 4% of the net occupiable floor area. The means to open the windows must be readily accessible to building occupants.

Credit Interpretation Rulings

In addition to LEED for Commercial Interiors Credit Interpretation Rulings (CIRs), applicable LEED for New Construction CIRs concerning this credit may also apply to LEED for Commercial Interiors projects.

Shared multi-occupant spaces include gymnasiums, weight, fitness and aerobics training rooms, cafeterias, conference rooms and libraries.

Approach and Implementation

Conventional buildings too frequently are built as sealed space where the occupants have no control. A more desirable approach provides individuals the controls to adjust the thermal conditions for a more comfortable environment. The components of an individual's thermal comfort include air temperature and velocity, the amount of outside air and moisture content.

Strategies

Operable windows are perhaps the occupants' desired building feature. In commercial interior projects where the space is being selected, the project team will have some say. Other means of providing thermal comfort involve planning and design consideration.

Planning Phase

The design team should determine the level of individual control desired. When occupying a portion of an existing building, assess the capabilities of the central HVAC systems, confirming it will be able to provide the desired level of thermal comfort.

Design Phase

Design the building with comfort controls to suit both individual needs and those of groups in shared spaces. ASHRAE Standard 55-2004 identifies the factors of thermal comfort and the process for developing comfort criteria for a building space and the occupants of that space. Strategies to consider include designs with operable windows, hybrid designs incorporating operable windows and mechanical systems, or mechanical systems alone.

Individual control of comfort with mechanical systems may be integrated into the overall systems design by enabling individual adjustment of selected comfort parameters, such as individual thermostats, individual diffusers (located at floor, desk or overhead), and individual radiant panels. Occupancy sensors can also be integrated in the design to automatically turn down the thermostat and reduce airflow when occupants are away, helping reduce energy use.

Occupancy

Educate occupants on individual control of their office space environment. Maintain the HVAC equipment, recalibrating controls as recommended by the manufacturers.

Synergies and Trade-Offs

First-time costs of added thermal comfort are often justified by the benefits of user satisfaction and productivity. Alteration of the ventilation and temperature scheme may change the energy performance of the building and may require commissioning and Measurement & Verification attention. Controllability of systems may not be possible for occupants in existing buildings being rehabilitated, especially with regard to operable windows, so choosing the space to meet the owner's needs and objectives is important. The degree of occupant controls will affect the performance of the ventilation system. Daylighting and view strategies are affected by the controlling requirements of the operable windows in this credit.

Calculations

Individual Thermal Comfort

To satisfy this portion of the requirement, start by identifying those workstation locations intended for individual use. The count should include private offices, open plan workstations, reception stations, ticket booths, etc. Confirm that 50% or more of individuals occupying these locations have at least one means of individual control over thermal comfort.

Operable windows may be used in lieu of individual controls for those occupants located within 20 ft. of the exterior wall and within 10 ft. of either side of the operable part of the window. The operable portion of the window will need to comply with the free-opening size criteria of ASHRAE Standard 62.1-2004 section 5.1; the minimum area of the window that may be opened is 4% of the net occupiable floor area. For the limits used in this credit, an area 20 ft. by 20 ft. per window, the opening size would need to be 16 sq.ft.

Shared Multi-Occupant Spaces

To satisfy this portion of the requirement, start by identifying those areas where transient groups share spaces, such as conference rooms, break rooms and lecture halls. Confirm that there is at least one means of control over thermal comfort that is accessible. Meeting spaces that can be subdivided, as with a movable wall in a convention hall, must be designed so occupants in each area have control of their individual area.

Submittal Documentation

Complete the LEED for Commercial Interiors Submittal Template declaring that the required thermal comfort controls are provided. Demonstrate compliance by providing a narrative describing the project's thermal comfort design and controls strategy. Include plans showing how at least 50% of the occupants are provided at least one individual control that enables adjustment to suit individual needs and preferences.

Identify all shared multi-occupant spaces and provide detail on how groups have access to the controls to provide thermal comfort within these spaces.

Additional Documentation

For potential use during submittal review, it is suggested that the project team obtain and retain information on the temperature and air-flow controls. Calculations on the sizes of windows that may be opened and their positions should be developed and submitted when used in lieu of individual controls.

Considerations

Cost

The most frequent reported occupant complaints involve thermal discomfort. Greater thermal comfort may increase occupant performance and attendance and, at least, will reduce complaints. According to the Rocky Mountain Institute's Green Developments in Real Estate, office worker salaries are estimated to be

72 times higher than energy costs, and they account for 92% of the life-cycle costs of a building; with this in mind, thermal comfort can have a tremendous effect on overall costs. Case studies have shown productivity increases from 1% to 16%, saving companies millions of dollars per year.

Additional controllability may add to first costs of a project, however, these costs are generally offset by energy savings through lower conditioned temperatures, natural ventilation and less solar gain through proper use of shading devices. Conversely, abuse of personal controls such as setting thermostats too high or leaving windows open during non-working hours increases energy costs. Therefore, it is important to educate occupants on the design and function of system controls.

Regional Considerations

Local weather and ambient air conditions must be considered when determining the feasibility of operable windows for projects. For example, in areas that are prone to extreme temperatures for a majority of the year, or urban areas where traffic and air pollution are problematic, operable windows may not be an appropriate addition to a building.

Resources

Please see the USGBC Web site at www. usgbc.org/resources for more specific resources on materials sources and other technical information.

Web Sites

Center for the Built Environment

www.cbe.berkeley.edu

This University of California, Berkeley research center provides information on underfloor air distribution technologies and other topics. See the publications page for articles such as "A Field Study of PEM (Personal Environmental Module)

Performance in Bank of America's San Francisco Office Buildings."

"Do Green Buildings Enhance the Wellbeing of Workers? Yes,"

Environmental Design + Construction

www.edcmag.com/CDA/ ArticleInformation/coverstory/ BNPCoverStoryItem/0,4118,19794,00. html

An article by Judith Heerwagen in the July/August 2000 edition, of Environmental Design + Construction quantifies the effects of green building environments on productivity.

Print Media

Controls and Automation for Facilities Managers: Applications Engineering, by Viktor Boed, CRC Press, 1998.

Definitions

Shared (Group) Multi-Occupant Spaces include conference rooms, classrooms and other indoor spaces used as a place of congregation for presentations, trainings, etc. Individuals using these spaces share the lighting and temperature controls and they should have, at a minimum, a separate zone with accessible thermostat and an air-flow control.

Individual Occupant Spaces are typically private offices and open office plans with workstations.

Non-Occupied Spaces include all rooms used by maintenance personnel that are not open for use by occupants. Included in this category are janitorial, storage and equipment rooms, and closets.

Non-Regularly Occupied Spaces include corridors, hallways, lobbies, break rooms, copy rooms, storage rooms, kitchens, restrooms, stairwells, etc.

Thermal Comfort

Compliance

Intent

Provide a thermally comfortable environment that supports the productivity and well-being of tenant space occupants.

Requirements

Comply with ASHRAE Standard 55-2004, Thermal Environmental Conditions for Human Occupancy.

Submittals

Provide the LEED for Commercial Interiors Submittal Template, signed by the engineer or responsible party, declaring that the project complies with ASHRAE Standard 55-2004. Include documentation of compliance according to ASHRAE Standard 55-2004, Section 6.1.1, Documentation.

Potential Technologies & Strategies

Establish comfort criteria per the standard and design the tenant space envelope and HVAC system to maintain these comfort ranges.

Summary of Referenced Standard

ANSI/ASHRAE Standard 55-2004: Thermal Environmental Conditions for Human Occupancy, American Society of Heating, Refrigerating and Air-Conditioning Engineers (ASHRAE)

www.ashrae.org

(800) 527-4723

This standard specifies the combinations of indoor thermal environmental factors and personal factors that produce thermal environmental conditions acceptable to predicted percentage of the occupants within a defined space and provides methodology to be used for most applications including naturally ventilated spaces. The designer may choose, in agreement with the owner or owner's representative the level of thermal comfort and appropriate exceedance. Standard addresses six factors that define conditions for thermal comfort which are metabolic rate and clothing insulation (personal factors) as well as air temperature, radiant temperature, air speed and humidity (environmental variables). These factors vary with time but the standard specifically addresses the thermal comfort in steady state. Project space's existing HVAC system design, outdoor conditions, occupant clothing, and occupant activity level are all incorporated into the engineer's assessment of the ability of the building to comply with the desired comfort criteria. The standard further describes appropriate instruments and procedures for measurement of thermal environment conditions. Documentation of the comfort criteria and the logic of the engineer's assessment are requirements for compliance to the standard (See Section 6. Compliance).

Credit Interpretation Rulings

Credit Interpretation Rulings made to LEED for Commercial Interiors project requests, and unless inapplicable, to LEED for New Construction project requests apply to LEED for Commercial Interiors projects for both EQ Credits 7.1 and 7.2.

EQ Credit 7.1

The project needs to demonstrate that humidity is controlled, or demonstrate through modeling/analysis that humidity control will not be necessary to maintain comfort. To achieve the point, the project could demonstrate that the building sequence of operations addresses humidity control, whether automatically or manually. The point would not be achieved simply because the mechanical system has an effect on humidity. (For example, the presence of an air conditioning system alone does not imply that humidity is controlled, merely that the system affects humidity.)

Approach and Implementation

If properly designed, built, and operated, a green space provides its occupants with comfortable indoor conditions that support their health and wellbeing. Although often associated only with air temperature, thermal comfort is a complex issue, impacted by environmental conditions (air temperature, radiant temperature, humidity and air speed) and personal factors (metabolic rate and clothing level) as well as personal preferences of occupants.

Compliance

Building conditioning systems, including both active HVAC systems and natural ventilation systems, are designed and installed in buildings to enhance thermal comfort for building occupants. These building conditioning systems may serve other functions as well, including providing ventilation air and providing thermal conditioning for equipment and processes. Designing and installing building conditioning systems to provide thermal comfort as efficiently and effectively as possible is a central challenge for many green buildings.

Strategies

There are three basic approaches to providing thermal comfort in project space:

- Active Conditioning (e.g. mechanical HVAC systems)
- Passive Conditioning (e.g. natural ventilation)
- Mixed-mode conditioning—employing a combination of active and passive systems

The owner should make a decision as to which of the conditioning approaches are desired and find a space that satisfies the preferred conditioning system. ASHRAE Standard 55-2004 provides thermal comfort standards, with an optional alternate approach specifically for naturally ventilated spaces. The selected space should be evaluated to determine that the space can be made to meet the desired comfort criteria identified by the future occupant.

ASHRAE 55-2004 uses the Predicted Mean Vote (PMV) model which incorporates heat balance principles to relate the personal and environmental thermal comfort factors based on the thermal sensation scale that shows seven levels ranging from +3 (hot) to -3 (cold). The PMV model is applicable to air speeds not greater than 0.20 m/s (40 fpm). For naturally ventilated spaces, the standard notes that field experiments have shown that occupants' thermal responses depend in part on the outdoor climate and may differ from thermal responses in buildings with centralized HVAC systems. This is primarily because of the different thermal experiences, changes in clothing, availability of control, and shifts in occupant expectations. The standard provides an optional method of compliance, intended for naturally ventilated spaces. This optional method provides indoor tempera-

ture ranges as a function of mean monthly outdoor temperatures-assuming light, sedentary activity but independent of humidity, air speed and clothing considerations. The optional method in section 5.3 of the standard utilizes a chart with a broad temperature range and is based on the adaptive model of thermal comfort (which also accounts for people's clothing adaptation). This chart is derived from a global database with measures being taken in office buildings.

Synergies and Trade-Offs

An active HVAC system generally will provide a higher degree of control over indoor thermal comfort conditions than a passive conditioning system. Capital, energy, and lifecycle costs, however, are generally higher for an active HVAC system than for a naturally ventilated system.

Natural ventilation and other passive conditioning approaches are often dependent on occupants managing the system (e.g. opening windows or closing blinds at appropriate times) to meet the comfort criteria. Active conditioning systems generally rely on central automation systems to comply with little or no direct occupant control.

Planning Phase

While researching for a lease or rental space, the design team should decide early on whether a passive approach will provide thermal comfort conditions in the desired project space or whether an active HVAC system or mixed-mode approach will need to be employed. This decision may be influenced by the desired type of space and cost, as well as the owner's desired impact on the organization.

Design Phase

Using ASHRAE Standard 55-2004, the design team and the owner in collaboration should identify the environmental parameters required to maintain the desired thermal comfort in the project space and then identify the conditioning systems (whether active or passive) available at the leased space to provide these conditions.

Lighting systems and other internal HVAC loads can also be integrated to the monitoring system, as feasible, to allow for thermal comfort without excess energy consumption.

There are many well established HVAC load calculation methodologies to assist designers in sizing and selecting HVAC equipment in order to provide thermal comfort conditions. Natural ventilation approach may be more difficult to evaluate in design and require more intensive analysis and/or reliance on experience and precedents. For naturally ventilated buildings CIBSE AM10 presents strategies that can be implemented to the selected space, however attention should be given to the lease requirements of the building to ensure the modifications desired by the owner and the design team may be implemented.

Operation Phase

For mechanical conditioning, the operating setpoints and parameters of the HVAC system will be a primary influence on thermal comfort conditions in the project space. Many facility operators in mechanically air-conditioned spaces spend significant effort and time adjusting thermostat setpoints and other operational parameters in order to limit complaints associated with poor thermal comfort. Systems where individual occupants are provided some amount of direct control over temperature and/or air movement generally yield fewer thermal comfort complaints.

The maxim "passive buildings, active occupants" fits the natural ventilation model well. Occupants generally take a primary role in managing thermal comfort conditions in naturally ventilated buildings by opening and closing windows as necessary and appropriate. Thermal comfort

in naturally conditioned buildings is also somewhat more variable and tied to the ambient conditions than in mechanically conditioned buildings where systems are often designed to maintain consistent conditions through all periods of occupancy.

Submittal Documentation

Complete the LEED for Commercial Interiors Submittal Template declaration that the project space is in compliance with ASHRAE Standard 55-2004.

Section 5.2 Method

When the compliance path outlined in Section 5.2 is followed, include documentation of compliance according to the Section 6.1.1 of the standard. .For LEED for Commercial Interiors projects, the documentation may be summarized in a narrative that describes the approach followed in complying with ASHRAE Standard 55-2004. When applicable, the narrative should include the following –

- The design criteria of the system(s) in terms of indoor temperature and humidity, including any tolerances or ranges; based on design outdoor ambient conditions and total indoor loads;

- Values assumed for comfort parameters, clothing and metabolic rate;

- Design outdoor, ambient conditions;

- Internal heating and cooling loads;

- System capacities (mechanical and/or natural ventilation) necessary to attain the design indoor conditions at design outdoor ambient conditions;

- Any limitations of the system(s) to control the thermal environment;

- The overall space supplied by the system(s) shown in a plan view layout, with individual control zones, registers, terminal units, operable windows, and other thermal control devices identified;

- Areas within any zone that lie outside the comfort control areas or where people should not be permanently located should be identified; and

- A description of how controls are intended to be adjusted and the recommended settings for various times of day, season, or occupancy load should be provided, including a block-diagram control schematic if appropriate.

Refer to ASHRAE Standard 55-2004, Section 6.1.1, Documentation, for more information.

Section 5.3 Naturally Ventilated Buildings

When Section 5.3 is used for naturally ventilated buildings, complete the calculations predicting the indoor temperature and humidity conditions under various ambient conditions; include a clear explanation of the calculation methodology. The standard includes a figure that demonstrates the acceptable thermal comfort levels based on indoor operative temperature vs. mean monthly outdoor air temperature. The projects need to comply with ASHRAE 55-2004 and achieve this credit by utilizing natural ventilation approach.

Other Exhibits

Plans, controls schematics, photographs and computer software calculation outputs may be provided, as necessary and appropriate, in support of the narrative.

Additional Documentation

If the submittal is complete, there should be no additional information required during review.

Exemplary Performance

No established criteria has been set for exemplary performance for EQ Credit 7.1.

Note: The Resources and Definitions for EQ Credit 7.1 can be found at the end of the EQ Credit 7.2 section.

**1 point
in addition to
EQ Credit 7.1**

Thermal Comfort
Monitoring

Intent

Provide a thermally comfortable environment that supports the productivity and well-being of tenant space occupants.

Requirements

Provide a permanent monitoring system to ensure building performance to the desired comfort criteria as determined by EQ Credit 7.1, Thermal Comfort, Compliance.

Submittals

Provide the LEED for Commercial Interiors Submittal Template, signed by the engineer or responsible party, that identifies the comfort criteria, strategy for ensuring performance to the comfort criteria, description of the permanent monitoring system implemented, and process for corrective action.

Potential Technologies & Strategies

ASHRAE Standard 55-2004 Paragraph 7 Evaluation of the Thermal Environment provides guidance on measurement of building performance parameters and two methods for validating performance: (a) Survey Occupants and (b) Analyze Environment Variables. The permanent monitoring system required here may apply either approach, survey or technical system, where the process or system is integrated into the standard operating processes of the building.

Credit Interpretation Rulings

Credit Interpretation Rulings made to LEED for Commercial Interiors project requests, and unless inapplicable, to LEED for New Construction project requests apply to LEED for Commercial Interiors projects for both EQ Credits 7.1 and 7.2.

When properly designed, built and operated, a green space provides its occupants with comfortable indoor conditions that support their health and wellbeing. Since poor thermal comfort is the primary occupant complaint in many facilities, a well managed and responsive green space have systems in place to gauge whether occupant comfort is being maintained or can be improved.

Strategies

Since thermal comfort is inherently subjective and is psychological as much as physiological, regularly surveying occupants may be the best way to determine if a facility is "comfortable". Sporadic occupant complaints about thermal comfort may not be an appropriate indicator of overall thermal comfort but rather an indicator of local or personal dissatisfaction. Providing a systematic process and mechanism for all occupants to provide feedback about their thermal comfort will help building operators adjust and maintain thermal comfort in the building.

Analyzing environment variables (typically by monitoring space temperature and relative humidity) is an alternate approach to determining if a facility is providing thermal comfort for its occupants. Temperature, humidity and other environmental monitoring systems provide facility operators with objective data to determine if the building space conditions meet the design intent and/or if they are being maintained consistently through the occupied periods.

Synergies and Trade-Offs

Thermal comfort monitoring (via occupant surveying or monitoring environmental variables) may add capital, operations and maintenance costs to a facility. The building systems, building use, and occupants change with time requiring ongoing maintenance and perhaps improvements to thermal comfort performance. Reducing thermal comfort problems and complaints contributes to occupant performance and may allow facility operations and maintenance staff to focus on other critical areas.

Planning Phase

Once the project space that has the desired conditioning system is selected, the design team should identify the type of monitoring system employed in the space, if any. The decision about how to monitor thermal comfort (via occupant surveying, monitoring environmental conditions or both) should be evaluated in the planning phase as this may impact HVAC system design decisions.

Design Phase

The design team should identify the environmental parameters in EQ Credit 7.1 to maintain performance to the comfort criteria in the selected space and then provide a monitoring system to be able to control and maintain these conditions. Any space temperature sensors, humidity sensors, or other sensors that are required to monitor space thermal comfort conditions should be integrated into the HVAC design. If the occupants will be surveyed, the guidelines and a sample thermal environment survey is available in detail in ASHRAE 55-2004.

Operations Phase

Facility operators should develop procedures to regularly (for every operating mode) survey building occupants about thermal comfort conditions. This survey may be administered in person, over the

SS	WE	EA	MR	EQ	ID
				Credit 7	

phone, over networked computers, or on paper but should be consistently applied and available for participation by all regular occupants. The survey may encompass other indoor environmental quality considerations (such as lighting or acoustics) as well, although this is not required for this LEED for Commercial Interiors credit.

Another way of monitoring comfort criteria is to employ a monitoring system that will be able to control non directional air speed, air temperature and humidity under all expected operating conditions. Maintenance and operations personnel need to verify that the system is functioning properly and that the comfort criteria determined earlier is being maintained by taking readings and assessing the thermal comfort parameters that are identified by the owner and the design team. Periodic verifications and adjusments to the system to maintain the set comfort criteria contributes to occupant performance and keeps the systems up to date, to deliver the design intent.

Even though credit 7.2 doesn't require a monitoring system and occupant surveying to verify the thermal comfort conditions, it might be beneficial for the owner and design teams to employ both options in their operations and maintenance plan especially for determining and tracking options to corrective action.

Submittal Documentation

Complete the LEED for Commercial Interiors Submittal Template, providing a description of the comfort criteria, a strategy for ensuring performance to the comfort criteria, description of the permanent monitoring system and the process used for corrective action.

Because EQ Credit 7.2 may not be earned until the requirements of EQ Credit 7.1 have been satisfied, the following items may be included in a common narrative:

- A description of the permanent monitoring system implemented: environmental monitoring or occupant surveying

- If environmental monitoring is employed, a description of the quantity, type, and location of space temperature and humidity sensors, along with the data monitoring and reporting procedures

- If occupant surveying is employed, a description of the survey techniques and frequency, including the survey results reporting procedures

- A description of the process for corrective action based on data from the thermal comfort monitoring system

Considerations

Costs

Depending on the specific approach and project space limitations, providing the thermal comfort conditions as defined by ASHRAE Standard 55–2004 may increase or decrease the cost of designing, constructing and operating the facility.

The choices that are made while finding the project space will shape the cost implications of this credit. If the owner selects a space that has mechanical systems, the design team has to evaluate the existing system to determine if maintaining the comfort criteria is feasible from a system and monitoring point of view and whether there is a need for modifications or changes to the overall system. This might affect lease agreements, which might reduce or increase the overall cost of the project.

If the owner selects a space that has a natural ventilation system, the above mentioned feasibility procedure should be carried out to evaluate cost implications. The selected space might have operable windows but may or may not provide the comfort criteria established by the owner and the design team. Natural ventilation systems consume less energy, and may have reduced maintenance costs compared to the HVAC systems.

Cost implications may be major if the selected space has a natural ventilation system and the owner prefers a mechanical system or vice versa. It is important to identify the conditioning preferences and comfort criteria in the planning phase to minimize cost impact and to sign a lease agreement that meets the owner's needs.

Regional Considerations

ASHRAE Standard 55–2004 provides alternate thermal comfort criteria based on presumed seasonal changes in occupants' clothing levels. This assumption may or may not be valid for facilities and for different regions of the country. Designers should consider and anticipate occupants' clothing levels and likely metabolic rate in determining the indoor thermal comfort criteria.

A natural ventilation approach is more typical in mild and temperate climates, although there are precedents for naturally conditioned buildings in all climates.

Environmental Issues

For many facilities, the HVAC systems which maintain indoor thermal comfort are the largest energy end-use. A successful green building should minimize the energy use associated with building conditioning—along with the associated energy cost, fuel consumption and air emissions—while maintaining thermal comfort conditions that enhance the occupants' wellbeing.

Resources

Please see the USGBC Web site at www. usgbc.org/resources for more specific resources on materials sources and other technical information.

Web Sites

Advanced Desiccant Cooling & Dehumidification Program

www.nrel.gov/desiccantcool

A research and development program of the U.S. Department of Energy that works with industry to realize the potential of desiccant systems for reducing energy consumption and improving indoor air quality and comfort.

NIST Multizone Modeling Software

www.bfrl.nist.gov/IAQanalysis/Software.htm

The National Institute of Standards and Technology provides software such as CONTAMW, a multizone indoor air quality and ventilation analysis computer program designed to predict airflows and contaminant concentrations.

The Whole Building Design Guide

www.wbdg.org/design/ieq.php

The Indoor Environmental Quality section provides a wealth of resources including definitions, fundamentals, materials and tools.

Print Media

ASHRAE Standard 62.1–2004: Ventilation for Acceptable Indoor Air Quality, ASHRAE, 2004.

ASHRAE Standard 111–1988: Practices for Measurement, Testing, Adjusting and Balancing of Building Heating, Ventilation, Air-Conditioning and Refrigeration Systems, ASHRAE, 1988.

Dehumidification Enhancements for 100-Percent-Outside-Air AHUs: Parts I, II and III by Donald Gatley, *Heating Piping and Air Conditioning Magazine*, September, October and November, 2000 (available as fee-based downloads at HPAC.com)

Humidity Control Design Guide by L. Harriman, G.W. Brundett and R. Kittler, ASHRAE, 2000.

SS	WE	EA	MR	EQ	ID
				Credit 7	

The Impact of Part-Load Air-Conditioner Operation on Dehumidification Performance: Validating a Latent Capacity Degradation Model, Hugh Henderson, IAQ and Energy 1998 Using ASHRAE Standards 62 and 90.1 Conference Papers, ASHRAE, 1998.

"The New Comfort Equation For Indoor Air Quality" by P.O. Fanger, *ASHRAE Journal*, October, pp. 33-38, 1989.

Selecting HVAC Systems for Schools, by Arthur Wheeler and Walter Kunz, Jr., Maryland State Department of Education, 1994.

Thermal Comfort, by P.O. Fanger, McGraw Hill, 1973.

Thermal Delight in Architecture, by Lisa Heschong, MIT Press, 1979.

"Unplanned Airflows and Moisture Problems" by T. Brennan, J. Cummings and J. Lstiburek, *ASHRAE Journal*, November, 2000

Definitions

Natural Ventilation provides acceptable air-change effectiveness and thermal comfort without the use of mechanical heating and cooling equipment. The natural effect of wind, stack effect and interior/exterior temperature differentials induce air circulation and replacement. Airflow is fan-assisted only when necessary.

The **Occupied Zone** is the region normally occupied by people within a space, generally considered to be between the floor and 6 ft. above the floor and more than 3.3 ft. from outside walls/windows or fixed heating, ventilating or air-conditioning equipment and 1 ft. from internal walls. (ASHRAE 55-2004)

Relative Humidity is the ratio of partial density of water vapor in the air to the saturation density of water vapor at the same temperature and the same total pressure. (ASHRAE 55-2004)

Thermal Comfort is a condition of mind experienced by building occupants expressing satisfaction with the thermal environment.

Comfort Criteria is specific original design conditions that shall at least include temperature (air, radiant and surface), humidity and air speed as well as outdoor temperature design conditions, outdoor humidity design conditions, clothing (seasonal) and activity expected. (ASHRAE 55-2004)

Daylight and Views
Daylight 75% of Spaces

1 point

Intent

Provide the occupants with a connection between indoor spaces and the outdoors through the introduction of daylight and views into the regularly occupied areas of the tenant space.

Requirements

For at least 75% of all regularly occupied areas:

- Achieve a minimum Daylight Factor of 2% (excluding all direct sunlight penetrations)

OR

- Using a computer simulation model, achieve at least 25 footcandles.

AND

- Provide daylight redirection and/or glare control devices to ensure daylight effectiveness.

Exceptions for areas where tasks would be hindered by the use of daylight will be considered on their merits.

Submittals

- Provide the LEED for Commercial Interiors Submittal Template, signed by the responsible party indicating the required daylighting is accomplished in at least 75% of the regularly occupied areas.

- Provide area calculations that define the daylight zones and provide a summary of daylight factor prediction calculations through manual methods or a summary of computer simulations illustrating that the footcandle levels have been achieved.

Potential Technologies & Strategies

Design the space to maximize interior daylighting and view opportunities. Strategies to consider include lower partition heights, interior shading devices, interior glazing and photo-integrated light sensors. Predict daylight factors via manual calculations or model daylighting strategies with a physical or computer model to assess footcandle levels and daylight factors achieved. Modeling must demonstrate 25 horizontal footcandles under clear sky conditions, at noon, on the equinox, at 30 in. above the floor. Any portion of a room achieving the requirements can qualify for this credit.

Daylight and Views
Daylight 90% of Spaces

Intent

Provide for the occupants a connection between indoor spaces and the outdoor environment through the introduction of daylight and views into the regularly occupied areas of the tenant space.

Requirements

For at least 90% of all regularly occupied areas:

- Achieve a minimum Daylight Factor of 2% (excluding all direct sunlight penetrations)

OR

- Using a computer simulation model, achieve at least 25 footcandles.

AND

- Provide daylight redirection and/or glare control devices to ensure daylight effectiveness.

Exceptions for areas where tasks would be hindered by the use of daylight will be considered on their merits.

Submittals

- Provide the LEED for Commercial Interiors Submittal Template, signed by the responsible party indicating the required daylighting is accomplished in at least 90% of the regularly occupied areas.

- Provide area calculations that define the daylight zones and provide a summary of daylight factor prediction calculations through manual methods or a summary of computer simulations illustrating that the footcandle levels have been achieved.

Potential Technologies & Strategies

Design the space to maximize interior daylighting and view opportunities. Strategies to consider include lower partition heights, interior shading devices, interior glazing, and photo-integrated light sensors. Predict daylight factors via manual calculations or model daylighting strategies with a physical or computer model to assess footcandle levels and daylight factors achieved. Modeling must demonstrate 25 horizontal footcandles under clear sky conditions, at noon, on the equinox, at 30 inches above the floor. Any portion of a room achieving the requirements can qualify for this credit.

Credit Interpretation Rulings

Credit Interpretation Rulings (CIRs) made to LEED for Commercial Interiors project requests, and unless inapplicable, to LEED for New Construction project requests concerning LEED for New Construction v2.1 EQ Credit 8.1, apply to LEED for Commercial Interiors projects for both EQ Credits 8.1 and 8.2.

Spaces where tasks would be hindered by the use of daylight may be excluded. Computer labs are a possible example.

Laboratory spaces may only be exempt if adequate justification is provided confirming the spaces are infrequently used or that daylighting would interfere with the research being conducted.

Support spaces for storage are excluded. Stacks in libraries may be excluded provided the primary function of the area is storage. Other support areas that may be included are kitchens and dining areas in residential applications. Exceptions to the requirement are solely based on visual considerations and not based on sound; office spaces affected by airplane noise cannot be exempted from the credit calculations.

Animal holding areas are not exempt from the requirements for this credit.

Approach and Implementation

Strategies

For commercial interior projects, where the project team may not have the opportunity to design the fenestration, the selection of a building that supports daylighting is critical. Determine if daylighting and direct line of sight to the outdoors is available. Some buildings' potential for natural daylighting is limited by site constraints or structures that prohibit daylight penetration.

Evaluate the impact of the selected building's orientation on possible daylighting options; opt for designs with shallow floor plates, courtyards, atriums, clerestory windows, skylights. Evaluate the potential to add interior light shelves, exterior fins, louvers and adjustable blinds. See **Figure 1**, which illustrates various daylighting strategies.

Figure 1: An illustration of Various Daylighting Strategies

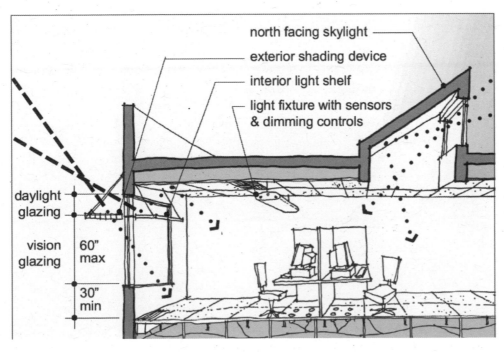

The desired amount of daylight will differ depending on the tasks occurring in a daylit space. Daylit spaces often have several daylight zones with differing target light levels. In addition to light levels, daylighting strategies should address interior color schemes, direct beam penetration and integration with the electric lighting system.

Glare control is perhaps the most common failure in daylighting strategies. Glare is defined as any excessively bright source of light within the visual field that creates discomfort or loss in visibility. Large window areas provide generous amounts of daylight to the task area. If not controlled properly, this daylight can produce unwanted glare and affect the lighting quality. Measures to control glare include light shelves, louvers, blinds, fins and shades. Typically low luminance ratios and lighting of primary surfaces will enhance visual quality.

Technologies

Computer modeling software can be used to simulate daylighting conditions. Daylighting software produces continuous daylight contours to simulate the daylighting conditions of interior spaces and to account for combined effects of multiple windows within a daylit space.

Photo-responsive controls for electric lighting can be incorporated into daylighting strategies to maintain consistent light levels and to minimize occupant perception of the transition from natural light to artificial light. These controls result in energy savings by reducing electric lighting in high daylight conditions while preserving footcandle levels on the task surface.

Synergies and Trade-Offs

The selected building may have limited daylighting potential due to their orientation, number and size of building openings and floor plate dimensions. Vertical site elements such as neighboring buildings and trees may reduce the potential for daylighting. Finally, light sensors and automatic controls will affect the energy performance of the building and will require commissioning and Measurement & Verification attention. Glazing parameters directly affect the heat gain and loss of the building which may result in increased energy use. It is important to address the glazing properly not only for energy usage but also for visual quality.

Calculations

Compliance with the requirements for this credit may be determined by either following the daylight calculation methodology outlined in the following paragraphs to determine daylight factor, or by using daylighting simulation software to determine point-by-point illumination levels (footcandles) measured at desk height (30" above the finished floor).

Areas to include in the daylighting calculations include all regularly occupied spaces such as office spaces, meeting areas and cafeterias. Areas that should not be considered include support areas for copying, storage, mechanical equipment, laundry and restrooms.

The daylighting calculation methodology below can be applied to approximate the daylight factor for each regularly occupied room in the building. The Daylight Factor (DF) is the ratio of exterior illumination to interior illumination and is expressed as a percentage. The variables used to determine the daylight factor include the floor area, window area, window geometry, visible transmittance (Tvis) and window height. This calculation method aims to provide a minimum 2% DF at the back of a space.

The Daylight Factor calculation method is designed to indentify daylighting conditions based on room and window geometry and visible transmittance based on meeting the performance criteria for overcast sky conditions. Currently this calculation method does not take into account light shelves, partitions, significant exterior obstructions or exterior reflecting surfaces. Daylight simulation calculation method is highly recommended where daylighting strategies go beyond the current capability to the Daylight Factor Calculation Method.

Daylight Factor

1. Create a spreadsheet and identify all regularly occupied rooms/areas. Determine the floor area of each applicable room using construction documents.

2. For each room/area identified, calculate the window area and use **Table 1** to indicate the acceptable window types. Note that window areas above 7'-6" are considered to be daylight glazing. Glazing at this height is the most effective at distributing daylight deep into the interior space. Window areas from 2'-6" to 7'-6" are considered to be vision glazing. These window areas are primarily used for viewing and lighting interior spaces close to the building perimeter. Window areas below 2'6" do not contribute to daylighting of interior spaces and are to be excluded from the calculations.

Table 1: Daylight Design Criteria

Window Type	Geometry Factor	Minimum T_{vis}	Height Factor	Best Practice Glare Control
sidelight daylight glazing	0.1	0.7	1.4	Adjustable blinds / Interior light shelves / Fixed translucent exterior shading devices
sidelighting vision glazing	0.1	0.4	0.8	Adjustable blinds / Exterior shading devices
toplighting vertical monitor	0.2	0.4	1.0	Fixed interior / Adjustable exterior blinds
toplighting sawtooth monitor	0.33	0.4	1.0	Fixed interior / Exterior louvers
toplighting horizontal skylights	0.5	0.4	1.0	Interior fins / Exterior fins / Louvers

Equation 1: Daylight Factor

$$\text{Daylight Factor} = \frac{\text{Window Area [SF]}}{\text{Floor Area [SF]}} \times \text{Window Geometry} \times \frac{\text{Actual } T_{vis}}{\text{Minimum } T_{vis}} \times \text{Window Height Factor}$$

3. For each window type, insert the appropriate geometry and height factors as listed in **Table 1**. The geometry factor indicates the effectiveness of a particular aperture to distribute daylight relative to window location. The height factor accounts for where light is introduced to the space.

4. For each window type, indicate the visible transmittance (Tvis), a variable number that differs for each product. Minimum Tvis is the recommended level of transmittance for selected glazing.

5. Calculate the Daylight Factor for each window type using **Equation 1**. For rooms/areas with more than one window type, sum all window types to obtain a total Daylight Factor for the room/area.

6. If the total daylight factor for a room/area is 2% or greater, then the square footage of the room/area is applicable to the credit.

7. Sum the square footage of all applicable rooms/areas and divide by the total square footage of all regularly occupied spaces. If this percentage is equal to or greater than 75%, then the project qualifies for the first

point of this credit. If this percentage is equal to or greater than 90%, then the project qualifies for both points under 8.1 and 8.2.

8. Note that glare control is also required for each window. **Table 1** provides best-practice glare control measures for different window types. Create another spreadsheet entry that identifies the type of glare control applied to each window type. The type of glare control selected for each window does not affect the daylight factor calculations. **Table 3** provides a glare control charge that projects can utilize.

Table 2 provides an example of daylighting calculations for a typical office space. All of the offices are considered to be regularly occupied spaces, while support areas such as hallways, foyers, storage areas, mechanical rooms and restrooms are not considered to be regularly occupied. The example qualifies for the first point of this credit because it exceeds the minimum square footage for daylit area and includes glare control on all windows in daylit rooms.

Table 2: Sample Daylighting Calculations

Room	Floor Area [SF]	Glazing Area [SF]	Window Geometry Type	Window Geometry Factor	Transmittance (Tvis) Actual	Transmittance (Tvis) Minimum	Window Height Factor	Daylight Factor Each	Daylight Factor Room	Daylit Area [SF]	Glare Control Type
101 Office	820	120	vision	0.1	0.9	0.4	0.8	2.6%	3.3%	820	2
		40	daylight	0.1	0.7	0.7	1.4	0.7%			3
102 Conference	330	30	vision	0.1	0.9	0.4	0.8	1.6%	1.8%	0	2
		5	daylight	0.1	0.7	0.7	1.4	0.2%			3
103a Open Office	2250	330	vision	0.1	0.9	0.4	0.8	2.6%	3.3%	2250	2
Daylit Area		110	daylight	0.1	0.7	0.7	1.4	0.7%			3
103b Open Office	685	0	vision	0.1	0.9	0.4	0.8	0.0%	0.0%	0	
Non-Daylit Area		0	daylight	0.1	0.7	0.7	1.4	0.0%			
104 Office	250	25	vision	0.1	0.9	0.4	0.8	1.8%	2.1%	250	2
		5	daylight	0.1	0.7	0.7	1.4	0.3%			3
105 Office	250	25	vision	0.1	0.9	0.4	0.8	1.8%	2.1%	250	2
		5	daylight	0.1	0.7	0.7	1.4	0.3%			3
Total	4,585									3,570	

Percentage of Daylit Area	78%
Points Awarded EQc8.1 (75%)	1
Points Awarded EQc8.2 (90%)	0

Table 3: Glare Control Chart

Type	Description
1	Fixed Exterior Shading Devices
2	Light Shelf, Exterior
3	Light Shelf, Interior
4	Interior Blinds
5	Pull-Down Shade
6	Fritted Glazing
7	Drapes
8	Electronic Black-Out Glazing

Daylight Simulation Model

1. Create a daylight simulation model for the building, or each regularly occupied space with glazing. The model should include appropriate glazing factors as well as representative surface reflectance settings for interior finishes.

2. For each applicable room/area, include a horizontal calculation grid at 30 inches above the floor. This grid will represent the typical workplane height. The calculation grid should be set at approximately 2 foot intervals to provide a detailed illumination diagram for each area. (For larger areas, it may be necessary to increase the grid size for clarity.)

3. Calculate the daylight illumination for each applicable space using the following daylight criteria: clear sky conditions at 12:00 noon on the equinox (March 21/ September 21) for the project's specific geographic location. **Figure 2** illustrates a sample daylight analysis for an office space.

4. Create a spreadsheet and identify all regularly occupied rooms/areas. Determine the floor area of each applicable room using construction documents. Provide the minimum illumination level (footcandles), determined through the simulation model, for each space.

5. If the minimum illumination for a room/area is 25 footcandles or greater, then the square footage of the room/area is applicable to the credit. (See Note 1 below for further information)

6. Sum the square footage of all daylit rooms/areas and divide by the total square footage of all regularly occupied spaces. If this percentage is equal to or greater than 75%, then the project qualifies for the first point of this credit. If this percentage is equal to or greater than 90%, then the

Figure 2: Sample Daylight Simulation Model Output

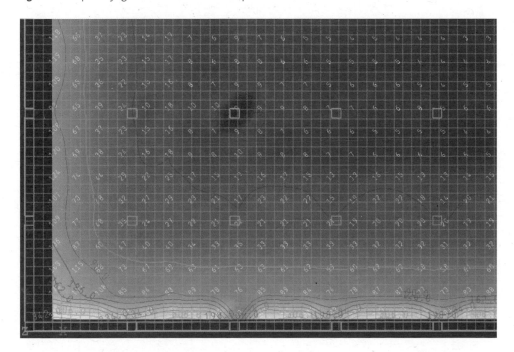

project qualifies for both points under 8.1 and 8.2.

7. Note that glare control is also required for each window. **Table 1** provides best-practice glare control measures for different window types. Create another spreadsheet entry that identifies the type of glare control applied to each window type. The type of glare control selected for each window does not affect the daylight factor calculations. **Table 3** provides a glare control chart that the projects can utilize.

NOTE 1: This credit can be approached so that 100% of each room does not have to meet the 2% daylight factor or the minimum 25 footcandle requirement. In order to do so, the portion of the room with a 2% (or higher) daylight factor or 25 footcandle minimum illumination would count towards the percentage of all space occupied for critical visual tasks. The portion of the room not meeting the daylight factor or illumination criteria would not count towards the compliant area total, but would be considered in the calculation of total area calculation. For the calculation spreadsheet, the two portions of the room (the one meeting the minimum daylight factor or illumination and the one not meeting the requirements) would be counted as separate spaces (See **Table 2** – Room 103 "Open Office"). The square footage of all compliant spaces is tallied and then divided over the total square footage of all regularly occupied spaces. If the percentage is equal to or greater than 75%, then the project qualifies for one point under this Credit (EQ Credit 8.1); if the percentage is equal to or greater than 90%, the project qualifies for two points under this credit (EQ Credit 8.1 / 8.2).

Submittal Documentation

Complete the LEED for Commercial Interiors Submittal Templates for the credits to be attained. Submit the completed calculations when the manual approach has

been used. When computer simulation has been done, provide a summary report illustrating that the footcandle levels have been achieved. The plans need to relate to the actual floor plan.

Additional Documentation

When the initial submittal is complete, no additional documentation should be needed.

Exemplary Performance

The availability of two points in EQ Credits 8.1 and 8.2 preclude the opportunity to earn a third point using the same criteria.

Considerations

Daylighting improves the indoor environment of buildings by exposing occupants to natural light. Studies have demonstrated that productivity increases dramatically for those building occupants working in daylit areas. In addition, daylighting decreases energy costs for buildings by providing natural solar lighting. A well-designed daylit building is estimated to reduce lighting energy use by 50% to 80% (Sustainable Building Technical Manual, chapter IV.7, page 90).

Daylighting design involves a careful balance of heat gain and loss, glare control, visual quality and variations in daylight availability. Shading devices, light shelves, courtyards, atriums and window glazing are all strategies employed in daylighting design. Important considerations include selected building's orientation, window size and spacing, glass selection, reflectance of interior finishes and locations of interior walls.

Environmental Issues

Daylighting reduces the need for electric lighting of building interiors, resulting in decreased energy use. This conserves natural resources and reduces air pollution impacts due to energy production and consumption. Daylit spaces also increase occupant productivity and reduce absenteeism and illness.

Economic Issues

Specialized glazing can increase initial costs for a project and can lead to excessive heat gain if not designed properly. Glazing provides less insulating effects compared to standard walls, resulting in higher energy use and requiring additional maintenance. However, offices with sufficient natural daylight have proven to increase occupant productivity and comfort. In most cases, occupant salaries significantly outweigh first costs of incorporating daylighting measures into a building design. Studies of schools and stores have shown that daylighting can improve student performance and retail sales (see the Resources section).

Daylighting can significantly reduce artificial lighting requirements and energy costs in many commercial and industrial buildings, as well as schools, libraries and hospitals. Daylighting, combined with energy-efficient lighting and electronic ballasts, can reduce the lighting power density in some office buildings by up to 30%.

Community Issues

Daylighting and outdoor views provide a connection with the building site and adjacent sites, creating a more integrated neighborhood. Daylit spaces increase occupant productivity and reduce illness and absenteeism.

Resources

Please see the USGBC Web site at www.usgbc.org/resources for more specific resources on materials sources and other technical information.

Web Sites

Analysis of the Performance of Students in Daylit Schools

www.innovativedesign.net/studentperformance.htm

Nicklas and Bailey's 1996 study of three daylit schools in North Carolina.

The Art of Daylighting

www.edcmag.com/CDA/ArticleInformation/features/BNP__Features__Item/0,4120,18800,00.html

This Environmental Design + Construction article provides a solid introduction to daylighting.

New Buildings Institute's Productivity and Building Science Program

www.newbuildings.org/downloads/FinalAttachments/PIER_Final_Report(P500-03-082).pdf

Provides case studies and report on the benefits of daylighting.

Radiance Software

radsite.lbl.gov

Free daylighting simulation software from the Lawrence Berkeley National Laboratory

Tips for Daylighting with Windows

eande.lbl.gov/BTP/pub/designguide/download.html

A daylighting comprehensive guide from Lawrence Berkeley National Laboratory

The Whole Building Design Guide

Daylighting: www.wbdg.org/design/daylighting.php?r=ieq

Lighting Controls: www.wbdg.org/design/electriclighting.php?r=ieq

The Daylighting and Lighting Controls sections provide a wealth of resources including definitions, fundamentals, materials and tools.

Print Media

"Daylighting Design" by Benjamin Evans, in *Time-Saver Standards for Architectural Design Data*, McGraw-Hill, Inc., 1997.

Daylighting for Sustainable Design by Mary Guzowski, McGraw-Hill, Inc., 1999.

Daylighting Performance and Design by Gregg D. Ander, John Wiley & Sons, 1997.

Sustainable Building Technical Manual, Public Technology, Inc., 1996 (www.pti.org)

Definitions

Daylight Factor is the ratio of interior illuminance at a given point on a given plane (usually the workplane) to the exterior illuminance under known overcast sky conditions. LEED uses a simplified approach for its credit compliance calculations. The variables used to determine the daylight factor include the floor area, window area, window geometry, visible transmittance (Tvis) and window height.)

Daylighting is the controlled admission of natural light into a space through glazing with the intent of reducing or eliminating electric lighting. By utilizing solar light, daylighting creates a stimulating and productive environment for building occupants.

Non-Occupied Spaces include all rooms used by maintenance personnel that are not open for use by occupants. Included in this category are janitorial, storage and equipment rooms, and closets.

Non-Regularly Occupied Spaces include corridors, hallways, lobbies, break rooms, copy rooms, storage rooms, kitchens, restrooms, stairwells, etc.

Regularly Occupied Spaces are areas where workers are seated or standing as they work inside a building; in residential applications it refers to living and family rooms.

Visible Light Transmittance (T_{vis}) is the ratio of total transmitted light to total incident light. In other words, it is the amount of visible spectrum (380 – 780 nanometers) light passing through a glazing surface divided by the amount of light striking the glazing surface. A higher Tvis value indicates that a greater amount of visible spectrum incident light is passing through the glazing.

Daylight and Views

Views for 90% Seated Spaces

Intent

Provide for the occupants a connection between indoor spaces and the outdoor environment through the introduction of daylight and views into the regularly occupied areas of the tenant space.

Requirements

Achieve a direct line-of-sight to the outdoor environment (vision glazing between 2'-6" and 7'-6") for building occupants in 90% of all regularly occupied areas. Determine the area with direct line of sight by totaling the regularly occupied square footage that meets the following criteria:

- In plan view, the area is within sight lines drawn from perimeter vision glazing.
- In section view, a direct sight line can be drawn from a point 42 in. above the floor to perimeter vision glazing.

Line of sight may be drawn through interior glazing. For private offices, the entire square footage of the office can be counted if 75% or more of the area has direct line of sight to perimeter vision glazing. If less than 75% of the area has direct line of sight then only the area with the direct line of sight will be counted towards meeting the credit requirement not the whole office area. For multi-occupant spaces, the actual square footage with direct line of sight to perimeter vision glazing is counted.

Submittals

Provide the LEED for Commercial Interiors Submittal Template and calculations signed by the architect, interior designer or other responsible party describing, demonstrating and declaring that the building occupants in 90% of regularly occupied areas will have direct lines of site to perimeter glazing.

Provide floor plans and representative sections highlighting the areas with direct line of sight and showing interior partitions and perimeter windows with respect to the view at 42 in. above the floor.

Potential Technologies & Strategies

Design the space to maximize view opportunities. Strategies to consider include lower partition heights and interior glazing.

Credit Interpretation Rulings

Credit Interpretation Rulings (CIRs) made to LEED for Commercial Interiors project requests, apply to LEED for Commercial Interiors projects. Where similarities exist with LEED for New Construction v2.1, EQ Credit 8.2 Views for 90% of Spaces, the rulings issued may apply.

This credit in LEED for Commercial Interiors has two distinct differences from the similar LEED for New Construction credit. First, the perspective in this credit is taken from the seated position, requiring there be no obstructions above that height in the view. Second, for LEED for Commercial Interiors projects, the determination of the horizontal view must be made with the furniture installed.

Approach and Implementation

There are two calculations required to determine achievement of this credit–Direct Line of Sight to Perimeter Glazing and Horizontal View at 42 Inches.

The Direct Line of Sight to Perimeter Glazing determination is an area calculation, and confirms that 90% of the occupied area is designed so there is the potential for views from regularly occupied areas. It is based on vision glazing (2'-6" – 7'-6"), and the location of full height interior partitions. Movable furniture is not included in this portion of the credit calculation. See **Figure 1**.

Generally the architect, when determining the interior wall locations and placement of borrowed lites, is responsible for satisfying this portion of the credit requirement. A successful design strategy for offices locates open plan areas along the exterior walls, while placing private offices and areas not regularly occupied to the core of the building.

The Horizontal Views at 42 Inches determination confirms that the available views are maintained once the furniture has been installed. See **Figure 2**.

Generally the interior designer, while laying out and specifying the furniture, is responsible for satisfying this portion of the credit requirement. Maintaining the views for spaces near the core is a primary design objective. One successful approach for open plan offices configures workstations so the high panels, which often include storage, run perpendicular to the exterior windows. Low or glazed panels are then run parallel to the windows keeping the views open to interior spaces.

Regularly occupied spaces include office spaces, conference rooms and cafeterias. Areas that need not be considered include support areas for copying, storage, mechanical equipment, laundry and restrooms.

Table 1: Determination of Compliance, EQ Credit 8.3

Room	Regularly Occupied Floor Area [SF]	Plan Area of Direct Line of Sight to Perimeter Vision Glazing [SF]	Calculated Area of Direct Line of Sight to Perimeter Vision Glazing [SF]	Horizontal View at 42 Inches [Yes/No]	Compliant Area [SF]
101 Office	820	790	820	Yes	820
102 Conference	330	280	330	Yes	330
103 Open Office	4,935	4,641	2,641	Yes	4,641
104 Office	250	201	250	No	0
105 Office	250	175	175	Yes	175
Total	6,585				5,966

Percent Access to Views [5,966 / 6,585] 90.6% Credit Earned

Figure 1: Direct Line of Sight to Perimeter Vision Glazing, used in the area determination

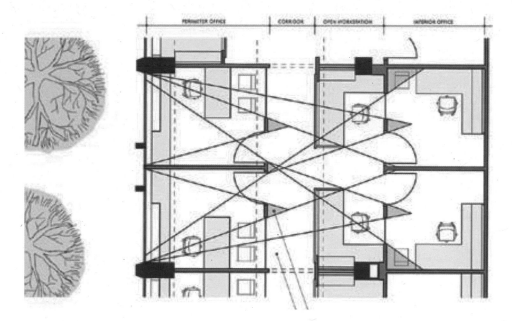

Figure 2: Horizontal View at 42 Inches, used to confirm view is maintained with furniture installed

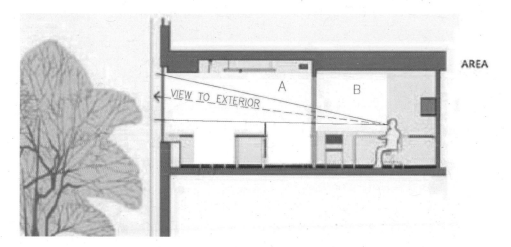

Calculations

Direct Line of Sight to Perimeter Vision Glazing

1. Create a spreadsheet and identify all regularly occupied rooms/areas. Determine the floor area of each applicable room using construction documents. See **Table 1**.

2. Using a floor plan, construct line of sight geometries at each window to determine the fraction of the regularly occupied room/area that has direct line of sight to the outdoors. Note: line of sight can pass through interior glazing but not through doorways with solid doors.

3. For private offices, if the percentage of floor area with direct line of sight is equal to or greater than 75% (i.e., only the corners are non-compliant), you may enter the entire square footage of that room in the spreadsheet as meeting the credit requirement. If less than 75% of the room has direct line of sight, you must estimate the compliant floor area and enter that value in the spreadsheet.

4. For multi-occupant spaces, such as open work areas and conference rooms, estimate the actual square footage with direct line of sight to perimeter vision glazing.

Horizontal View at 42 Inches

1. Using representative building sections showing the furniture, draw a line at 42 in. across the section to establish the height of the perimeter glazing and any obstruction to it. Draw one or more representative sight lines from a point at 42in. in the regularly occupied space(s) to the perimeter vision glazing.

2. For each space where the view, taken at 42 in. above the floor, is maintained, enter a YES in the spreadsheet in the "Horizontal View" column of **Table 1**. If a room has direct line of site on the floor plan but does not have an unobstructed view at 42 in., the floor area of that room may not be counted as meeting the credit requirement and should be marked as NO in the table.

Total the area that is determined to meet all criteria above and divide it by the total regularly occupied area to determine if the building meets the 90% access to views requirement.

Submittal Documentation

Complete the LEED for Commercial Interiors Submittal Templates for the credits to be attained. Submit the completed calculations similar to **Table 1**, along with floor plans to support the values used. Provide representative sections with the furniture shown that demonstrate that the available views are maintained.

Additional Documentation

When the initial submittal is complete, no additional documentation should be needed.

Exemplary Performance

No threshold has been established for exemplary performance for EQ Credit 8.3.

Considerations

Review the Considerations included with EQ Credits 8.1 and 8.2.

References

Review the References included with EQ Credits 8.1 and 8.2.

Definitions

Direct Line of Sight to Perimeter Vision Glazing is the approach used to determine the calculated area of regularly occupied areas with direct line of sight to perimeter vision glazing. The area determination includes full height partitions and other fixed construction prior to installation of furniture.

Horizontal View at 42 Inches is the approach used to confirm that the direct line of sight to perimeter vision glazing remains available from a seated position. It uses section drawings that include the installed furniture to make the determination.

Non-Occupied Spaces include all rooms used by maintenance personnel that are not open for use by occupants. Included in this category are janitorial, storage and equipment rooms, and closets.

Non-Regularly Occupied Spaces include corridors, hallways, lobbies, break rooms, copy rooms, storage rooms, kitchens, restrooms, stairwells, etc.

Regularly Occupied Spaces are areas where workers are seated or standing as they work inside the space.

Vision Glazing is that portion of exterior windows above 2' - 6" and below 7' -6" that permits a view to the outside of the project space.

Innovation & Design Process

Sustainable design strategies and measures are constantly evolving and improving. New technologies are continually introduced to the marketplace and up-to-date scientific research influences building design strategies. The purpose of this LEED category is to recognize projects for innovative building features and sustainable building knowledge.

Occasionally, a strategy results in building performance that greatly exceeds those required in an existing LEED credit. Other strategies may not be addressed by any LEED prerequisite or credit but warrant consideration for their sustainability benefits. And expertise in sustainable building essential to the design and construction process may also merit further evaluation. These issues are addressed in this category.

Overview of LEED® Credits

ID Credit 1
Innovation in Design

ID Credit 2
LEED® Accredited Professional

There are 5 points available in the Innovation & Design Process category.

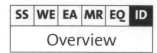

Innovation in Design

Intent

Provide design teams and projects the opportunity to be awarded points for exceptional performance above the requirements set by the LEED Green Building Rating System and/or innovative performance in Green Building categories not specifically addressed by the LEED Green Building Rating System.

Requirements

Credit 1.1 (1 point)   Identify the intent of the proposed innovation credit, the proposed requirements for compliance, the proposed submittals to demonstrate compliance, and the design approach (strategies) that might be used to meet the requirements.

Credit 1.2 (1 point)   Same as Credit 1.1

Credit 1.3 (1 point)   Same as Credit 1.1

Credit 1.4 (1 point)   Same as Credit 1.1

Submittals

Provide the proposal(s) within the LEED for Commercial Interiors Submittal Templates [including intent, requirements, submittals and possible design approach (strategies)] with relevant evidence of performance achieved.

Potential Technologies & Strategies

Substantially exceed a LEED performance credit such as energy performance or water efficiency. Apply strategies or measures that are not covered by LEED such as acoustic performance, or education of occupants or community development.

Credit Interpretation Rulings

In addition to LEED for Commercial Interiors Credit Interpretation Rulings (CIRs), applicable LEED for New Construction CIRs concerning this credit may also apply to LEED for Commercial Interiors projects.

It is USGBC policy to only review four ID credits at one time for each certification submittal. This approach maintains fairness and consistency for all projects.

Should an ID credit be denied in the Preliminary LEED Review, you may replace it with another proposal in the supplementary submittal at no additional cost. Note, however, that this will only afford that new proposal one opportunity to be evaluated.

LEED for New Construction ID1.1 CIR (9/24/01—9/24/01) outlines the path for achieving an innovation credit for an Educational Outreach Program.

LEED for New Construction ID1.1 CIR (4/8/04—4/8/04) outlines the path for achieving an innovation credit for Green Housekeeping.

Approach and Implementation

There are two types of innovation strategies that qualify under this credit. The first type includes those strategies that greatly exceed the requirements of existing LEED credits. For instance, a project that incorporates recycled materials or water efficiency measures that greatly exceed the requirements of their respective LEED credits would be appropriate for this credit.

As a general rule of thumb, ID credits for exemplary performance are awarded for doubling the credit requirements and/or achieving the next incremental percentage threshold. For instance an ID credit for exemplary performance in water use reduction (WE Credit 1) would require a minimum of 40% savings (20% = WEc1.1; 30% = WEc1.2, etc.).

Points for exemplary performance are available only for those credits where the outcome provides outstanding, measurable benefits to the environment and/or building occupants.

The second type of innovation strategies are those that are not addressed by any existing LEED credits. Only those strategies that have significant environmental benefits are applicable.

For example, simple signage in a building would not be considered a significant educational effort by itself. But a visitor's center and interactive display, coupled with a Web site and video would be an appropriate level of effort for earning an innovation credit. In other words, substantial efforts must be applied to merit innovation credits.

There are three basic criteria for achieving an innovation credit for a category not specifically addressed by LEED:

1. The project must demonstrate quantitative performance improvements for environmental benefit (establishing a baseline for standard performance for comparison to the final design),

2. The process or specification must be comprehensive, and

3. There must be the ability for other projects to duplicate the formula that your project developed for the innovation credit.

Credit for one project at a specific point in time does not constitute automatic approval for a similar strategy in a future project.

Innovation credits are not awarded for the use of a particular product or design strategy if the technology aids in the achievement of an existing LEED credit.

Approved ID credits may be pursued by any LEED project, but the project team must sufficiently document the achievement using the LEED credit equivalence process outlined under "Submittals."

Submittal Documentation

The LEED credit equivalence process includes identifying the proposed innovation credit intent, the proposed requirement(s) for compliance, the proposed submittal(s) to demonstrate compliance, and a summary of potential design approaches that may be used to meet the requirements.

A separate set of submittals is required for each point awarded and no strategy can achieve more than one point. Four independent sustainability measures may be applied to this credit.

Considerations

Synergy with LEED for Commercial Interiors SS Credit 1

LEED for Commercial Interiors SS Credit 1, Option L allows projects to propose a half point for any other quantifiable environmental performance achieved by the building in which the tenant space is located. This can include innovative and/or exceptional performance that could be awarded Innovation in Design credits in other LEED rating systems. But, while Option L provides design teams the opportunity to be awarded points for exceptional and/or innovative performance in the *core building*, the Innovation in Design section provides design teams the opportunity to be awarded points for exceptional and/or innovative performance in the tenant improvement space only.

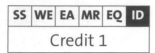

LEED Accredited Professional

1 point

Intent

Support and encourage the design integration required by a LEED Green Building project and streamline the application and certification process.

Requirement

At least one principal participant of the project team has successfully completed the LEED Professional Accreditation Exam.

Submittals

Provide the LEED for Commercial Interiors Submittal Template stating the LEED Accredited Professional's name, title, company and contact information. Include a copy of this person's LEED Accredited Professional Certificate.

Potential Technologies & Strategies

Attending a LEED for Commercial Interiors Technical Review Training Workshop is recommended but not required. Study the LEED for Commercial Interiors Reference Guide. Successfully pass the LEED Professional Accreditation Exam.

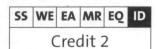

SS	WE	EA	MR	EQ	**ID**

Credit 2

Credit Interpretation Rulings

In addition to LEED for Commercial Interiors Credit Interpretation Rulings (CIRs), applicable LEED for New Construction CIRs concerning this credit may also apply to LEED for Commercial Interiors projects.

This credit can be achieved by having the professional accredited prior to the application for certification.

Green Building Concerns

LEED Accredited Professionals have the expertise required to design a building to LEED standards and to coordinate the documentation process that is necessary for LEED certification. The Accredited Professional understands the importance of integrated design and the need to consider interactions between the prerequisites and credits and their respective criteria. Architects, engineers, interior designers, consultants, owners and others who have a strong interest in sustainable building design are all appropriate candidates for accreditation. The Accredited Professional should be the champion for the project's LEED application and this person should be an integral member of the project design team.

Strategies

To become a LEED Accredited Professional, the LEED Professional Accreditation Exam must be successfully passed. To prepare for the exam, it is helpful to attend a LEED Workshop offered by, or authorized by, USGBC. Workshops include details on prerequisites and credits, calculation and documentation examples, and case studies from projects that have achieved certification.

For more information on workshops and the Accreditation Exam, visit the Education section of the USGBC Web site at www.usgbc.org.